# New
# General
# Mathematics 4

## J B Channon MA
formerly Assistant Master at Rugby School

## A McLeish Smith BA
formerly Second Master at Lawrence Sheriff School,
Rugby

## H C Head MA
Assistant Master at Rugby School

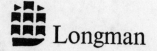
Longman

LONGMAN GROUP LIMITED
Longman House,
Burnt Mill, Harlow, Essex CM20 2JE, England
and Associated Companies throughout the World.

© J. B. Channon and A. McLeish Smith 1959
© New edition, Longman Group Ltd, 1971

First published 1959
New edition first published 1971
Tenth impression 1985

ISBN (with answers) 0 582 31847 5
ISBN (without answers) 0 582 31846 7

Produced by Longman Group (FE) Ltd
Printed in Hong Kong

# *Preface*

This set of four books is based on the authors' **General Mathematics** series, which has been completely rewritten in order to meet modern demands. Decimal currency has been used throughout, and in Books 1 and 2 the metric system of measures has supplanted the Imperial system almost completely, though a few questions and examples still remain in which Imperial units are used. Books 3 and 4 are completely metric. SI units have been used extensively but not exclusively; in particular the eminently useful centimetre and litre have been retained.

With the introduction of decimal currency it is assumed that pupils at primary level will have acquired some knowledge of decimal notation—place value, multiplication and division by a whole number and so on.

The more ponderous and less useful features of traditional textbooks will not be found here, and their omission has left room for chapters on those new topics which appear to the authors to be of permanent value, and which are in no danger of being eliminated from the syllabus once the experimental period of trial and error is over. Such topics as binary numbers, statistics, set theory, matrices, vectors, probability and linear programming must find a place in any series of books which is attempting to fit pupils for the modern world of technological development, and all of these subjects are dealt with in this series.

At the time of writing the future of geometry is still in a state of considerable uncertainty and, for this reason, more of the subject is retained than some teachers may consider necessary. These chapters can of course be disregarded by those who wish to do so, but they are there for those who believe that the study of geometry still has something to offer to the intelligent pupil.

The last two sets of Revision Examples consist entirely of questions selected from past G.C.E. examination papers, and the authors would like to express their gratitude to the examining bodies mentioned below for their permission to reproduce these questions, and also for allowing metrication of many problems originally set in Imperial units. These problems have in fact been altered as little as possible, and their nature and intention remains unchanged; such questions are distinguished by an asterisk, as (C)*.

Cambridge Local Examinations Syndicate
Northern Universities Joint Matriculation Board
Oxford Local Examinations
Oxford and Cambridge School Examination Board (including M.E.I.)
University of London
Welsh Joint Education Committee
Southern Universities' Joint Board for School Examinations

Rugby 1971

J.B.C.
A.McL.S.
H.C.H.

# *Theorems*

# *Constructions*

# *Contents*

v

## Contents

# *Tables*

## LENGTH

10 millimetres (mm) = 1 centimetre (cm)

10 cm = 1 decimetre (dm)

10 dm = 1 metre (m) = 1 000 mm

10 m = 1 decametre (dam)

10 dam = 1 hectometre (hm)

10 hm = 1 kilometre (km) = 1 000 m

*The decimetre, decametre and hectometre are very rarely used*

## AREA

100 sq mm (mm²) = 1 sq cm (cm²)

100 sq cm = 1 sq dm (dm²)

and so on

1 sq dam (dam²) = 1 are (a) = 100 m²

100 ares = 1 sq hm (hm²) = 1 hectare (ha) = 10 000 m²

100 ha = 1 sq km (km²)

*The hectare is the only unit in which the prefix hecto is in common use*

## VOLUME

1 000 cu mm (mm³) = 1 cu cm (cm³)

1 000 cu cm = 1 cu dm (dm³)

and so on

## CAPACITY

10 millilitres (ml) = 1 centilitre (cl)

10 cl = 1 decilitre (dl)

10 dl = 1 litre (l) = 1 000 ml

1 litre = 1 dm³ = 1 000 cm³

## MASS

10 milligrammes (mg) = 1 centigramme (cg)

10 cg = 1 decigramme (dg)

10 dg = 1 gramme (g) = 1 000 mg

10 g = 1 decagramme (dag)

10 dag = 1 hectogramme (hg)

10 hg = 1 kilogramme (kg) = 1 000 g

1 000 kg = 1 tonne (t)

*The centigramme, decigramme, decagramme and hectogramme are very rarely used*

# Chapter 1

# Compound interest

When money is invested at **Simple Interest** the investor receives the interest at regular intervals, the principal remaining unchanged. At **Compound Interest** the interest is added to the principal at the end of each interval. Thus the principal itself steadily increases, and the interest becomes greater for successive intervals.

The working is usually arranged in a tabulated form, and the interest is calculated by inspection. For example 4% of £218·62 is found by multiplying £218·62 by 4, and moving the digits two places to the right (to divide by 100),

i.e. 4% of £218·62 = £2·186 2 × 4 = £8·744 8.

Four places of decimals are usually sufficient for an answer to the nearest penny, and any digits after the fourth decimal place may be omitted.

The total interest cannot be calculated directly; the amount is found first, and then the principal is subtracted to leave the interest.

**Example 1** *Find to the nearest penny the compound interest on* £371·86 *for 3 years at 4% per annum.*

| | | |
|---|---|---|
| 1st year | Principal | £371·86 |
| | Interest 4% | 14·874 4 |
| 2nd year | Principal | 386·734 4 |
| | Interest 4% | 15·469 2 . . . |
| 3rd year | Principal | 402·203 6 |
| | Interest 4% | 16·088 0 . . . |
| | Amount | 418·291 6 |
| | | = £418·29 to nearest penny |
| | Principal | = £371·86 |
| | Compound Interest | = £46·43 |

**Example 2** *Find to the nearest penny the amount of* £141·36 *in* 2 *years at* $4\frac{3}{4}$% *per annum.*

| 1st year | Principal | £141·36 | |
|---|---|---|---|
| | 4% | 5·654 4 | |
| | Interest $\{$ $\frac{1}{2}$% | 0·706 8 | ($\frac{1}{2}$% is $\frac{1}{8}$ of 4%) |
| | $\frac{1}{4}$% | 0·353 4 | ($\frac{1}{4}$% is $\frac{1}{2}$ of $\frac{1}{2}$%) |
| 2nd year | Principal | 148·074 6 | |
| | 4% | 5·922 8 . . . | |
| | Interest $\{$ $\frac{1}{2}$% | 0·740 3 . . . | |
| | $\frac{1}{4}$% | 0·370 2 . . . | |
| | Amount | 155·107 9 | |
| | | = £155·11 to nearest penny | |

If the interest is to be added half-yearly and the rate is 6% per annum, then the interest must be calculated and added each half-year at the rate of 3%.

**Example 3** *In order to raise money to buy a house, a man borrows* £2 400 *at* 4% *per annum, interest to be added half-yearly, and arranges to pay back* £150 *at the end of each half-year. How much does he still owe after* $1\frac{1}{2}$ *years?*

| 1st half-year | Total debt | £2 400 |
|---|---|---|
| | Interest 2% | 48 |
| | | 2 448 |
| | Repayment | 150 |
| 2nd half-year | Total debt | 2 298 |
| | Interest 2% | 45·96 |
| | | 2 343·96 |
| | Repayment | 150 |
| 3rd half-year | Total debt | 2 193·96 |
| | Interest 2% | 43·879 2 |
| | | 2 237·839 2 |
| | Repayment | 150 |
| Total debt after $1\frac{1}{2}$ years | | 2 087·839 2 |
| | | = £2 087·84 to nearest penny |

**Exercise 1**

*In this exercise all answers should be to the nearest penny.*

Find the amount at compound interest for each of the following:

|   |   |   |   |   |   |   |   |   |   |
|---|---|---|---|---|---|---|---|---|---|
| 1 | £250 | for 2 years at 4% per annum |
| 2 | £500 | ,, | 3 | ,, | ,, | 5% | ,, | ,, |
| 3 | £400 | ,, | 2 | ,, | ,, | 3% | ,, | ,, |
| 4 | £620 | ,, | 3 | ,, | ,, | 2% | ,, | ,, |
| 5 | £128 | ,, | 3 | ,, | ,, | 6% | ,, | ,, |
| 6 | £83·50 | ,, | 2 | ,, | ,, | 7% | ,, | ,, |
| 7 | £26·20 | ,, | 3 | ,, | ,, | 5% | ,, | ,, |
| 8 | £124·75 | ,, | 2 | ,, | ,, | 2% | ,, | ,, |
| 9 | £211·50 | ,, | 4 | ,, | ,, | 2% | ,, | ,, |
| 10 | £54·43 | ,, | 3 | ,, | ,, | 1% | ,, | ,, |
| 11 | £176·61 | ,, | 2 | ,, | ,, | 3% | ,, | ,, |
| 12 | £312·34 | ,, | 2 | ,, | ,, | 7% | ,, | ,, |

Find the compound interest on

|   |   |   |   |   |   |   |   |   |   |
|---|---|---|---|---|---|---|---|---|---|
| 13 | £46·72 | for 2 years at 5% per annum |
| 14 | £132·61 | ,, | 3 | ,, | ,, | 4% | ,, | ,, |
| 15 | £407·39 | ,, | 3 | ,, | ,, | 2% | ,, | ,, |
| 16 | £52·53 | ,, | 4 | ,, | ,, | 2% | ,, | ,, |
| 17 | £125·68 | ,, | 3 | ,, | ,, | 4% | ,, | ,, |
| 18 | £215·66 | ,, | 3 | ,, | ,, | 4% | ,, | ,, |
| 19 | £163·36 | ,, | 3 | ,, | ,, | 5% | ,, | ,, |
| 20 | £232·76 | ,, | 3 | ,, | ,, | 4% | ,, | ,, |
| 21 | £409·90 | ,, | 4 | ,, | ,, | 5% | ,, | ,, |
| 22 | £185·47 | ,, | 3 | ,, | ,, | 4% | ,, | ,, |
| 23 | £213·38 | ,, | 3 | ,, | ,, | 4% | ,, | ,, |
| 24 | £95·87 | ,, | 3 | ,, | ,, | 6% | ,, | ,, |
| 25 | £298·43 | ,, | 3 | ,, | ,, | 4% | ,, | ,, |

Find the amount at compound interest for each of the following:

26 £160 for 2 years at $3\frac{1}{2}\%$ per annum

27 £68 ,, 3 ,, ,, $2\frac{1}{4}\%$ ,, ,,

28 £157·61 ,, 2 ,, ,, $1\frac{1}{2}\%$ ,, ,,

29 £162·72 ,, 3 ,, ,, $2\frac{1}{2}\%$ ,, ,,

30 £296·43 ,, 2 ,, ,, $2\frac{3}{4}\%$ ,, ,,

Find the compound interest on

31 £205·48 for 2 years at $3\frac{1}{2}\%$ per annum

32 £48·93 ,, 3 ,, ,, $1\frac{3}{4}\%$ ,, ,,

33 £132·42 ,, 2 ,, ,, $4\frac{3}{4}\%$ ,, ,,

34 £516·17 ,, 3 ,, ,, $3\frac{3}{4}\%$ ,, ,,

35 £316·84 ,, 2 ,, ,, $4\frac{3}{4}\%$ ,, ,,

36 £100 is invested at $6\%$ per annum compound interest, the interest being added half-yearly. Find the amount after 2 years.

37 Find the sum to which £240 will amount in $2\frac{1}{2}$ years, if it is invested at $4\%$ per annum compound interest, the interest being added half-yearly.

38 Find the compound interest on £314·30 in $1\frac{1}{2}$ years, if interest at $2\frac{1}{2}\%$ per annum is added half-yearly.

39 Find the compound interest on £436·70 for $1\frac{1}{4}$ years at $8\%$ per annum, if interest is added quarterly.

40 Find the sum to which £281·37 will amount after 2 years, if compound interest at $4\frac{1}{2}\%$ per annum is added half-yearly.

41 If £162·42 is invested at $6\%$ per annum, compound interest being added quarterly, find the amount after a year.

42 A man wishing to buy a house borrows £2 000 at $5\%$ per annum compound interest, and undertakes to repay £300 at the end of each year. How much does he still owe when he has made his third repayment?

43 The value of a car depreciates each year by $12\frac{1}{2}\%$ of the value at the beginning of the year. If a car cost £1 024 new, find its value after 3 years.

**44** A man borrows £760 at 4% compound interest. At the end of the first year he pays back £270. After another year he repays £280. At the end of the third year he clears the debt completely. What is his final payment?

**45** Is it better to earn interest at 4% annually or 1% quarterly? Find the actual annual rate per cent if interest is added at 1% quarterly (3 sig. fig.).

**46** £1 860 is invested for 2 years at 5% per annum compound interest. Find how much more profitable it would be to have the interest added half-yearly, rather than annually.

**47** In any year, the depreciation in the value of a car is reckoned as a percentage of the value at the beginning of the year. If the depreciation is 25% in the first year, 20% in the second, and 15% in each subsequent year, find the value of a car after 4 years if it cost £1 080 when new (nearest tenth of £1).

**48** A man invests £650 at 4% compound interest, and adds £150 to the capital at the end of each year. Find the amount after 4 years.

**49** A man wishing to create a fund for his son's education invests £300 in a building society at $4\frac{1}{2}$% compound interest when his son is born, and adds £80 at the end of each year. How big is the fund when the boy is 4 years old (nearest tenth of £1)?

**50** A man borrows £1 850 at 6% compound interest, and arranges to pay back £450 at the end of each year. How much does he still owe when he has made his fourth repayment?

**51** The population of a town increases by $2\frac{1}{2}$% each year. Three years ago the population was exactly 448 000. What is it now?

**52** A man estimates that he will need £7 000 for house purchase in 3 years' time. He invests £5 500 in a building society at 5% per annum compound interest, adds £250 to his investment at the end of the first year, and adds a further £350 at the end of the second. By how much will the sum available after 3 years be greater or less than the £7 000 needed?

**53** A man wishing to provide for his son's university education invested £300 at $3\frac{1}{2}$% compound interest on 1 October 1965.

He added another £300 on 1 October 1966, and did the same again on 1 October 1967. The son began his university career in October 1968, and the father withdrew £330 on 1 October of that year. He withdrew another £330 on 1 October 1969, and then took all that remained on 1 October 1970. How much did he receive at the final withdrawal?

# Chapter 2

# *Shares and stocks. Investments*

## Shares

Imagine that a man has invented something which he knows to be good and which he thinks that people would buy readily if it were on sale in the shops. Unfortunately he has not enough money to set in motion all the complicated processes which are necessary before his product reaches the retailer (machinery, workshops, advertising, etc.), and it is unlikely that he will be able to borrow enough from his friends to do so, even if he himself is capable of doing all this preliminary work.

He therefore puts himself into the hands of a **Company Promoter** (who is an expert in this kind of work), who agrees to **float** a company to manufacture and sell the product. The Promoter's first step will be to issue a **prospectus** explaining what the inventor is trying to do and how he is trying to do it, and inviting the general public to buy **shares** in the limited company which is being formed for the purpose.

These shares will probably be of value 25p, 50p or £1 (though in fact the value may be almost any sum of money): let us suppose that they are £1 shares in this case.

The prospectus will offer for sale (say) 20 000 £1 shares, as it is estimated that £20 000 will comfortably cover the preliminary costs of the flotation. Members of the public read the prospectus and, if they think the product likely to be successful, will buy shares at £1 each; that is to say, they will **invest** money in the company.

When enough money has been paid in, manufacture begins. If the product is popular, more people will want to invest money in the company and the price of the shares will rise, perhaps to £1·50 or more. The distinction between the **nominal value** (£1) of a share and its **market value** (£1·50) is extremely important.

Members of the public generally invest money for one of two reasons: either (i) in the hope that the value of the shares will

7

rise, so that they will make a profit when they sell them, or (ii) in order to obtain an income from their investment.

The income arises as a result of the profits made by the company. At the end of a year's trading the books of the company are made up, and the directors decide how much of the profit is available for distribution among the shareholders (generally after they have paid part of it away in the form of taxation and kept part back as a reserve fund to allow for the depreciation of machinery, etc.).

Suppose that in this particular case the whole of the £20 000 was subscribed and that the profit available for distribution in a given year was £1 500. £1 500 is $7\frac{1}{2}\%$ of £20 000; therefore the directors announce that a **dividend** of $7\frac{1}{2}\%$ will be paid to the shareholders. Notice that dividend is not the same as interest: the former is the share of the profit which the investor receives because he is a member of the company and is therefore entitled to share in its fortunes and misfortunes, while the latter is paid on money lent.

This means that each £1 share receives a dividend of $7\frac{1}{2}\%$ of £1 (i.e. $7\frac{1}{2}$p) and *this dividend is quite independent of the price which the shareholder has paid for his share.*

If for instance he paid £1·50, then his return is $7\frac{1}{2}$p on £1·50 (i.e. 5% on his investment): on the other hand, if he had been lucky enough to buy at 75p, then the return on his investment would have been 10% ($7\frac{1}{2}$p on 75p).

There are a number of different types of share which may be offered to the investor, who is free to choose the type of investment which suits his needs. The most important of these (which are given in order of reliability as producers of interest) are as follows:

1. **Debentures** or **Bonds.** These are issued in return for money lent to buy the land on which the factory stands and to erect the essential buildings and plant, so that the holders of this class of security are in fact the owners of part of the company's estate and are entitled to demand payment of interest on the money lent, however well or badly the company may be doing.

2. **Preference shares.** Holders of these are entitled to receive payment of their dividends before any other class of shareholder.

Preference shares always receive a fixed rate of dividend, and the holder can never get more than this rate, however well the company may do. Preference shares may also be participating or cumulative or both: **participating** means that the shareholder may, after having received his fixed rate of income, receive yet a further share of the profits after the claims of all the other shareholders have been met: **cumulative** means that, if the full rate of interest has not been paid in any one year or series of years, the accumulated debt to the shareholder must be paid off before the rest of the shareholders receive any dividend at all.

The above classes of share are very well protected, and therefore the holder of them will not expect to receive a high rate of interest on his holdings.

3. **Ordinary shares.** These pay a dividend which is entirely dependent on the fortunes of the company: in good years the investor will get a high rate of interest: in bad years he may get nothing at all.

4. **Deferred shares.** These are not entitled to any dividend until a fixed minimum rate has been paid on all other classes of share.

The Stock Exchange quotes the prices of shares in **pence and fractions of a penny (without the p)** unless the price is £10 or more, in which case the price is given in pounds and fractions of a pound,

$$\text{e.g.} \quad £5·65\tfrac{3}{4} \text{ is quoted as } 565\tfrac{3}{4},$$
$$\text{and} \quad £12·75 \text{ ,, \quad ,, \quad ,, } £12\tfrac{3}{4}.$$

**Example 1** *An investor buys* 200 £1 *shares at* 125p *and receives a dividend of* 4%. (*i*) *How much does he pay for the shares?* (*ii*) *What is his dividend in cash?* (*iii*) *What rate of interest does he get on his money?*

(i) Money invested $= 200 \times £1·25 = £250.$

(ii) Dividend $= 4\%$ of £200 $= £8.$

(iii) £250 cash earns £8 interest

$\therefore$ £100 cash earns £8 $\times \frac{100}{250}$ interest $= £3·2$

$\therefore$ rate of interest $= 3·2\%.$

9

*Alternatively*

(iii) Dividend on one share = 4% of £1 = 4p

∴ 125p cash earns 4p interest

∴ 100p cash earns $4 \times \frac{100}{125}$p = 3·2p

∴ rate of interest = 3·2%.

**Example 2** *A man invests* £300 *in* 50p *shares when their price is* 40p. *(i) How many shares does he buy? A dividend of* 5½% *is declared and he subsequently sells the shares at* 43p. *(ii) What is his cash dividend? (iii) How much profit does he make on the sale?*

(i) Number of shares = $\dfrac{£300}{40p} = \dfrac{30\,000p}{40p} = 750$.

(ii) Nominal value of 750 50p shares = 37 500p = £375

∴ dividend = 5½% of £375 = £20·625 ≏ £20·62.

(iii) Profit on one share ≈ 43p − 40p = 3p

∴ profit on 750 shares = 750 × 3p = 2 250p = £22·50.

**Example 3** *A certain* 25p *share stands at* 28p. *What yield is secured on money invested if the dividend is* 7%?

Dividend on one share = 7% of 25p = $1\frac{3}{4}$p

28p cash earns dividend $1\frac{3}{4}$p

∴ 100p cash earns dividend $\frac{100}{28} \times 1\frac{3}{4}$p = $6\frac{1}{4}$p

∴ yield is $6\frac{1}{4}$%.

*N.B.* From Example 3 it can be seen the yield on money invested is given immediately by the formula

$$\text{Yield \%} = \frac{\text{Nominal value}}{\text{Cash value}} \times \text{Dividend \%}.$$

### Exercise 2a

**1** Calculate the cost of

(i) 50 Barclay's Bank £1 shares at 374p.

(ii) 100 Cunard £1 shares at 56¼p.

(iii) 500 British American Tobacco 50p shares at 502p.

(iv) 240 Lotus 25p shares at 53¾p.

(v) 125 Cerebos 25p shares at 56p.

**2** How many shares can be bought for £240 invested in

 (i) Lake George 25p shares at 48p?
 (ii) Anglo-Oriental rubber shares (10p) at 25p?
(iii) British Leyland 25p shares at 31¼p?
(iv) Scottish and Newcastle Breweries £1 shares at 320p?
 (v) Shell £1 shares at 187½p?

**3** What profit does a man make who buys 200 Plessey shares at 95p and sells them at 156¾p?

**4** An investor held 250 Tate & Lyle £1 shares, for which he paid £1·75½ per share, and had to sell out at £1·23½ per share. How much did he lose?

**5** A man sold 150 Strand Electric shares at 152½p and by so doing made a profit of £130·50. At what price had he bought the shares?

**6** An investor held 600 Burmah Oil £1 shares which he bought at 475p. He sold half his holding at 560p and the rest during a crisis, when the prices had slumped. At what price did he sell the last 300 shares if he neither gained nor lost on the whole transaction?

**7** If the investor in no. 6 had sold 400 shares at 560p and the rest at 367½p, when the slump was at its worst, what profit or loss would he have made on the whole transaction?

**8** A holder of 500 British Timken £1 shares, which he bought at 225¾p, resolved not to sell them until he could clear £600 on the transaction. The highest price the shares reached was 342p. Did he get the opportunity he wanted or not?

**9** A man sold 440 En-Tout-Cas Preferred 20p shares at 28p and re-invested the whole amount in Unilever £1 shares at 385p. How many of the latter shares did he buy?

**10** A speculator sold 250 British Petroleum £1 shares at a price which enabled him to buy 900 £1 shares of a new Stewart & Lloyds issue, the issued price being 175p. He sold these shares a few days later at 182½p. What price did he get for each B.P. share, and how much cash had he in hand at the end?

In Examples 11 to 18 find the actual dividend paid to buyers at the prices stated, and find also the percentage yield on the money invested, giving the percentage as an exact fraction.

**11** 200 Skefko Ball Bearing £1 shares at 160p: dividend 10%.

**12** 500 Perry & Co. £1 shares at 125p: dividend 15%.

**13** 320 Shell Transport £1 shares at 675p: dividend $18\frac{3}{4}$%.

**14** 400 Sunday Pictorial 25p shares at 100p: dividend 30%.

**15** 150 Stoll Theatres 20p shares at 100p: dividend 7%.

**16** 630 Bristol Aeroplane 50p shares at 90p: dividend 10%.

**17** 2 000 Rugby Portland Cement 25p shares at $101\frac{1}{4}$p: dividend 18%.

**18** 440 G.U.S. 25p shares at 189p: dividend 63%.

Which of the following investments (nos. 19 to 23) produce the better percentage yield on money invested?

**19** (i) Austin Reed £1 shares at 110p: dividend 11%,
　　(ii) John Oakey £1 shares at 250p: dividend 20%.

**20** (i) B.L.M. 25p shares at 85p: dividend $12\frac{1}{2}$%,
　　(ii) Meccano 25p shares at $63\frac{3}{4}$p: dividend $8\frac{1}{2}$%.

**21** (i) Huntley & Palmers 4% Preference £1 shares at 75p,
　　(ii) Army & Navy Stores 50p shares at $67\frac{1}{2}$p: dividend $7\frac{1}{2}$%.

**22** (i) Eucryl 10p shares at 16p: dividend 12%,
　　(ii) Super Air-Seals 15p shares at 50p: dividend 25%.

**23** (i) Horlicks 25p shares at $113\frac{3}{4}$p: dividend 35%,
　　(ii) Price & Pierce £1 shares at $272\frac{1}{2}$p: dividend 20%.

**24** In 1956 the dividend on each Woolworth's 25p share was 18p. What rate per cent was paid, and what percentage return did an investor get on his money if he paid £2·40 per share?

**25** Odeon $4\frac{1}{4}$% £1 Preference shares stand at 38p. How many shares must an investor buy in order to obtain an annual income of £85, and how much will he have to pay for them? What will be his percentage return on the money invested? (3 sig. fig.)

**26** A man invested £299·52 in Northampton Breweries £1 shares at 312p and sold the shares two months later at 285½p. If expenses amounted to £6·63, how much did the investment cost him altogether?

**27** An investor bought 100 Odhams Press 50p shares at 113½p, received a half-year's dividend of 12½%, and then sold the shares at 118½p. If the costs of buying and selling amounted to £1·06, how much did he gain on the whole transaction?

**28** A man received a legacy of 800 Hawker Siddeley £1 shares which he sold at 194p after getting a dividend of 17½%. The cost of selling the shares was £7·55. How much cash had he in hand after the sale had been completed?

**29** An investor held 500 15p shares in British Ropes which he sold at 37¼p after having received a half-year's dividend of 12%. He reinvested the proceeds of the sale in Paton & Baldwin £1 shares at 186¼p, subsequently receiving a second half-year's dividend of 10% on the latter shares. How many shares was he able to buy, and what was his total income for the year?

**30** A man invests £355, partly in British Leyland 25p shares at 35p, and partly in British Aluminium £1 shares at 320p. The two concerns pay dividends of 12½% and 12% respectively, and the incomes he gets from them are equal. What sums did he invest in each?

**Stock**

There is no essential difference between **Shares** and **Stock,** but shares cannot be subdivided (i.e. it is not possible to buy or sell a fraction of a share) while stock can be dealt with in any amount whatsoever in £ p. The price of stock is invariably based on a **par** value of £100 so that, if a stock is quoted at 78¼, £100 stock can be bought or sold for £78·25 cash.

It is important to use the words *cash* and *stock* to avoid confusion in working, as in the following examples.

**Example 4** *How much Mackeson* 4% *Debenture stock at 74 can be bought for* £246·05?

£74 cash buys £100 stock

$\therefore$ £246·05 cash buys £100 $\times \dfrac{246·05}{74}$ stock

$\qquad = $ £332·50 stock.

**Example 5** *What income is received from the investment in Example 4, and what is the yield per cent on the money invested?*

(*N.B.* The income is £4 on £100 stock or on £74 cash.)
On £74 cash the income is £4

$\therefore$ on £246·05 cash the income is £4 $\times \dfrac{246·05}{74} = $ £13·30.

On £74 cash the income is £4

$\therefore$ on £100 cash the income is £4 $\times \dfrac{100}{74} \backsimeq$ £5·40, i.e. 5·4%.

**Example 6** *A man sold* £1 000 *of* 3½% *Conversion stock at 84 and reinvested in British Electricity* 4½% *stock at 90. By how much did he improve his original income?*

Original income = 3½% of £1 000 = £35.
Selling price of Conversion stock = £840.
In B.E. stock £90 cash yields income £4½

$\therefore$ in B.E. stock £840 cash yields income £4½ $\times \dfrac{840}{90} = $ £42

$\therefore$ improvement in income is £7.

**Exercise 2b**

*Give all answers to the nearest penny.*

**1** Find the cost of
    (i) £500 Associated Biscuit 4¾% loan stock at 92.
    (ii) £350 3½% Conversion stock at 83.
    (iii) £520 Birmingham 2¾% loan at 98½.

    (iv) £580 Barclay Perkins 3% mortgage debentures at 71.

    (v) £225 Edinburgh 4½% Preference stock at 73½.

**2** What is the gross income from each of the investments in no. 1 ?

**3** How much stock is obtained from investing
    (i) £172·50 in Olympia 4% debentures at 69,
    (ii) £310 in Norvic 5% loan at 93,
    (iii) £260 in Brown 5½% debentures at 104,
    (iv) £600 in British Gas 3½% stock at 80½,
    (v) £500 in New Brunswick 5% stock at 110 ?

**4** What is the gross income from each of the investments in no. 3 ?

**5** What is the percentage return on each of the investments in no. 3 ?

**6** How much will have to be invested in Aberdeen 3% stock at 65 in order to produce an income of £40 annually ?

**7** What is the price of Sudan 4½% stock if an investment of £200 produces an annual income of £10 ?

**8** What rate per cent is paid by Victory Bonds at 92 if an income of £35 is yielded by an investment of £805 ?

**9** An investment in 3½% Conversion Loan yields an income of £120. What is the cash value of the stock if it stands at 73½ ?

**10** £487·50 invested in 2½% Treasury Loan produces an income of £25. What is the price of the stock ?

**11** How much will have to be invested in John Dickinson 5% First Preference stock at 92½ in order to produce an income of £54 ?

**12** An investment of £765 in Olympia stock at 68 yields an income of £45. Find the percentage rate paid by the stock.

**13** What is the price of Hampstead Gardens 5½% Debenture stock if a yield of £12·50 is secured by an investment of £212·50 ?

**14** £1 021·25 invested at 95 in Duff Developments yields an income of £64·50. At what percentage is the stock rated?

**15** A holding of Namdang Tea 4% debentures at 74 produces an income of £32·50. How much is the holding worth?

**16** Which of the following pairs of stocks gives the better rate of interest on money invested?
   (i) Stoke on Trent 5¼% at par *or* West Hartlepool 3% at 75.
   (ii) Sudan 3¼% at 91 *or* Newfoundland 3% at 87.
   (iii) P. & O. 3½% debentures at 59½ *or* Cunard 6% at 101.
   (iv) Sydney C.C. 5¼% at 98 *or* Montreal 3% debentures at 58.
   (v) Dover Harbour 3¾% at 77 *or* 4¼% at 87.

**17** What is the price of Pears' 5% debentures if money invested earns 6¼%?

**18** Money invested in Odhams 3½% debentures earns 4⅔% interest. What is the price of the stock?

**19** If the return on an investment in Odeon 3¼% is 5%, find the price of the stock.

**20** Peel River stock paid a dividend of 17½%, which represented a rate of 12½% to the investor. What was the price of the stock?

**21** A man invested £770 in City & Industrial 5% stock at 75 and sold out later at 79. What did he gain?

**22** An investor put £494 into Rollmaker's 4¼% stock at 78 and, by selling out at the right moment, gained £57. At what price did he sell the stock?

**23** A holder of £2 000 Exchequer 2½% stock sold at 84 and with the proceeds bought Dunlop 3½% stock at 73½. How much stock did he buy, and what was the improvement in his income?

**24** A man invested £380 in British Lion 4% at 84 and was forced to sell out at a loss a year later. If the loss of capital value exactly equalled the amount of the one dividend received, at what price did he sell?

**Investments**

There are various ways of comparing the merits of different methods of investing money, but perhaps the most important point to consider is whether the sum of money invested remains constant (apart from interest added) or whether its value rises and falls with the cost of living, inflation, devaluation and so on.

Examples of the first kind of investment are the National Savings Bank (formerly the Post Office Savings Bank) and Building Societies. The second kind includes shares and stocks, generally known as **equities.**

In our modern society it seems inevitable that the price of everything should rise, which means that the buying power of money becomes less. For example, it has been stated that £1 in 1959 became worth only 74p in 1969, so that a pair of shoes which cost £3 in 1959 would probably have cost about £4 in 1969. Hence if a man had £100 invested in a building society in 1959 and drew his interest each year, then in 1969 he would still have had the nominal sum of £100 invested, but this would have bought only what £74 would have bought in 1959. On the other hand he would have had the security of a completely safe investment, with a very satisfactory rate of interest. In 1969 this rate of interest was generally 5% free of income tax, which means that the building society paid the investor's income tax direct to the Inland Revenue, and paid to the investor the 5% which remained. This was equivalent to the investor receiving about 8½% gross, and then paying income tax on it.

The value of shares in any one company is liable to fall as well as rise, but over the years the general tendency is for the value of equities to rise. If the man who had £100 invested in a building society in 1959 had withdrawn the money and invested it in equities, he would probably have found that in 1969 these equities would have been worth about £130, thus roughly keeping pace with the cost of living. On the other hand he could have been unlucky, and the value of his £100 could have fallen.

17

## Unit Trusts

A man with £1 000 to invest in equities would almost certainly not put it all into shares in any one company, but would consider it wiser to invest perhaps £200 in each of five companies, thus spreading the risk. Alternatively he could aim at even greater safety by buying units in a **Unit Trust**. In effect this would mean that he, and many others like him, would be handing over money to a group of experts who would invest it jointly in a large number of companies. If the investment is spread over, say, 200 companies, then any bad results from some of the companies would probably be offset by the more profitable ones.

There are many unit trusts, each with its own particular aims, to meet the needs of all kinds of investor. Save and Prosper have, among others, Income Units and Capital Units. With Income Units the money is invested mainly in companies which are likely to produce a good annual yield, with only moderate prospects of capital growth, giving a return (in 1970) of about $6\frac{1}{2}\%$ (gross, subject to income tax). On the other hand with Capital Units the annual yield is of secondary importance (less than 2%), and the money is invested in companies whose shares are most likely to rise in value. A man with a high income who pays income tax and surtax would not be particularly enthusiastic about increasing his income, knowing that perhaps three-quarters of the increase would go to the Inland Revenue. He would prefer to invest in Capital Units, whose value would probably have risen considerably by the time he needed the money on retirement ten or twenty years later.

Other examples of specialised unit trusts are Ebor Commodity Units, invested mainly in companies covering a wide range of commodities (gold, copper, rubber, coffee, copra, timber and so on), and Unicorn '500' Units, invested not in the well-known large companies, but rather in young, small companies which are likely to grow.

Some unit trusts do not specialise, but invest in a general cross-section of companies.

# Chapter 3

# *Harder simultaneous equations (one linear, one quadratic)*

**Example 1** *Solve the equations* $3x + y = 10$, $2x^2 + y^2 = 19$.

$$3x + y = 10 \qquad \text{(i)}$$
$$2x^2 + y^2 = 19 \qquad \text{(ii)}$$

From (i) $\qquad\qquad y = 10 - 3x.$

Substituting for $y$ in (ii),

$$2x^2 + (10 - 3x)^2 = 19$$
$$\therefore\ 2x^2 + 100 - 60x + 9x^2 = 19$$
$$\therefore\ 11x^2 - 60x + 81 = 0$$
$$\therefore\ (x - 3)(11x - 27) = 0$$
$$\therefore\ x = 3 \quad \text{or} \quad \tfrac{27}{11}.$$

When $x = 3$, $y = 10 - 3 \times 3 = 10 - 9 = 1$

,, $x = \tfrac{27}{11}$, $y = 10 - 3 \times \tfrac{27}{11} = 10 - \tfrac{81}{11} = \tfrac{29}{11}$.

*Ans.* $(3, 1)$; $(2\tfrac{5}{11}, 2\tfrac{7}{11})$.

Notice particularly that when the values of $x$ have been found, the corresponding values of $y$ are found by substituting back in the *linear* equation.

**Example 2** *If* $A = \{x, y : 3x + 4y = 11\}$ *and* $B = \{x, y : xy = 2\}$, *find* $A \cap B$.

$$3x + 4y = 11 \qquad \text{(i)}$$
$$xy = 2 \qquad \text{(ii)}$$

From (ii) $\qquad\qquad x = \dfrac{2}{y}.$

Substituting for $x$ in (i),

$$3 \times \frac{2}{y} + 4y = 11$$
$$\therefore\ 4y^2 - 11y + 6 = 0$$
$$\therefore\ (y - 2)(4y - 3) = 0$$
$$\therefore\ y = 2 \quad \text{or} \quad \tfrac{3}{4}.$$

19

When $y = 2$, $x = \frac{2}{2} = 1$

„ $y = \frac{3}{4}$, $x = \dfrac{2}{\frac{3}{4}} = \dfrac{8}{3} = 2\frac{2}{3}$.

*Ans.* $\{(1, 2); (2\frac{2}{3}, \frac{3}{4})\}$

Notice that the answers are given in the form of a vector $(x, y)$, so that it is clear which $x$ corresponds to which $y$.

In both these examples one letter is expressed in terms of the other from one equation, and then a substitution is made in the other equation, which produces an equation involving one letter only. This method will always lead to a solution, but is not necessarily the best, as may be seen from the following example.

**Example 3** *Solve the equations* $3x - y = 3$, $9x^2 - y^2 = 45$.

$$9x^2 - y^2 = 45$$
$$\therefore (3x - y)(3x + y) = 45$$
$$\therefore 3(3x + y) = 45 \quad \text{since} \quad 3x - y = 3 \quad \text{(i)}$$
$$\therefore 3x + y = 15 \quad \text{(ii)}$$

Adding (i) and (ii), $\quad 6x = 18$, $\quad \therefore x = 3$
Subtracting (i) from (ii), $2y = 12$, $\quad \therefore y = 6$.

*Ans.* (3, 6)

This method can always be used when one of the given equations can be expressed in factors, and one of these factors occurs in the other equation.

**Exercise 3**

Nos. 1 to 5 are suitable for class discussion. In nos. 6–10 the method of Example 3 should be used.

**1** $3x^2 - 4y = -1$
$\quad 2x - y = 1$

**2** $x^2 + y^2 = 34$
$\quad x + y = 2$

**3** $2x^2 + y^2 = 19$
$\quad x + 3y = 0$

**4** $9y^2 + 8x = 12$
$\quad 2x + 3y = 4$

**5** $xy + 3x = 3$
$\quad 3x + y = 7$

**6** $x^2 - y^2 = 27$
$\quad x + y = 3$

**7** $x^2 - 4y^2 = 9$
$x + 2y = 1$

**8** $4x^2 - y^2 = 15$
$2x - y = 5$

**9** $4x^2 - 9y^2 = 19$
$2x + 3y = 1$

**10** $5x^2 - 3xy = 9$
$5x - 3y = 3$

**11** $2xy + 6y - x - 3 = 0$
$2y - x = 5$

**12** $3x^2 - xy = 0$
$2y - 5x = 1$

**13** $3x - 4y = 2$
$xy = 2$

**14** $25x^2 - y^2 = 36$
$5x + y = 2$

**15** $x^2 - xy + 8 = 0$
$2x - y = 2$

**16** $x + 2y = 2$
$x^2 - 6y^2 = 10$

**17** $x^2 + 4y^2 = 65$
$x + 2y = 3$

**18** $x^2 - y = 13$
$x - y = 11$

**19** $xy + 3 = 0$
$2x + y = 1$

**20** $2x^2 - 5xy = 0$
$3y - x = 1$

**21** $2x - 5y = 7$
$xy = 6$

**22** $3x + 2y + 1 = 0$
$3x^2 - y^2 = 2$

**23** $xy + 6 = 0$
$2x - 3y + 15 = 0$

**24** $2y^2 - 9x^2 = 4$
$3x + 2y = 2$

**25** $3x + 4y = 7$
$2xy + 3 = 0$

**26** $3x^2 - 5xy = 8$
$5y - 2x = 2$

**27** $xy + 2x^2 = 3$
$3x + 2y = 1$

**28** $2x^2 + 3xy - 2y^2 = 8$
$2x - y = 1$

**29** $xy + 5x - 2y - 10 = 0$
$2x + y = 1$

**30** $x - 2y = 2$
$(x - y)(x + 2y) = 18$

**31** $8y + x = 1$

$x + \dfrac{2}{y} = 1$

**32** $2x^2 + 3xy - 7y^2 = 122$
$3y = x + 14$

**33** $x^2 + 5y^2 = 14$
$x - 5y = 2$

**34** $xy - 3x + y = 5$
$xy - 4x - 2y = 2$

**35** $2x - 3y = 12$
$4x^2 + 2xy - 3y^2 = 12$

**36** $\dfrac{1}{y} - \dfrac{1}{x} = \dfrac{1}{60}$
$3y - 2x = 6$

**37** $\dfrac{1}{x} + \dfrac{2}{y} = 8$

$3x + 5y = 3$

**38** $(x + 1)(y - 2) = 6$
$(x - 1)(y + 2) = 20$

**39** $5x^2 - 3xy - 2y^2 = 0$
$x + 2y = 6$

**40** $4x^2 + 2xy - y^2 = 1$
$4x + 3y = 1$

# Chapter 4

# *Inequalities (2)*

In Book 3, Chapter 21, some linear inequalities were considered. There remains one type, in which fractions are involved, which presents its own peculiar difficulties.

## Inequalities with fractions

It has already been shown that, when both sides of an inequality are multiplied by a negative number, the effect is to reverse the inequality (e.g. $5 > 4$, but $-5 < -4$).

Therefore, when both sides of an inequality are multiplied by $x$, the cases of $x$ positive and $x$ negative must be carefully distinguished.

**Example 1** $\dfrac{6}{x} > 3$.

(i) If $x > 0$        $6 > 3x$

$\left. \begin{array}{l} \therefore \ x < 2 \\ \text{But } x > 0 \end{array} \right\}$   $\therefore \ 0 < x < 2$

(ii) If $x < 0$        $6 < 3x$

$\left. \begin{array}{l} \therefore \ x > 2 \\ \text{But } x < 0 \end{array} \right\}$   $\therefore$ there is no negative solution

$\therefore$ the complete solution is $0 < x < 2$.

*N.B.* The situation which arises when $x = 0$ is not considered here, since the value of $\dfrac{6}{0}$ has not yet been defined.

**Example 2** $\left\{ x : \dfrac{6}{x} < -3 \right\}$.

(i) If $x > 0$        $6 < -3x$

$\therefore \ -x > 2$

$\left. \begin{array}{l} \therefore \ x < -2 \\ \text{But } x > 0 \end{array} \right\}$   $\therefore$ there is no positive solution

23

(ii) If $x < 0$        $6 > -3x$

$\therefore -x < 2$

$\left.\begin{array}{c} \therefore \ x > -2 \\ \text{But } x < 0 \end{array}\right\}$   $\therefore -2 < x < 0$

$\therefore$ the complete solution is $\{x : -2 < x < 0\}$.

**Example 3** $\dfrac{6}{x} > 3$.

The argument is as in Example 1, but solution $0 < x < 2$.

**Exercise 4a**

Solve the following inequalities:

**1** $\dfrac{6}{x} < 2$   **2** $\dfrac{6}{x} > -2$   **3** $\left\{ x : \dfrac{10}{x} > 5 \right\}$

**4** $\left\{ x : \dfrac{24}{x} < -6 \right\}$   **5** $18 \leqslant \dfrac{3}{x}$   **6** $\left\{ x : \dfrac{4}{x} - 20 > 0 \right\}$

**7** $\dfrac{30}{x} + 3 \leqslant 0$        **8** $\left\{ x : \dfrac{2}{x} < \dfrac{5}{x} + 2 \right\}$

**9** $\left\{ x : 2\left( \dfrac{2}{x} - \dfrac{1}{3} \right) > -\dfrac{1}{6} \right\}$   **10** $\dfrac{1}{3x} < \dfrac{1}{2x} + \dfrac{1}{4}$

**11** $\left\{ x : \dfrac{1}{5x} > \dfrac{4}{15x} - \dfrac{1}{20} \right\}$   **12** $\dfrac{5}{3x} + \dfrac{3}{4} > \dfrac{1}{12}$

## Quadratic inequalities

If $a$ and $b$ are two numbers the equation $ab = 0$ can be satisfied only if *either* $a = 0$ *or* $b = 0$.

In the inequality $ab > 0$ (i.e. the product of $a$ and $b$ has to be $+$) the two numbers must be either both $+$ or both $-$ ($+ \times + = +$ and $- \times - = +$).

In the inequality $ab < 0$ (i.e. the product of $a$ and $b$ has to be $-$) one of the two numbers must be $+$ and the other $-$ ($+ \times - = -$ and $- \times + = -$).

**Example 4** $(x - 3)(x - 5) > 0.$

*Either* (i) $x - 3 > 0$ *and* $x - 5 > 0$

∴ $x > 3$ *and* $x > 5$

∴ solution is $x > 5$

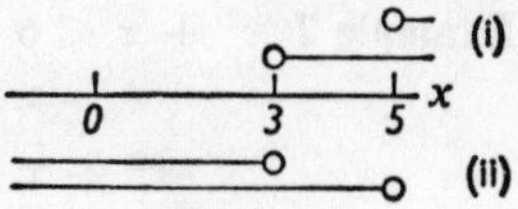

Fig. 1

*or* (ii) $x - 3 < 0$ *and* $x - 5 < 0$

∴ $x < 3$ *and* $x < 5$

∴ solution is $x < 3$

∴ complete solution is $x > 5$ *or* $x < 3.$

Notice here that, if $x > 3$ *and* $x > 5$, the solution is the intersection of two sets $\{x : x > 3\} \cap \{x : x > 5\} = \{x : x > 5\}.$

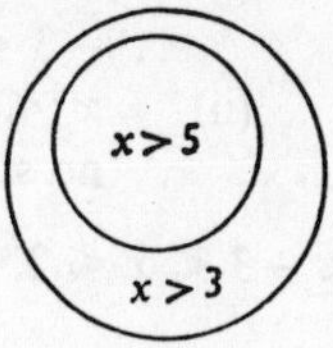

Fig. 2

**Example 5** $\{x : (x - 3)(x - 5) < 0\}.$

*Either* (i) $\{x : x - 3 > 0\} \cap \{x : x - 5 < 0\}$

$= \{x : x > 3\} \cap \{x : x < 5\}$

$= \{x : 3 < x < 5\}$

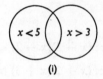

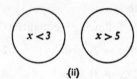

(i)                               (ii)

Fig. 3

*or* (ii) $\{x : x - 3 < 0\} \cap \{x : x - 5 > 0\}$

$= \{x : x < 3\} \cap \{x : x > 5\}$

$= \phi$

*Ans.* $\{x : 3 < x < 5\}.$

**Example 6** $x^2 > 4.$

$$x^2 > 4$$
$$\therefore x^2 - 4 > 0$$
$$\therefore (x + 2)(x - 2) > 0$$

Continue as in Example 4.

*Ans.* $x < -2$ *or* $x > 2;$

in set notation $\{x : x < -2\} \cup \{x : x > 2\}.$

*New General Mathematics*

**Example 7** $x^2 + x \leqslant 6$.

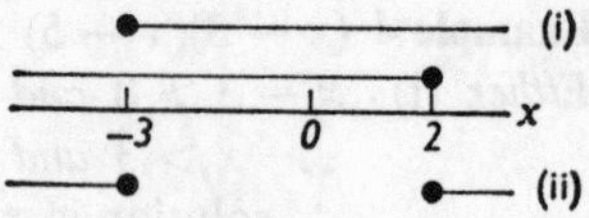

$$x^2 + x \leqslant 6$$
$$\therefore \; x^2 + x - 6 \leqslant 0$$
$$\therefore \; (x + 3)(x - 2) \leqslant 0$$

Fig. 4

*Either* (i) $\quad x \geqslant -3 \; and \; x \leqslant 2$
$$\therefore \; -3 \leqslant x \leqslant 2$$
*or* (ii) $\quad x \leqslant -3 \; and \; x \geqslant 2$
$$\therefore \; \text{no solution}$$

*Ans.* $-3 \leqslant x \leqslant 2$.

N.B. $(x - a)^2 > 0$ True for all values of $x$ *except* $x = a$.
$(x - a)^2 \geqslant 0$ True for all values of $x$.
$(x - a)^2 < 0$ Impossible for real values of $x$.
$(x - a)^2 \leqslant 0$ True only for $x = a$.

**Exercise 4b**

Solve the following inequalities:

**1** $(x - 3)(x - 2) > 0$    **2** $\{x : (x - 3)(x - 2) < 0\}$

**3** $(x + 2)(x + 3) < 0$    **4** $\{x : (x + 2)(x + 3) > 0\}$

**5** $x^2 - 36 > 0$    **6** $\{x : x^2 < 100\}$

**7** $\{x : (x + 2)(x - 3) < 0\}$    **8** $(x - 4)(x + 1) > 0$

**9** $2x^2 \geqslant 32$    **10** $x^2 > x + 12$

**11** $\{x : x^2 + 4x \leqslant 12\}$    **12** $\{x : 2x^2 + 7x \geqslant 4\}$

**13** $2x^2 < x + 6$    **14** $4x^2 + 4x \geqslant 15$

**15** $\{x : 4x^2 + 4x \leqslant 0\}$    **16** $\dfrac{8}{x} > x - 2$

**17** $3x - 8 \geqslant \dfrac{3}{x}$    **18** $\left\{x : \dfrac{6}{x^2} < 6 + \dfrac{5}{x}\right\}$

*Reminder*: the curves shown in Fig. 5 will be needed in the next exercise.

26

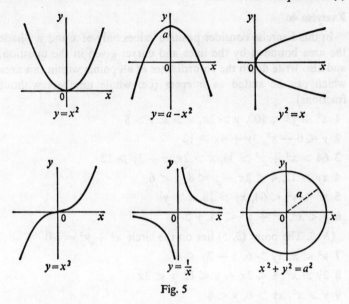

$y = x^2$

$y = a - x^2$

$y^2 = x$

$y = x^3$

$y = \frac{1}{x}$

$x^2 + y^2 = a^2$

Fig. 5

**Example 8** *Show on a diagram the area bounded by* $y \geqslant x^3$, $2y > 9x$, $y < 27$, $x \geqslant 1$ *for positive values of x and y.*

The required area is shown shaded in Fig. 6. Notice that, as in Book 3, Chapter 21, dotted lines indicate a > or < boundary and solid lines a ⩾ or ⩽ boundary.

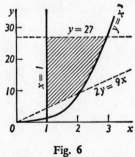

Fig. 6

27

**Exercise 4c**

In this Exercise consider positive values only of $x$ and $y$. Shade the area bounded by the lines and curves given in the question, and also write down the co-ordinates of all points within this area which can be stated as integers (i.e. whole numbers without fractions).

**1** $x^2 + y^2 < 100, y > 2x, x > 2, y > 8$

**2** $y \leqslant 6 - x^2, 3y + 4x \geqslant 12$

**3** $64 > x^2 + y^2 > 36, x > 2y, x + 3y \geqslant 12$

**4** $xy \geqslant 12, 4 < 2x - y < 8, y < 6$

**5** $x^2 + y^2 \leqslant 64, xy > 18, x > y$

**6** $y < x^2, x^2 + y^2 \leqslant 34, y > 3$

(*N.B.* The point (3, 5) lies on the circle $x^2 + y^2 = 34$)

**7** $y^2 < x, xy > 6, x - 2y \leqslant 4$

**8** $2y > x^2, 8 \leqslant 2x + y \leqslant 12, y < 3x$

**9** $y \geqslant x^3, xy > 6, y < 8$

**10** $y \geqslant x^2 + 4, 2x + y \geqslant 12, x^2 + y^2 < 100$

**11** $2y > x^2 + 4, y < x^3, y \leqslant 7$

**12** $y > 10 - x^2, x^2 + y^2 < 45, y > x$

**13** $y^2 < 2x, 25 \geqslant x^2 + y^2 \geqslant 9, x + y > 4, y > 1$

**14** $2y > x^3, y > 8 - x^2, 4 < y - x < 6$

# Chapter 5

# *Trigonometrical ratios of an obtuse angle*

The trigonometrical ratios of an acute angle in a right-angled triangle have already been defined.

In Fig. 7, $\sin \theta = \dfrac{\text{opp.}}{\text{hyp.}} = \dfrac{MP}{OP}$

$\cos \theta = \dfrac{\text{adj.}}{\text{hyp.}} = \dfrac{OM}{OP}$

$\tan \theta = \dfrac{\text{opp.}}{\text{adj.}} = \dfrac{MP}{OM}$

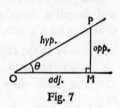

Fig. 7

When the angle $\theta$ is obtuse, some clarification is needed, as $\theta$ is no longer an angle in a triangle of which one side is clearly opposite to $\theta$, and another adjacent.

In Fig. 7, with $\theta$ acute, any point P was taken on one arm of the angle, and a perpendicular was drawn from P to the other arm, cutting it in M.

In Fig. 8, with $\theta$ obtuse, any point P is taken on one arm of the angle, and the perpendicular from P cuts *the other arm produced* in M.

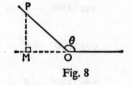

Fig. 8

The ratios are now defined as before,

i.e.   $\sin \theta = \dfrac{MP}{OP}$

$\cos \theta = \dfrac{OM}{OP}$

$\tan \theta = \dfrac{MP}{OM}$

29

In Fig. 9, $\overline{AOB}$ is a diameter of the circle. Draw radii $\overline{OP}$ and $\overline{OQ}$ so that $B\hat{O}P = \theta$ and $Q\hat{O}A = \theta$, $\theta$ being acute.

Then $B\hat{O}Q = 180° - \theta$, which is obtuse.

Draw $\overline{PM}$, $\overline{QN} \perp \overline{AB}$.

Triangles OPM, OQN are clearly congruent, and corresponding sides are equal.

Using the convention for positive and negative lengths as with co-ordinates on a graph,

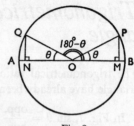

Fig. 9

i.e. +ve to the right, −ve to the left,
+ve upwards, −ve downwards,

ON is negative, since it is measured to the left, and
NQ „ positive, „ „ „ „ upwards.

Hence ON = − OM
and NQ = MP.

The oblique lengths OP and OQ are taken to be positive outwards from O, and are equal.

Then

$$\sin (180° - \theta) = \frac{NQ}{OQ} = \frac{MP}{OP} = \sin \theta$$

$$\cos (180° - \theta) = \frac{ON}{OQ} = \frac{-OM}{OP} = -\frac{OM}{OP} = -\cos \theta$$

$$\tan (180° - \theta) = \frac{NQ}{ON} = \frac{MP}{-OM} = -\frac{MP}{OM} = -\tan \theta$$

Hence
the sine of an angle = the sine of its supplement,
the cosine of an angle = *minus* the cosine of its supplement,
the tangent of an angle = *minus* the tangent of its supplement.

For example,
sin 160° = sin (180° − 20°) = sin 20° = 0·342 0
cos 160° = cos (180° − 20°) = − cos 20° = − 0·939 7
tan 160° = tan (180° − 20°) = − tan 20° = − 0·364 0

The graphs of the three ratios of angles from 0° to 180° may now be drawn.

The values of sin $\theta$ as $\theta$ varies from 0° to 90° are found from the tables, giving the graph from A to B in Fig. 10. Then since, for example, sin 120° = sin 60° and sin 150° = sin 30°, the graph will be symmetrical about the line $\overline{MB}$, and all the values of sin $\theta$ from 0° to 90° will be repeated in reverse order, giving the graph from B to C.

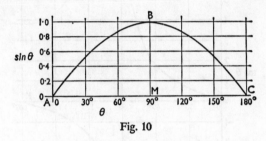

Fig. 10

Notice that the sine of any angle between 0° and 180° is positive.

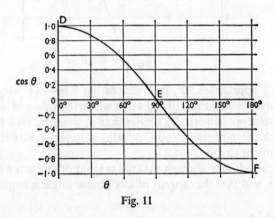

Fig. 11

Fig. 11 shows the graph of cos $\theta$. The values of cos $\theta$ as $\theta$ varies from 0° to 90° are found from the tables, giving the graph from D to E. Then since, for example, cos 120° = $-$ cos 60° and cos 150° = $-$ cos 30°, the values of cos $\theta$ already found between

31

D and E are repeated in reverse order, and in a negative direction (i.e. downwards). This gives the graph from E to F.

Notice that the cosine of any acute angle is positive, and that the cosine of any obtuse angle is negative.

The graph of tan $\theta$ is similarly drawn and is as in Fig. 12, with tan 120° = — tan 60°, tan 150° = — tan 30°, and so on. Notice

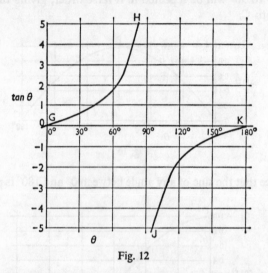

Fig. 12

that as $\theta$ approaches 90°, the value of tan $\theta$ becomes very great. Compare this with Figs. 10 and 11, in which the values of sin $\theta$ and cos $\theta$ are never numerically greater than 1, since each is a fraction in which the numerator (opp. or adj.) is never greater than the denominator (hyp.).

It is clear from the graph that the tangent of any acute angle is positive, and that the tangent of any obtuse angle is negative.

### Exercise 5a

Write down in decimal form the values of the following:

**1** sin 110°          **2** cos 110°          **3** tan 110°

**4** sin 153°          **5** sin 98°          **6** cos 106°

**7** cos 142°    **8** tan 167°    **9** tan 93°

**10** cos 128°    **11** sin 156° 30'    **12** tan 173° 45'

**13** cos 161° 20'    **14** tan 131° 50'    **15** sin 93° 17'

**16** cos 135° 39'    **17** cos 103° 7'    **18** tan 118° 53'

**19** sin 178° 35'    **20** tan 92° 29'    **21** cos 90° 18'

**22** sin 164° 47'    **23** cos 118° 16'    **24** cos 121° 31'

**25** tan 95° 10'

If $\theta$ lies between 0° and 180° and cos $\theta$ is given, then $\theta$ can be found, and there is **only one** value for $\theta$.

For example, if cos $\theta$ = 0·287 4, then from the tables, $\theta$ = 73° 18'.

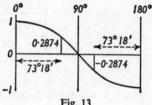

Fig. 13

If cos $\theta$ = −0·287 4, then
$\theta$ = 180° − 73° 18'
= 106° 42'

This is easily seen from the sketch-graph in Fig. 13.

Similarly if tan $\theta$ is given, there is only one value for $\theta$ lying between 0° and 180°.

If tan $\theta$ = 2·164 2, then from the tables, $\theta$ = 65° 12'.

If tan $\theta$ = −2·164 2, then
$\theta$ = 180° − 65° 12'
= 114° 48'

This is illustrated in the sketch-graph in Fig. 14.

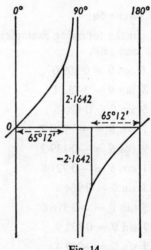

Fig. 14

If, however, sin $\theta$ is known, there are two possible values for $\theta$ between 0° and 180°.

For example, if sin $\theta$ = 0·936 1, then from the tables, $\theta$ = 69° 24'.

But sin 69° 24′ = sin (180° − 69° 24′) = sin 110° 36′.
Hence if sin θ = 0·936 1, θ could be either 69° 24′ or 110° 36′.
The sketch graph in Fig. 15 should make this clear.

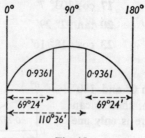

Fig. 15

If sin θ = −0·936 1, then θ does not lie between 0° and 180°.

## Exercise 5b

In the following examples, find the values of θ lying between 0° and 180°.

**1** cos θ = 0·809 0          **2** cos θ = −0·809 0

**3** tan θ = 3·732 1          **4** tan θ = −3·732 1

**5** sin θ = 0·920 5          **6** tan θ = −1·962 6

**7** cos θ = −0·939 7        **8** sin θ = 0·422 6

**9** cos θ = −0·139 2        **10** tan θ = −0·624 9

**11** cos θ = −0·727 8       **12** sin θ = 0·608 8

**13** sin θ = 0·964 6        **14** tan θ = −2·106 0

**15** tan θ = −0·316 6       **16** cos θ = −0·425 3

**17** sin θ = 0·832 9        **18** tan θ = −0·723 0

**19** sin θ = 0·959 4        **20** cos θ = −0·784 6

**21** tan θ = −1·678 6       **22** sin θ = 0·262 8

**23** sin θ = 0·744 9        **24** tan θ = −12·34

**25** cos θ = −0·952 4

# Chapter 6

## *Connections between the trigonometrical ratios*

In Fig. 16, a perpendicular is drawn from one arm of the angle $\theta$ to the other, and the lengths of the sides of the right-angled triangle so formed are $m$, $n$ and $d$ units respectively.

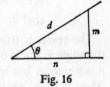

Fig. 16

Then
$$\frac{\sin \theta}{\cos \theta} = \frac{\dfrac{m}{d}}{\dfrac{n}{d}} = \frac{m}{n} = \tan \theta$$

$$\therefore \ \tan \theta = \frac{\sin \theta}{\cos \theta}.$$

Also, since $\quad \cot \theta = \dfrac{1}{\tan \theta}, \quad \cot \theta = \dfrac{\cos \theta}{\sin \theta}.$

The square of a ratio is usually written without brackets, e.g. $(\sin \theta)^2$ is written as $\sin^2 \theta$.

$$\sin^2 \theta + \cos^2 \theta = \frac{m^2}{d^2} + \frac{n^2}{d^2}$$

$$= \frac{m^2 + n^2}{d^2}$$

$$= \frac{d^2}{d^2} \qquad (m^2 + n^2 = d^2, Pythag.)$$

$$= 1.$$

$$\therefore \ \sin^2 \theta + \cos^2 \theta = 1.$$

This result is, in effect, an alternative version of the theorem of Pythagoras,

$$\text{for} \quad m^2 + n^2 = d^2$$
$$\therefore \frac{m^2}{d^2} + \frac{n^2}{d^2} = 1$$
$$\therefore \sin^2 \theta + \cos^2 \theta = 1.$$

Notice also the following forms of the same statement:

$$\sin^2 \theta = 1 - \cos^2 \theta$$
$$\cos^2 \theta = 1 - \sin^2 \theta.$$

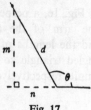

Fig. 17

The result is true whatever the size of the angle $\theta$. If $\theta$ is obtuse as in Fig. 17, the $n$ is negative, but $n^2$ is positive as before. Also, if $\theta$ is an obtuse angle, $\cos \theta$ is negative, but $\cos^2 \theta$ is positive.

**Example 1** *If* $\sin \theta = \frac{5}{13}$, *find the value of* $\cos \theta$.

$$\sin^2 \theta + \cos^2 \theta = 1$$
$$\therefore \cos^2 \theta = 1 - \sin^2 \theta$$
$$= 1 - \frac{25}{169}$$
$$= \frac{144}{169}$$
$$\therefore \cos \theta = \pm \frac{12}{13}.$$

If $\theta$ is acute, then $\cos \theta = \frac{12}{13}$.
If $\theta$ is obtuse, then $\cos \theta = -\frac{12}{13}$.

*Alternatively*, draw a triangle PQR right-angled at R, with angle $\theta$ at Q. Then if RP is 5 units, QP must be 13 units, since $\sin \theta = \frac{5}{13}$.

$$QR^2 = 13^2 - 5^2 = 144$$
$$\therefore QR = 12 \text{ units}$$
$$\therefore \cos \theta = \frac{QR}{QP} = \frac{12}{13}.$$

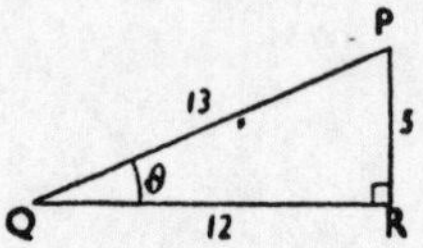

Fig. 18

This result is true only if $\theta$ is acute.
If $\theta$ is obtuse, then $\cos \theta = -\frac{12}{13}$.

**Example 2** *If tan θ = 1·7, find the values of sin θ and cos θ.*

Since tan θ is positive, θ cannot be obtuse.
Draw △PQR right-angled at R, with angle θ at Q.
If QR = 10 cm, then RP = 17 cm, since tan θ = 1·7 = $\frac{17}{10}$.

Fig. 19

$$PQ^2 = 17^2 + 10^2 = 289 + 100 = 389$$

∴ PQ = √389 cm

∴ sin θ = $\dfrac{17}{\sqrt{389}}$

= 0·861 8

| No. | Log. |
|---|---|
| 17 | 1·230 4 |
| √389 | 2·589 9 ÷ 2 ≃ 1·295 0 |
| 0·861 8 | 1̄·935 4 |

and   cos θ = $\dfrac{10}{\sqrt{389}}$

= 0·507 0.

| No. | Log. |
|---|---|
| 10 | 1·000 0 |
| √389 | 2·589 9 ÷ 2 ≃ 1·295 0 |
| 0·507 0 | 1̄·705 0 |

**Example 3** *Find the value of cot 36° sin 36°.*

$$\cot 36° \sin 36° = \frac{\cos 36°}{\sin 36°} \times \sin 36°$$
$$= \cos 36°$$
$$= 0·809 0.$$

**Example 4** *If θ is acute and sin θ = s, find cos θ and tan θ in terms of s.*

Draw a right-angled triangle as in Fig. 20, so that sin θ = $\dfrac{s}{1}$.

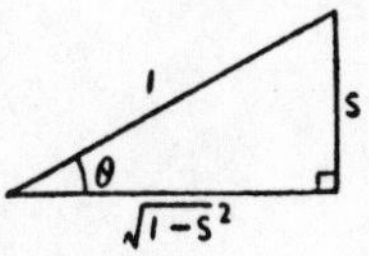

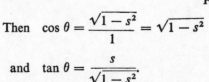

Fig. 20

Then   cos θ = $\dfrac{\sqrt{1 - s^2}}{1} = \sqrt{1 - s^2}$

and   tan θ = $\dfrac{s}{\sqrt{1 - s^2}}$.

# New General Mathematics

## Exercise 6

*Trigonometrical tables should not be used in nos. 1–10.*
*In nos. 1–12 the angle $\theta$ may be assumed to be acute.*

1 If $\quad \cos \theta = \frac{4}{5}, \quad$ find $\sin \theta$ and $\tan \theta$

2 „ $\quad \sin \theta = \frac{12}{13}, \quad$ „ $\cos \theta$ „ $\tan \theta$

3 „ $\quad \tan \theta = \frac{8}{15}, \quad$ „ $\sin \theta$ „ $\cos \theta$

4 „ $\quad \sin \theta = \frac{7}{25}, \quad$ „ $\cos \theta$ „ $\tan \theta$

5 „ $\quad \cos \theta = \frac{40}{41}, \quad$ „ $\sin \theta$ „ $\tan \theta$

6 „ $\quad \tan \theta = \frac{5}{7}, \quad$ „ $\sin \theta$ „ $\cos \theta$, to 3 sig. fig.

7 „ $\quad \tan \theta = 2 \cdot 1, \quad$ „ $\sin \theta$ „ $\cos \theta$, „ „ „ „

8 „ $\quad \sin \theta = \frac{3}{7}, \quad$ „ $\cos \theta$ „ $\tan \theta$, „ „ „ „

9 „ $\quad \sec \theta = 3, \quad$ „ $\sin \theta$ „ $\tan \theta$, „ „ „ „

10 „ $\quad \cos \theta = 0 \cdot 4, \quad$ „ $\sin \theta$ „ $\tan \theta$, „ „ „ „

11 „ $\quad \tan \theta = t, \quad$ „ $\sin \theta$ „ $\cos \theta$ in terms of $t$

12 „ $\quad \operatorname{cosec} \theta = x, \quad$ „ $\cos \theta$ „ $\tan \theta$ „ „ „ $x$

With as little working as possible, find the value of

13 $\dfrac{\sin 62°}{\cos 62°}$ 　　　14 $\tan 34° \cos 34°$ 　　　15 $\tan 19° \operatorname{cosec} 19°$

# Chapter 7

# *Monetary systems and exchange*

A national of any country expects to pay and to be paid in the currency of his own country when he is living there: a French merchant or tradesman will not accept pounds or dollars in France, but requires francs in payment and will settle his debts in francs; an American requires dollars; an Indian rupees, and so on.

Before the two world wars most countries were on the 'gold standard' and gold was the common base on which the value of one form of currency in terms of another could be calculated.

For instance the mass of an English sovereign (£1 in gold) was compared with the mass of an American $10 gold piece, and it was a simple calculation to find that £1 was equivalent to $4·86.

In the same way all countries on the gold standard were able to work out their **mint par of exchange,** so that transactions between countries or their nationals could be quickly and smoothly carried out.

Those countries whose base was silver and not gold made similar arrangements amongst themselves, and were also linked to the gold countries by comparable calculations.

Unfortunately one effect of the two wars was to make it impossible for most countries to remain on the gold standard (for reasons which are far too complex to go into here), so that the common basis of calculation was no longer available, and consequently the various currencies had to be linked together in agreed ratios.

The table below shows the currency units in use by a number of countries and their approximate relations to the £ sterling. It is important to realise that these relations are only agreed values, and are liable to revision by the countries concerned, should circumstances result in the agreed values ceasing to reflect the real values (in terms of purchasing power) of the currencies involved.

| Country | Local unit | Units to £1 |
|---|---|---|
| U.S.A. | Dollar ($) | 2·40 |
| Canada | Dollar ($) | 2·60 |
| Holland | Florin (fl) | 8·70 |
| Belgium | Franc (f) | 119·60 |
| Denmark | Kroner (k) | 17·90 |
| West Germany | Deutschmark (DM) | 8·84 |
| Portugal | Escudo (e) | 68·50 |
| Italy | Lira (lr) | 1 500·00 |
| Norway | Kroner (k) | 17·15 |
| France | Franc (F) | 13·34 |
| Sweden | Kronor (k) | 12·42 |
| Switzerland | Franc (f) | 10·42 |
| Spain | Peseta (pt) | 167·75 |
| Greece | Drachma (dr) | 71·65 |

In fact the day-to-day quotations of foreign exchange in the daily papers will show continual slight variations from the figures given here, but in general tend to fluctuate round them.

In the examples given and in the exercise which follows, values are taken from this table unless other rates are quoted.

**Example 1** *If a traveller is allowed to take £50 abroad, how many florins will he have available for a holiday in Holland?*

$$£1 = 8·70 \text{ fl}$$
$$\therefore £50 = 50 \times 8·70 \text{ fl}$$
$$= 435 \text{ fl.}$$

**Example 2** *What is the value of a French 100-franc note to the nearest penny?*

$$13·34 \text{ F} = £1$$
$$\therefore 100 \text{ F} = £\frac{100}{13·34}$$
$$\simeq £7·50.$$

**Example 3** *How many American dollars can be bought for* 2 000 Portuguese escudos?

$$£1 = 68·50 \text{ escudos} = \$2·40$$

$$\therefore 2\ 000 \text{ escudos} = \$2·40 \times \frac{2\ 000}{68·50}$$

$$= \$\frac{4\ 800}{68·50}$$

$$\simeq \$70·07.$$

**Exercise 7**

1 How many (i) German Deutschmarks, (ii) Swedish kronor, (iii) American dollars, (iv) Swiss francs, (v) Italian lire, can be bought for £20?

2 Evaluate in £ to the nearest penny
  (i) 25 Canadian dollars,
  (ii) 5 000 Belgian francs,
  (iii) 300 Norwegian kroner,
  (iv) 600 Portuguese escudos,
  (v) 10 000 Italian lire.

3 How much does the value of an American $10 bill rise or fall if the rate changes from 2·41 to 2·39 (nearest penny)?

4 By what percentage has the value of the £ in terms of the American dollar depreciated since 1920, when the rate was 4·86?

5 What is the value of a Swiss franc to the nearest penny?

6 The Dutch have a large silver double-florin: what is this coin worth in pence, to the nearest penny?

In nos. 7 to 12 find the equivalent cost to the nearest penny.

7 Dinner on a French train, which costs about 12·5 francs.

8 A Vancouver haircut at $1·60.

9 A leather handbag which cost 16 000 lire in Naples.

10 A glass vase bought in Stockholm for 50 kronor.

11 A box of 100 Dutch cigars for 23·50 florins.

12 A week in Portugal, costing 1 650 escudos.

**13** An American intending to travel in Great Britain can buy for $20 in America a 'thrift token' ticket which entitles him to 1 600 km of second-class railway travel. What is the cost of a railway journey to him in pence per kilometre, to two decimal places?

**14** If ribbon in France costs 9·60 francs per metre, find in £ the cost of 20 metres (nearest penny).

**15** A bottle of wine which is sold for 2·30 francs in France costs 65p in England. By what percentage, to the nearest whole number, is the cost in England greater than that in France?

**16** Find in French francs the cost of 24 litres of petrol, which costs 7p per litre in England (nearest penny).

**17** A Scottish distillery exports whisky to America at £18·50 for a case of twelve bottles. If the retail price of a bottle of whisky in America is $8.80c, and taxation etc. amounts to $38 per case, what percentage profit does the American importer make on the sale?

**18** The cost of a ten-day winter sports holiday in Switzerland for a party of twenty schoolboys with two adults in charge of the party worked out at £25·30 for each boy, the adults paying nothing towards the cost. If the journey cost £13·20 per head, what did the hotel charge in francs per head per day?

**19** A traveller buys francs at 13·30 to the £ with a £5 'traveller's cheque'. He crosses into Italy and changes the francs into lire at the rate of 113 lire to the franc. He spends 6 500 lire in Italy and changes the remaining lire into sterling at 1 510 to the £. How much English money has he got back out of the original cheque (nearest penny)?

**20** Before the war an English importer bought articles in New York at $11.40c each. The cost of importing them to England was $68.40c per hundred, and the rate of exchange was then $4.56c to the £. The price of the articles has risen to $25.50c each; the cost of importing them is double what it was, and the rate of exchange is now $2.40c to the £. Find, in English money, the difference in the average cost of each article.

# Revision examples

## I

1 Find to the nearest penny the compound interest on £240 for 3 years at 4%.

2 One angle of a polygon is a right angle, and each of the other angles is 126°. Calculate the number of sides.

3 68·46 Portuguese escudos and 8·71 Dutch florins go to the £. How many escudos go to the florin?

4 Solve the equation $10 \sin x = 7$ for values of $x$ between 0° and 180°.

5 Solve the equations $xy + 6 = 0$, $x - 2y = 7$.

6 .A gang X can surface a kilometre of motorway in 15 days, and a gang Y can do the same in 10 days. The two gangs work together for two days, after which Y is withdrawn and sent to another job. How much longer will it take X to complete the kilometre?

7 Solve the equation $\dfrac{2}{x-4} + \dfrac{1}{x-2} + \dfrac{7}{x^2 - 6x + 8} = 0$.

8 $\overline{AB}$ is a fixed diameter of a given circle, and P a variable point on the circumference. $\overline{AP}$ is produced to X so that XP = PA. Find the locus of X.

9 Which British Electricity stock gives the better yield: $3\frac{1}{2}\%$ at 70 or $4\frac{1}{4}\%$ at 80? Find the effective rate per cent of each stock.

10 Solve the inequalities (i) $\dfrac{12}{x} < 4$ (ii) $(x - 2)(x - 4) > 0$

## II

1 (i) If $\sin \theta = \frac{3}{4}$, find the value of $4 \cos^2 \theta + \frac{1}{4}$.
 (ii) If $\sin \phi = \frac{3}{5}$ and $\phi$ is obtuse, find the value of $\cos \phi$.

2 Construct the incircle of a triangle with sides 6 cm, 7·5 cm and 9 cm, and measure its diameter.

43

**3** On each of three consecutive days a man bought £100 worth of dollars at 2·40, 2·38 and 2·41 respectively to the £. He then changed all the dollars back into sterling at 2·39. How much did he gain or lose altogether?

**4** Solve the equations $x - 2y = 2$, $x^2 - 4y^2 = 28$.

**5** The universal set $\mathscr{E}$ is made up of all the positive integers from 1 to 16 inclusive. The subset A consists of those members of $\mathscr{E}$ which are multiples of 3. The subset B consists of those members of $\mathscr{E}$ which are multiples of 4. List the members of the two sets A′ ∩ B and A ∩ B′.

**6** A 30°, 60°, 90° set-square with a 12-cm hypotenuse is supported with its shortest side on a table and the vertex 10 cm above the table. Find the angles between the table and (i) the hypotenuse, (ii) the third side.

**7** On a 300-km stretch of motorway a motorist averages 100 km h⁻¹ on the good surface, but only 40 km h⁻¹ on the parts which are being made up. If the average speed for the whole journey is 80 km h⁻¹, what length of road is under repair?

**8** ABCD is a parallelogram, and P, Q are the mid-points of $\overline{AB}$, $\overline{DC}$ respectively. $\overline{PC}$ cuts $\overline{BD}$ at X and $\overline{QA}$ cuts $\overline{BD}$ at Y. Prove that APCQ is a parallelogram, and also that

$$BX = XY = YD.$$

**9** Find to the nearest penny the compound interest on £76·68 for 3 years at 4%.

**10** Draw the graph of $t = \sqrt{0·2d}$, for values of $d$ from 2 to 10. Read off the value of $t$ when $d = 7$ and of $d$ when $t = 1·3$.

### III

**1** What is the effective rate of interest on money invested if British Aluminium £1 shares pay a 12% dividend and the shares were bought at 250p? How much did a man invest if his income from the investment was £55·20?

**2** In January 1957 three USAAF Stratojets completed a non-stop flight round the world in 45 h 19 min. If their route was

40 083 km long, find the average speed of the aircraft correct to 3 sig. fig.

**3** (i) Solve the equation $20 \tan x + 31 = 0$ for a value of $x$ between $0°$ and $180°$.

(ii) If $\tan x = 2·4$, evaluate without using tables

$$2 \sin x + 3 \cos x.$$

**4** Solve the inequalities (i) $\{x : \dfrac{15}{x} \geqslant 10\}$

(ii) $\{x : x^2 < 25\}$

**5** Solve the equations $x + 3y = 1$, $x^2 - 3y^2 = 13$.

**6** The value of a car bought for £1 500 depreciates at the rate of 12% per annum. What is the value of the car to the nearest tenth of £1 after 4 years?

**7** Two circles ABX, ABYP cut at A and B. $\overline{AY}$ is the tangent at A to the first circle, and $\overline{XB}$ is produced to cut the second circle at P (Fig. 21). Prove $\overline{AX} \parallel \overline{PY}$.

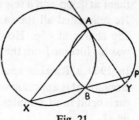

Fig. 21

**8** Brown and Smith run a 4-km race. Brown runs 1 km h⁻¹ faster than Smith and finishes a quarter of a kilometre ahead of him. How long does Brown take for the 4 km?

**9** A man on business in Greece changes £200 into drachmas at 71·65 to the £, spends 13 800 drachmas, and changes the rest back into sterling at the same rate as before. How much should he receive?

**10** Draw on the same diagram the graphs of $y = \dfrac{3}{x + 3}$ and $y = \dfrac{x + 2}{12}$, taking values of $x$ between 1 and 6.

Show that the intersection of the two graphs gives a solution of the equation $x^2 + 5x - 30 = 0$, and read off this solution.

## IV

1 Solve the equations $2x + 3y = 3, 4x^2 - 9y^2 = -27$.

2 Find to the nearest penny the compound interest on £311·09 for 3 years at $1\frac{1}{2}\%$ per annum.

3 (i) Express in standard form 238 500 and 0·000 004 7.

(ii) If $\hat{A}$ is obtuse and $\sin A = \frac{12}{13}$, what is the value of $\tan A$ (no tables to be used)?

4 In a triangle ABC, $AB = AC$. The bisectors of $\hat{B}$ and $\hat{C}$ meet $\overline{AC}$ and $\overline{AB}$ at X and Y respectively. Prove that $BY = CX$ and that $\overline{YX} \parallel \overline{BC}$.

5 A man who had 500 Imperial Tobacco £1 shares sold 300 of them at 250p and a few days later the remaining 200 at 210p. He reinvested all the cash he had received in Cammell Laird 25p shares at 65p. How many shares did he buy, and what was his income from the shares if they paid a dividend of 14%?

6 In 1960 a Russian sputnik, travelling round the earth in a circular orbit approximately 14 400 km in diameter, completed each orbit in 91 minutes. What was its speed in km h$^{-1}$ (3 sig. fig.)?

7 Fig. 22 shows a desk sloping at 30° to the horizontal, M being the mid-point of the top edge $\overline{AB}$ of the desk. Find the inclination to the horizontal of $\overline{BD}$ and of $\overline{MD}$.

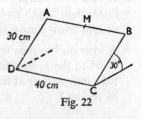

Fig. 22

8 A book which costs 6 francs in Paris is sold for 3·50 florins in Amsterdam. Which is the larger price, and by how many pence? (£1 = 13·32 F = 8·70 fl)

9 ABCD is a circle and the chords $\overline{AB}$, $\overline{DC}$ meet outside the circle at P. X is a point on $\overline{DP}$ such that $\overline{BX} \parallel \overline{AD}$. Prove that the circle BXC touches $\overline{AP}$ at B.

10 The vertices of a triangle are at (2,4), (4,−4), (−4,2). Find the vertices of the triangle which is the result of reflecting the

given triangle in the line $y = 0$ and then enlarging in the ratio
$3:2$ with $(0,0)$ as centre.

## V

**1** Evaluate (i) $\sqrt[3]{15 \cdot 6 \times 9 \cdot 37}$    (ii) $0 \cdot 482\ 3^3$

**2** Solve the equations $x + 2y = 12$, $x^2 + 4y^2 = 104$.

**3** In June 1968 a man bought 2 000 Ebor Commodity Units at
34p, and later that year he received a dividend of $0 \cdot 56$p per
unit. In January 1969 he sold all his units at 43p. Find his total
profit on the transaction.

**4** Evaluate without using tables (i) $\sin^2 29° + \sin^2 61°$

                                     (ii) $\tan 34° \times \sin 56° \times \operatorname{cosec} 34°$

**5** The catalogue price of a certain article is 136% of the cost
price, but the purchaser is allowed 5% discount off the catalogue price if he pays cash. What is the cash price if the cost
price is £25?

**6** (i) Express $0 \cdot 002$ and $0 \cdot 000\ 003$ in standard form. Hence find
the value of $0 \cdot 002 \times 0 \cdot 000\ 003$ in standard form.
(ii) Express 120 000 and $0 \cdot 04$ in standard form. Hence find
the value of $120\ 000 \div 0 \cdot 04$ in standard form.
(iii) Express $0 \cdot 005$ and $(0 \cdot 005)^3$ in standard form.
(iv) Express 810 000 and $\sqrt[4]{810\ 000}$ in standard form.

**7** If $\dfrac{7x + y}{x + 7y} = 3$, evaluate $\dfrac{7x - y}{x - 7y}$.

**8** Two circles touch externally at X, and P is any point on the
common tangent at X to the circles. $\overline{PA}$ is a tangent from P to
one circle and $\overline{PD}$ a tangent to the other, and the line $\overline{AD}$ cuts
the circles again at B and C.

    Prove $PA = PD$ and $A\hat{X}B = C\hat{X}D$.

**9** Over the last few years the cost of my tobacco has risen by 7p
per tin, with the result that I now get 3 tins fewer for £6·30 than
I did. What are the old and new prices per tin?

**10** Draw the graph of $\sin x + 2 \cos x$ for values of $x$ from $0°$ to
$180°$. Hence solve the equation $\sin x + 2 \cos x = 0$.

## VI

1 If 2 sec A + 5 = 0 and A is an angle of a triangle, what is the size of this angle?

2 Draw a circle of radius 6·4 cm and inscribe in it a triangle with angles of 50°, 60° and 70°. Measure the shortest side of the triangle.

3 In 1957 Sam Snead won the Dallas Open Golf tournament and his prize money amounted to $8 000 (about £2 780, according to the newspaper report). If these figures are correct, what was the rate of exchange at this time in dollars to the pound sterling, and what was one dollar worth to the nearest penny?

4 Solve the equations $x^2 + xy + y^2 = 12$, $x + y = 2$.

5 What is the compound interest on £127·58 for 2 years at $3\frac{1}{2}\%$ per annum (to the nearest penny)?

6 A rectangular block of wood 6 cm by 10 cm gets jammed across a gutter in such a position that the 10-cm side makes an angle of 24° with the gutter. Calculate the width of the gutter.

7 What was the effective rate of income on Guinness 50p shares bought at 212p if the dividend paid was 25%? Express the answer in £ per cent to the nearest penny.

8 $a = 2·76 \times 10^{19}$, $b = 3·81 \times 10^{-7}$, $c = 5·04 \times 10^{10}$. Evaluate $\dfrac{ab^2}{c}$, expressing the answer in standard form to 3 sig. fig.

9 ABCD is a parallelogram and E any point on $\overline{DC}$. $\overline{AE}$ meets $\overline{BD}$ at X and $\overline{BC}$ produced at Y. Prove

(i) $\triangle AXD = \triangle BXE$, (ii) $\triangle AEB = \triangle ADY$.

10 Draw the graph of $y = x^2 - 5x + 1$ for values of $x$ from 0 to 5. Hence solve the equation $x^2 - 5x + 2 = 0$.

## VII

1 A man borrowed £5 000 from the bank, paying 4% compound interest p.a. on the loan, on 1 January 1960. He repaid £1 000 on 31 December each year. What was the amount of his debt on 1 January 1964 (nearest penny)?

**2** Solve, for values of $x$ between $0°$ and $180°$, $13 \operatorname{cosec} x = 30$.

**3** Solve the equations $2x^2 - 3xy = 14$, $2x + 3y + 1 = 0$.

**4** Fig. 23 shows a portion of a cylinder 8 cm in radius and 16 cm high, O being the centre of the top surface and $A\hat{O}X = 120°$. If the cylinder is placed with the lines $\overline{AB}$ and $\overline{XY}$ vertical, calculate the angles made with the horizontal by (i) $\overline{AY}$, (ii) the triangle BOY.

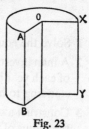

Fig. 23

**5** Solve the inequalities  (i) $\{x : \dfrac{16}{x} + 4 > 0\}$

(ii) $\{x : x^2 - 2x \geqslant 8\}$

**6** A seaside party sets out for a trip in a motor-boat to an island 7 km out from the harbour. On the outward journey they have the advantage of a 4 km h$^{-1}$ tide, but on the way home the tide is running against them at 5 km h$^{-1}$, so that the homeward journey takes 54 minutes longer than the journey out. What speed would the motor-boat make in slack water?

**7** $\overline{AC}$ is the diameter of a circle ABCD and Q any point on $\overline{AC}$. A line through Q perpendicular to $\overline{AC}$ cuts $\overline{AB}$ at P and $\overline{AD}$ at R. Prove that PQCB and RQCD are cyclic quadrilaterals, and that the line joining the centres of the circles PQCB and RQCD bisects $\overline{QC}$.

**8** A pyramid stands on a base which is a regular hexagon of side 2 m, and each of the slant-edges is 3 m long. Find the angle which (i) an edge, (ii) one of the triangular faces, makes with the base.

**9** Associated Electrical Industries highest and lowest prices for a £1 share in 1957 were 361p and 270p respectively. The total dividend during the year was 20%. How much did an investor lose who bought 150 shares at the top price and sold at the bottom, and what cash dividend did he receive?

**10** Draw on the same diagram graphs of $y = (4 - x)(x - 1)$ and $2y = x$ for values of $x$ from 0 to 5. Show that the intersections

49

of the graphs give the solutions of the equation $2x^2 - 9x + 8 = 0$, and write down these solutions.

## VIII

1 Solve the equations $xy + 4x - 3y = 2x + 3y = 12$.

2 A man invests £2 000 at 3% compound interest, and at the end of each year he adds £150 to his investment. Find the total sum standing to his credit after 4 years (to the nearest penny).

3 Construct a triangle ABC having $A\widehat{B}C = 50°$ and $AB = 10$ cm, the radius of the inscribed circle being 2·5 cm. Measure BC and CA.

4 If $A = \begin{pmatrix} 1 & 3 \\ 2 & 4 \end{pmatrix}$, $B = \begin{pmatrix} -2 & 1 \\ -3 & 4 \end{pmatrix}$ and $C = AB$, find the value of the matrix C. Find also the value of BA.

5 A sailing dinghy starting from a buoy A makes successive tacks of 5 km on a bearing of 063°, 4 km on a bearing of 163°, and finally 5 km on a bearing of $\theta°$. After completing the three tacks the dinghy has reached another buoy B which is due east of A. Find the distance from A to B direct, and the angle $\theta°$.

6 $y = \dfrac{3x - 2}{2x + 5}$. Express $x$ in terms of $y$, and evaluate $x$ if $x = 7y$.

7 £600 of $3\frac{1}{2}$% Conversion Loan is sold at $80\frac{1}{2}$ and the proceeds reinvested in Monsanto 25p shares at 84p, these shares paying a dividend of $13\frac{1}{2}$%. What is the change in the income received (nearest penny)?

8 A conical hole is formed in a metal block, the axis of the hole being at right angles to the face of the block. When a 1-cm diameter ball is dropped into the hole, the top of the ball is 4·8 cm below the face of the block: for a 2-cm diameter ball this distance is 0·4 cm. Calculate the included angle of the taper.

9 (i) Solve the equation $5x^2 + 16x + 7 = 0$, giving the roots to two places of decimals.
(ii) If one root of the equation $2x^2 + ax - 20 = 0$ is $2\frac{1}{2}$, find $a$ and the other root.

**10** Draw on the same diagram the graphs of sin $3x$ and cos $2x$ for values of $x$ from $0°$ to $60°$. Read off the solutions of the equation sin $3x =$ cos $2x$.

## IX

**1** Evaluate to 3 sig. fig.

   (i) $\dfrac{1 \cdot 76 \times 0 \cdot 68}{0 \cdot 19 \times 179}$     (ii) $0 \cdot 328\ 1^5$     (iii) $\sqrt[7]{57 \cdot 32}$

**2** Solve the equations
$$2x^2 + 3xy - 2y^2 = 0, \; 2x + y + 6 = 0.$$

**3** The £ is rated at \$2·40 and at 10·36 Swiss francs. How many Swiss francs can be bought for \$1 000 (nearest whole number)?

**4** ABCD is a parallelogram with E, F the mid-points of $\overline{BC}$, $\overline{CD}$ respectively. Prove $\triangle BEF = \frac{1}{4}\triangle BAF$.

**5** £376 was invested in London Tin 20p shares at 47p, which subsequently paid a dividend of 30%. How many shares were bought and what dividend was received from them? What percentage return on money invested does this dividend represent?

**6** In a group of girls it was found that 58 had been to France, 49 had been to Germany, and 36 had been to Holland. All had visited one or more of these countries except 3 girls who had never been abroad. Thirty-one had been to France only, 19 to Germany only, 10 to France and Germany but not Holland, and 39 had visited more than one country. By means of a Venn diagram find how many girls there were in the group.

**7** A £2 000 car is bought on the instalment system, the purchaser paying £500 down and agreeing to pay £500 quarterly until the debt is paid off. If interest is added quarterly at 6% per annum, what is the amount of the final payment (at the end of the fourth quarter)?

**8** The speed of light is 299 800 km s$^{-1}$.
(i) Express this speed in standard form $a \times 10^n$, where $n$ is an integer and $a$ a number between 1 and 10 (3 sig. fig.).

51

(ii) A 'light year' is the distance which light travels in one year. Express this distance in kilometres in standard form.

(iii) A star is $4 \cdot 9 \times 10^{18}$ kilometres from the earth. Express this distance in light years.

**9** A dealer bought a number of toys for £8. If he had been able to buy them for 5p each less than he did, he could have bought eight more for the same money. How many toys did he buy and at what price?

**10** Draw on the same diagram the graphs of $y = x^3 - 12x$ and $y + 9x = 2$ for values of $x$ from $-3$ to $+4$, taking a 2-cm scale for values of $x$ and 4 cm = 10 units for values of $y$. Hence solve the equation $x^3 - 3x - 2 = 0$.

## X

**1** (i) cos A $= \frac{2}{3}$. Evaluate 3 sin$^2$ A $- 1$.

(ii) B is an obtuse angle and sin B $= 0 \cdot 6$. What is the value of cos B?

(No tables to be used in this question.)

**2** Solve the equations $\dfrac{2}{x} - \dfrac{3}{y} = \dfrac{1}{6}$, $2x + 1 = y$.

**3** Show on a graph the area giving the solution-set of $x + 2y < 8$, $3x + 4 > y$, $y > 0$.

**4** The vertices of a triangle are at $(4,5)$, $(-5,1)$, $(3,-1)$. Find the vertices of the triangle which is the result of translating the given triangle through $(3,-2)$, and then reflecting it in the line $x = 0$.

**5** Solve the inequality $\dfrac{6}{x} > x - 1$.

**6** The hypotenuse of a right-angled triangle is $y + z$, the other two sides being $z$ and $x - y$. Express $y$ in terms of $x$ and $z$.

**7** A man borrows £2 000 at 3% compound interest, and at the end of each year he repays £150. Find how much he still owes after four years (nearest penny).

**8** Two circles touch internally at A and any other circle through A cuts them at B and C (Fig. 24). X is any point on the third circle, and $\overline{\text{XBP}}$, $\overline{\text{XCQ}}$ are straight lines. Prove that $\overline{\text{PQA}}$ is a straight line.

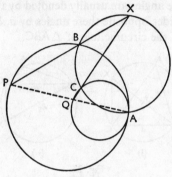

Fig. 24

**9** 200 Unilever £1 shares were bought at 525p and sold when the price had dropped to 450p, a $17\frac{1}{2}\%$ dividend having been paid in the meantime. The money was reinvested in British Gas $3\frac{1}{2}\%$ stock, and the income received was the same as before. What was the price of the stock?

**10** Solve graphically the equation cosec $x = 3 \sin x$, taking values of $x$ from 0° to 180°.

# Chapter 8

# *The sine formula*

In any $\triangle ABC$, the angles are usually denoted by the capital letters A, B, C and the sides opposite these angles by $a$, $b$, $c$ respectively. R is the radius of the circumcircle of $\triangle ABC$.

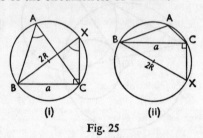

Fig. 25

**To prove** that

$$\frac{a}{\sin A} = \frac{b}{\sin B} = \frac{c}{\sin C} = 2R.$$

Draw the diameter $\overline{BX}$ of the circle ABC, and join $\overline{CX}$.

Then  $B\hat{C}X = 90°$           *∠ in semi ⊙*

In (i), with A acute,

     $\sin A = \sin B\hat{X}C$          *∠s in same segment*

            $= \dfrac{a}{2R}.$

In (ii), with A obtuse,

     $\sin A = \sin (180° - B\hat{X}C)$    *opp. ∠s of cyclic quad.*

          $= \sin B\hat{X}C$

          $= \dfrac{a}{2R}.$

$\therefore$ whether A is acute or obtuse,

     $\sin A = \dfrac{a}{2R}$

i.e. $\dfrac{a}{\sin A} = 2R.$

Similarly $\dfrac{b}{\sin B} = 2R$ and $\dfrac{c}{\sin C} = 2R.$

$\therefore \dfrac{a}{\sin A} = \dfrac{b}{\sin B} = \dfrac{c}{\sin C} = 2R.$

The principal use of this formula is for 'solving' triangles which are not right-angled, and in which **two angles and any side** are given.

It can also be used when **two sides and the angle opposite one of them** are given. Only one triangle can be drawn with these given facts, provided

(i)  that the given angle is obtuse, or

(ii) that if the given angle is acute, then the side opposite to it is the greater of the two given sides.

If the side opposite the given acute angle is less than the other given side, then there is ambiguity, i.e. two different triangles can be drawn with the same set of three facts. This case is dealt with on page 60.

In any case it is advisable to **draw a rough figure** to make sure that only one triangle can be drawn with the given facts.

The formula should never be used for the solution of triangles which are right-angled or isosceles, for which simpler methods are available.

**Example 1** *In* $\triangle$ABC, B $= 39°$, C $= 82°$, $a = 6.73$ *cm. Find c.*

$A = 180° - (39° + 82°)$
$\quad = 59°$

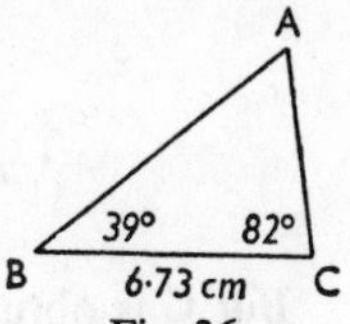

$\dfrac{c}{\sin C} = \dfrac{a}{\sin A}$

$\therefore \dfrac{c}{\sin 82°} = \dfrac{6.73}{\sin 59°}$

Fig. 26

$\therefore c = \dfrac{6.73}{\sin 59°} \times \sin 82°$

$\quad = 6.73 \sin 82° \operatorname{cosec} 59°$

$\quad \simeq 7.78$ cm.

| No. | Log. |
|---|---|
| 6.73 | 0.828 0 |
| sin 82° | $\bar{1}$.995 8 |
| cosec 59° | 0.066 9 |
| 7.775 | 0.890 7 |

55

*New General Mathematics*

*N.B.* (i) It is numerically simpler to multiply by cosec than to divide by sine.

(ii) In the logarithmic working, the tables of 'Log sines' and 'Log cosecants' are used, in order to avoid the double process of looking up the 'natural sine' and then finding its logarithm, and so on.

In Examples 2 and 3 which follow, remember that there are two angles between 0° and 180° with the same sine, since

$$\sin \theta = \sin (180° - \theta).$$

Notice also that **the greater angle is opposite the greater side,**

e.g. if $a > b$

then $\widehat{A} > \widehat{B}$, and conversely.

**Example 2** *Find the remaining angles of the* $\triangle ABC$ *in which* $a = 12.5$ *cm*, $c = 17.7$ *cm*, $C = 116°$.

The formula is rearranged in the form $\dfrac{\sin A}{a} = \dfrac{\sin C}{c}$, so that the unknown comes first.

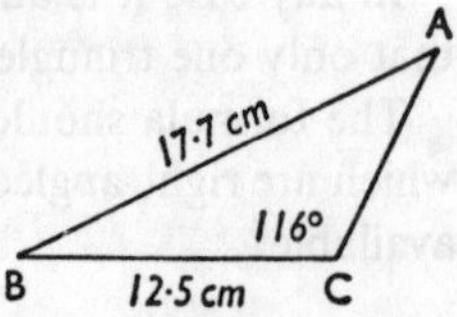

Fig. 27

$$\frac{\sin A}{12.5} = \frac{\sin 116°}{17.7}$$

$$\therefore \sin A = \frac{12.5 \sin 116°}{17.7}$$

$$= \frac{12.5 \sin 64°}{17.7}$$

$$\therefore A = 39° 24' \text{ or } 180° - 39° 24'$$
$$= 39° 24' \text{ or } 140° 36'.$$

But C is obtuse

$$\therefore A \text{ cannot be obtuse}$$

$$\therefore A = 39° 24'$$
$$\text{and} \quad B = 180° - (39° 24' + 116°)$$
$$= 180° - 155° 24'$$
$$= 24° 36'.$$

| No. | Log. |
|---|---|
| 12·5 | 1·096 9 |
| sin 64° | $\overline{1}$·953 7 |
| | 1·050 6 |
| 17·7 | 1·248 0 |
| sin 39° 24' | $\overline{1}$·802 6 |

**Example 3** *Solve completely the* △ABC *in which a = 7·1 cm,
b = 9·5 cm, B = 63° 18′ (i.e. find the three dimensions which are
not given).*

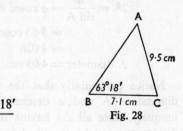

Fig. 28

$$\frac{\sin A}{a} = \frac{\sin B}{b}$$

$$\therefore \frac{\sin A}{7·1} = \frac{\sin 63° 18′}{9·5}$$

$$\therefore \sin A = \frac{7·1 \sin 63° 18′}{9·5}$$

$$\therefore A = 41° 53′ \text{ or } 180° - 41° 53′$$
$$= 41° 53′ \text{ or } 138° 7′.$$
But $a < b$

$$\therefore A < B$$
$$\therefore A = 41° 53′$$

| No. | Log. |
|---|---|
| 7·1 | 0·851 3 |
| sin 63° 18′ | $\overline{1}$·951 0 |
| | 0·802 3 |
| 9·5 | 0·977 7 |
| sin 41° 53′ | $\overline{1}$·824 6 |

and
$$C = 180° - (63° 18′ + 41° 53′)$$
$$= 180° - 105° 11′$$
$$= 74° 49′.$$

$$\frac{c}{\sin C} = \frac{b}{\sin B}$$

$$\therefore \frac{c}{\sin 74° 49′} = \frac{9·5}{\sin 63° 18′}$$

| No. | Log. |
|---|---|
| 9·5 | 0·977 7 |
| sin 74° 49′ | $\overline{1}$·984 5 |
| cosec 63° 18′ | 0·049 0 |
| 10·26 | 1·011 2 |

$$\therefore c = \frac{9·5 \sin 74° 49′}{\sin 63° 18′}$$

$$= 9·5 \sin 74° 49′ \text{ cosec } 63° 18′$$
$$= 10·26 \text{ cm}$$
$$= 10·3 \text{ cm to 3 sig. fig.}$$

$$\therefore A = 41° 53′, \quad C = 74° 49′, \quad c = 10·3 \text{ cm.}$$

IV—C

**Example 4** *Find the diameter of the circumcircle of* $\triangle ABC$ *in which* A = 73°, a = 3·85 cm.

$$2R = \frac{a}{\sin A} = a \operatorname{cosec} A$$

$$= 3·85 \operatorname{cosec} 73°$$

$$= 4·026$$

∴ diameter ≏ 4·03 cm.

| No. | Log. |
|---|---|
| 3·85 | 0·585 5 |
| cosec 73° | 0·019 4 |
| 4·026 | 0·604 9 |

Notice particularly that the two dimensions A and *a* determine R uniquely, since all $\triangle$s having these dimensions can be inscribed in the same $\odot$.

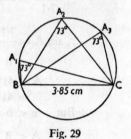

Fig. 29

**Exercise 8a**

1 Use Fig. 30 (i) to prove that $\dfrac{b}{\sin B} = \dfrac{c}{\sin C}$, and deduce the 'sine formula'.

2 Using Fig. 30 (ii), deduce the sine formula, as in no. 1.

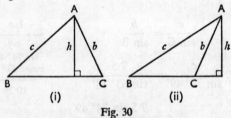

(i)                    (ii)

Fig. 30

3 A = 29°, B = 36°, b = 15·8 m. Find *a*.

4 A = 54° 12′, B = 71° 30′, a = 12·4 cm. Find *b*.

5 B = 104° 19′, C = 31° 17′, a = 29 cm. Find *c*.

6 A = 83°, a = 285 m, c = 216 m. Find C.

7 C = 53°, b = 3·56 m, c = 4·28 m. Find B.

8 Find the radii of the circumcircles in nos. 3 to 7.

Solve completely (i.e. find all the missing dimensions) the △s in which

**9** A = 115°, a = 65 m, b = 32 m.

**10** B = 25° 38′, C = 124° 22′, c = 39·2 m.

**11** B = 29° 46′, C = 51° 22′, a = 19·58 cm.

**12** A = 38° 18′, a = 252 m, b = 198 m.

**13** C = 96° 13′, b = 11·2 cm, c = 39·4 cm.

**14** A ship sails due west for 4 km. It then changes course and sails on a bearing of 197° until it is south-west of its starting point. How far is it then from its starting point?

**15** A surveyor starts from a point A and walks 285 m to B on a bearing of 078°. He then walks due south until he arrives at a point C which is 307 m from A. What is the bearing of A from C, and what is the distance BC?

**16** The bearing of a church from a point A is 319°, and from a point B 317 m due east of A the bearing of the church is 288°. How far is the church from A?

**17** A weight is hung from a horizontal beam by two strings, the shorter one being 2·6 m long and making 74° with the horizontal, while the longer makes 38° with the horizontal. What is the length of the longer string?

**18** A golfer's shot from the tee is 214 m, but is 40° off the correct line and his ball is 157 m from the hole. If his drive had been dead straight, how far short of the hole would he have been?

**19** Two ships P and Q leave a port simultaneously. P steams at 9 km h⁻¹ on a bearing of 159°. Q steams on a bearing of 215°. After an hour the bearing of Q from P is 256°. Find the speed of Q.

**20** Two of the guy wires which support a flag pole are attached to pegs (in the level ground) which are respectively due east and due west of the pole. If the wires make angles of 58° and 67° with the ground, and the pegs are 21 m apart, find the lengths of the wires.

**21** A target is placed at the top edge of a cliff, and A and B are two points of observation 57 m apart at sea level, both being due south of the target. If the angles of elevation of the target from A and B are 25° and 37° respectively, find to the nearest metre the distances of the target from A and B.

**22** The beams of two searchlights placed on level ground 3·9 km apart converge at an angle of 109° upon an aircraft vertically above the line joining the searchlights. If one of the beams makes 33° with the horizontal, how far is the aircraft from this searchlight?

**23** A scout wishing to reach a point due east of him finds a lake between him and his objective. He therefore crawls 220 m on a bearing of N 63° E, and then straight to the point on a line bearing S 24° E. How far was he from his objective at first?

## Ambiguous case

In $\triangle ABC$, suppose that $a$, $c$ and $C$ are given: then, so long as $a > c$ and $\hat{C}$ is acute, two triangles can be drawn from the data: $\triangle A_1BC$ in Fig. 31 (ii) and $\triangle A_2BC$ in Fig. 31 (iii).

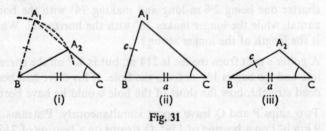

**Fig. 31**

In Fig. 31 (i) it will be seen that $\triangle A_1BA_2$ is isosceles and that $B\hat{A}_1C$ and $B\hat{A}_2C$ are supplementary. Hence in the $\triangle$s $BA_1C$ and $BA_2C$ the angles $A_1$ and $A_2$ are supplementary and have the same sine, but the length $b$ will be either $A_1C$ or $A_2C$.

This is known as 'the ambiguous case' (see Book 2, page 17) and worked Example 5 shows a complete numerical solution of such a case.

If the given angle C is obtuse there can be only one solution, because the angle A must then be acute.

Also, if $c > a$, only one $\triangle$ is possible (Fig. 32).

In all questions of this kind it is advisable to **draw a preliminary sketch** in order to determine whether or not the ambiguous case is involved.

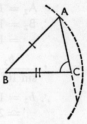

Fig. 32

**Example 5** *Solve completely the* $\triangle ABC$ *in which* $a = 13·3$ *cm,* $c = 12·4$ *cm,* $C = 64°\ 22'$.

$$\frac{\sin A}{a} = \frac{\sin C}{c}$$

$$\therefore \frac{\sin A}{13·3} = \frac{\sin 64°\ 22'}{12·4}$$

$$\therefore \sin A = \frac{13·3 \sin 64°\ 22'}{12·4}$$

$$\therefore A = 75°18' \quad \text{or} \quad 180° - 75°\ 18'$$
$$= 75°\ 18' \quad \text{or} \quad 104°\ 42'.$$

| No. | Log. |
|---|---|
| 13·3 | 1·123 9 |
| sin 64° 22′ | $\bar{1}$·955 0 |
| | 1·078 9 |
| 12·4 | 1·093 4 |
| sin 75° 18′ | $\bar{1}$·985 5 |

Fig. 33

Fig. 34

$$A_1 = 75°\ 18',$$
$$\therefore B_1 = 180° - (75°\ 18' + 64°\ 22')$$
$$= 40°\ 20'$$

$$\therefore \frac{b_1}{\sin 40°\ 20'} = \frac{12·4}{\sin 64°\ 22'}$$

$$\therefore b_1 = 12·4 \sin 40°\ 20' \operatorname{cosec} 64°22'$$
$$\simeq 8·90.$$

| No. | Log. |
|---|---|
| 12·4 | 1·093 4 |
| sin 40° 20′ | $\bar{1}$·811 1 |
| cosec 64° 22′ | 0·045 0 |
| 8·902 | 0·949 5 |

61

$$A_2 = 104° 42',$$
$$\therefore B_2 = 180° - (104° 42' + 64° 22')$$
$$= 10° 56'$$

$$\therefore \frac{b_2}{\sin 10° 56'} = \frac{12·4}{\sin 64° 22'}$$

$$\therefore b_2 = 12·4 \sin 10° 56' \cosec 64° 22'$$
$$\simeq 2·61.$$

| No. | Log. |
|---|---|
| 12·4 | 1·093 4 |
| sin 10° 56' | $\bar{1}$·278 1 |
| cosec 64° 22' | 0·045 0 |
| 2·609 | 0·416 5 |

$$Ans. \begin{cases} A = 75° 18', & B = 40° 20', & b = 8·90 \text{ cm.} \\ A = 104° 42', & B = 10° 56', & b = 2·61 \text{ cm.} \end{cases}$$

## Exercise 8b

Solve completely the triangles in which

**1** $A = 77° 43'$, $C = 41° 32'$, $b = 4·31$ cm.

**2** $B = 42° 16'$, $b = 1\,800$ m, $c = 2\,400$ m.

**3** $C = 15° 22'$, $a = 6·3$ m, $c = 2·5$ m.

**4** $A = 123° 7'$, $b = 12·7$ cm, $a = 18·1$ cm.

**5** $A = 38° 50'$, $a = 2·8$ cm, $c = 4·2$ cm.

**6** $A = 128° 17'$, $C = 30°7'$, $c = 15·6$ cm.

**7** $B = 65° 8'$, $a = 156$ m, $b = 146$ m.

**8** $A = 57° 20'$, $a = 4·5$ cm, $b = 5·1$ cm.

**9** Two ships leave a port in directions which diverge from one another by 47°. After an hour the ships are 11 km apart. If the faster ship is travelling at 14 km h$^{-1}$, what is the speed of the slower one?

**10** Two ships *Albatross* and *Bustard* are 2 000 m apart, *Bustard*'s bearing from *Albatross* being 067° 17'. *Albatross* locates a submarine on a bearing of 034° 58', and *Bustard* reports the submarine as being 1 580 m distant. How far is the submarine from *Albatross* (two possible answers), and what is its bearing from *Bustard* (two answers)?

**11** From a point on a straight road running east and west an enemy mortar is located 3 500 m away in a direction making 42° 28' with the road. If the effective range of the mortar is 2 500 m, what length of the road is covered by its fire?

**12** Two triangulation points A and B are 4·38 km apart, and the bearing of B from A is 126° 7'. A third point C, which is inaccessible from A, is found to be 3·54 km from B, and its bearing from A is 075° 32'. If C is slightly west of B, how far is it from A?

**13** Two boys set out from the same starting point simultaneously. David goes due north, and John runs on a bearing of 046°. When John has gone 440 m the boys are 400 m apart. How far is David then from the starting point?

**14** A helicopter is hovering at a point which is in the same vertical plane as two points A and B on the horizontal ground. Its distances from A and B are 850 m and 1 200 m respectively, and its angle of elevation when observed from B is 43°. Find AB correct to 3 significant figures.

**15** Three triangulation points A, B and C are such that B is due west of A, and C is on a bearing of 318° from A. If AC = 4·36 km and BC = 3·48 km, find the bearing of B from C.

# Chapter 9
# *The cosine formula*

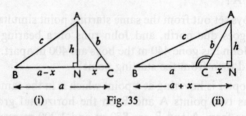

(i)        Fig. 35        (ii)

Consider Fig. 35.

In (i), with $A\widehat{C}B$ acute,

$$c^2 = (a - x)^2 + h^2$$
$$= a^2 - 2ax + x^2 + h^2$$
$$= a^2 - 2ax + b^2 \qquad x^2 + h^2 = b^2, \text{ Pythagoras}$$
$$= a^2 + b^2 - 2ab \cos C$$

$$In \triangle ACN, \frac{x}{b} = \cos C$$

$$\therefore x = b \cos C$$

In (ii), with $A\widehat{C}B$ obtuse,

$$c^2 = (a + x)^2 + h^2$$
$$= a^2 + 2ax + x^2 + h^2$$
$$= a^2 + 2ax + b^2 \qquad x^2 + h^2 = b^2, \text{ Pythagoras}$$
$$= a^2 + b^2 + 2a(-b \cos C)$$

$$In \triangle ACN, \ \frac{x}{b} = \cos A\widehat{C}N$$

$$= a^2 + b^2 - 2ab \cos C$$

$$= \cos (180° - C)$$
$$= -\cos C$$
$$\therefore x = -b \cos C$$

$\therefore$ in either case    $c^2 = a^2 + b^2 - 2\,ab \cos \mathbf{C}$

Similarly    $b^2 = a^2 + c^2 - 2\,ac \cos \mathbf{B}$

and    $a^2 = b^2 + c^2 - 2\,bc \cos \mathbf{A}$

This is the **cosine formula,** and it is used in numerical work for solving triangles in which two sides and the included angle are given, as in the following examples.

**Example 1** *Find the side* AB *of the* △ABC *in Fig.* 36.

$$x^2 = 2^2 + 3^2 - 2 \times 2 \times 3 \times \cos 80°$$
$$= 4 + 9 - 12 \times 0.173\,6$$
$$= 13 - 2.083\,2$$
$$= 10.916\,8$$
$$\therefore x = 3.305 \simeq 3.31$$
$$\therefore AB = 3.31 \text{ cm}.$$

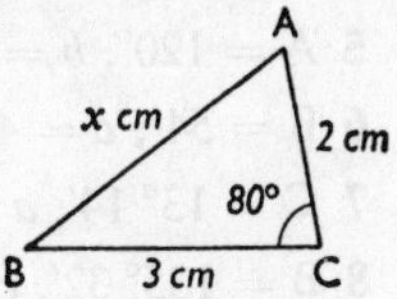

Fig. 36

**Example 2** *Find y in Fig.* 37.

$$y^2 = 5^2 + 3^2 - 2 \times 5 \times 3 \times \cos 102°$$
$$= 25 + 9 - 30\,(-\cos 78°)$$
$$= 34 + 30 \cos 78°$$
$$= 34 + 30 \times 0.207\,9$$
$$= 34 + 6.237$$
$$= 40.237$$
$$\therefore y = 6.343 \simeq 6.34.$$

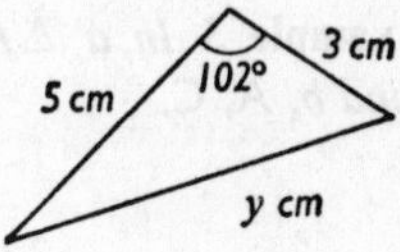

Fig. 37

Notice that (in Fig. 38)

if the side $c$ is opposite a right angle, $c^2 = a^2 + b^2$

„  „  „  $c$ „  „  an acute angle, $c^2 < a^2 + b^2$

„  „  „  $c$ „  „  an obtuse angle, $c^2 > a^2 + b^2$

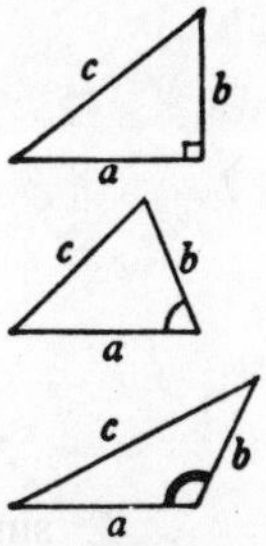

Fig. 38

Hence in Example 1 above, $x^2 < 2^2 + 3^2$
 i.e.  $x^2 < 13$
and in Example 2 above,  $y^2 > 5^2 + 3^2$
 i.e.  $y^2 > 34.$

## Exercise 9a

Calculate the side opposite the given angle in each of the △s ABC given.

**1** A = 49°, $b = 3$ cm, $c = 5$ cm.

**2** B = 46°, $c = 1$ cm, $a = 2$ cm.

*New General Mathematics*

**3** $C = 29°$, $a = 2$ m, $b = 3$ m.

**4** $A = 95°$, $b = 2$ m, $c = 1$ m.

**5** $A = 120°$, $b = 7$ cm, $c = 12$ cm.

**6** $B = 54°$, $c = 4$ cm, $a = 5$ cm.

**7** $C = 13° 14'$, $a = 10$ m, $b = 15$ m.

**8** $B = 135° 32'$, $c = 8$ cm, $a = 5$ cm.

**9** $A = 125° 23'$, $b = 2·4$ cm, $c = 5$ cm.

**10** $C = 47° 46'$, $a = 13·1$ m, $b = 24·2$ m.

**Example 3** *In a* $\triangle ABC$, $a = 6·7$ *cm*, $c = 2·3$ *cm*, $B = 46° 32'$. *Find* $b$, $A$, $C$.

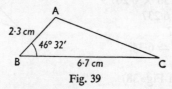

Fig. 39

$$b^2 = 2·3^2 + 6·7^2 - 2 \times 2·3 \times 6·7 \cos 46° 32'$$
$$= 5·29 + 44·89 - 4·6 \times 6·7 \cos 46° 32'$$
$$= 50·18 - 21·20$$
$$= 28·98$$
$$\therefore b = 5·383.$$

$$\frac{\sin C}{2·3} = \frac{\sin 46° 32'}{5·383}$$

$$\therefore \sin C = \frac{2·3 \sin 46° 32'}{5·383}$$

$$\therefore C = 18° 4'$$
$$\therefore A = 180° - (46° 32' + 18° 4')$$
$$= 115° 24'.$$

| No. | Log. |
|---|---|
| 4·6 | 0·662 8 |
| 6·7 | 0·826 1 |
| cos 46° 32" | $\bar{1}$·837 5 |
| 21·20 | 1·326 4 |

| No. | Log. |
|---|---|
| 2·3 | 0·361 7 |
| sin 46° 32' | $\bar{1}$·860 8 |
| | 0·222 5 |
| 5·383 | 0·731 0 |
| sin 18° 4' | $\bar{1}$·491 5 |

*Ans.* $b = 5·38$ cm, $C = 18° 4'$, $A = 115° 24'$.

*N.B.* (i) The cosine formula is used to find $b$.

(ii) The sine formula is used to find the angles.

(iii) The smaller of the two unknown angles is found first. If the sine formula had been used to find A in this example, log sin A would have been $\bar{1}\cdot955\,8$, which gives A $= 64° 35'$ *or* $115° 25'$. The smaller of the two angles must be acute, and this possible ambiguity does not arise.

### Exercise 9b

Find the unknown side and angles in the following △s ABC:

**1** A $= 66°$, $b = 4$ cm, $c = 5$ cm.

**2** C $= 74°$, $a = 10$ cm, $b = 5$ cm.

**3** C $= 139°$, $a = 8$ m, $b = 5$ m.

**4** B $= 95°$, $c = 200$ m, $a = 300$ m.

**5** A $= 58° 8'$, $b = 10$ m, $c = 8\cdot5$ m.

**6** B $= 126° 14'$, $c = 5\cdot6$ cm, $a = 5$ cm.

**7** C $= 25° 44'$, $b = 3\cdot5$ cm, $a = 6$ cm.

**8** A $= 140° 9'$, $b = 45$ m, $c = 24$ m.

**9** C $= 143° 17'$, $b = 3\cdot8$ cm, $a = 2\cdot3$ cm.

**10** B $= 34° 29'$, $c = 2\cdot8$ cm, $a = 5\cdot1$ cm.

The formula $a^2 = b^2 + c^2 - 2bc \cos A$ can be rearranged in the form

$$\cos A = \frac{b^2 + c^2 - a^2}{2bc}$$

and similarly $\cos B = \dfrac{c^2 + a^2 - b^2}{2ca}$

$$\cos C = \frac{a^2 + b^2 - c^2}{2ab}.$$

From this formula the angles of a △ can be found when all three sides are known.

*New General Mathematics*

**Example 4** *Find the angles of a $\triangle$ with sides 4 m, 5 m, 7 m.*

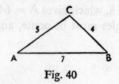

Fig. 40

Lettering the $\triangle$ as in Fig. 40,

$$\cos A = \frac{5^2 + 7^2 - 4^2}{2 \times 5 \times 7} = \frac{58}{70} = 0.828\,6$$

$$\therefore A = 34° 3'.$$

$$\cos B = \frac{4^2 + 7^2 - 5^2}{2 \times 4 \times 7} = \frac{40}{56} = 0.714\,3$$

$$\therefore B = 44° 25'.$$

$$\cos C = \frac{4^2 + 5^2 - 7^2}{2 \times 4 \times 5} = \frac{-8}{40} = -0.200\,0$$

$$\therefore C = 180° - 78° 28' = 101° 32'.$$

$$Check.\ A + B + C = 180°.$$

*N.B.* In questions of this type it is always worth while to calculate the three angles independently, using the cosine formula, and then check by adding, as in Example 4.

**Example 5** *Find the angles of $\triangle$s having sides (i) 400 m, 500 m, 700 m; (ii) 6·3 cm, 7·2 cm, 9·9 cm.*

In both these questions the problem is simplified by considering similar (i.e. equiangular) $\triangle$s having less complex numbers as sides.

e.g. in (i) $\qquad$ $400 : 500 : 700 = 4 : 5 : 7$

$\qquad \therefore$ solve the $\triangle$ with sides 4, 5 and 7, as in Example 4.

In (ii) $\qquad$ $6·3 : 7·2 : 9·9 = 63 : 72 : 99 = 7 : 8 : 11$

$\qquad \therefore$ solve the $\triangle$ with sides 7, 8 and 11 units.

In nos. 1–10 find the angles of the △s ABC whose sides are given in centimetres: find all three angles independently and check as in Example 4.

**1** $a = 5, b = 9, c = 10$  **2** $a = 8, b = 5, c = 7$

**3** $a = 9, b = 10, c = 6$  **4** $a = 5, b = 2, c = 4$

**5** $a = 5, b = 7, c = 9$  **6** $a = 45, b = 33, c = 21$

**7** $a = 5·2, b = 6·5, c = 7·8$  **8** $a = 7·2, b = 6·3, c = 9·9$

**9** $a = 14·4, b = 11·2, c = 7·6$  **10** $a = 2·7, b = 3·7, c = 3·1$

**11** ABC is a △ in which $a = 8$ m, $b = 7$ m, $c = 9$ m, and M is the mid-pt. of $\overline{BC}$. Find cos B (in △ABC) and hence AM. Do not find B in degrees and minutes.

**12** By writing down the expression for cos B
  (i) from △ABM in Fig. 41,
  (ii) from △ABC,
deduce the **Theorem of Apollonius**
  (i.e. $b^2 + c^2 = 2x^2 + 2y^2$).

Fig. 41

**13** In a △ABC, AB = 8 cm, BC = 4 cm, CA = 5 cm, and $\overline{BC}$ is produced to P so that CP = 4 cm. Use the cosine formula to find cos $A\hat{C}B$, and hence find AP.

**14** In a △PQR, PQ = 5 m, QR = 9 m, RP = 8 m. X is a point on $\overline{PR}$ such that PX = 6 m. Find QX.

**15** In Fig. 42 find $x$ and $\theta$. All lengths given are in centimetres.

**16** $\overline{AB}$ and $\overline{CD}$ are the parallel sides of a trapezium ABCD in which AB = 4 cm, BC = 5 cm, CD = 8 cm, DA = 6 cm.

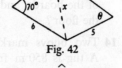

Fig. 42

Draw a line $\overline{BX} \parallel \overline{AD}$ to cut $\overline{CD}$ in X. Calculate $\hat{C}$ and BD.

**17** Calculate $y$ in Fig. 43. [First find cos $\theta$, but do not work out $\theta$.]

**18** Find the radii of the circumcircles of the △s in nos. 1, 2 and 3.

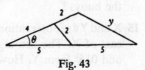

Fig. 43

*New General Mathematics*

**Exercise 9d**

**Miscellaneous problems involving sine and cosine formulae**

Solve completely the △s in which

**1** A = 78°, B = 43°, b = 29·4 m.

**2** A = 78° 14′, b = 8·72 cm, c = 6·39 cm.

**3** B = 45° 7′, a = 8·92 cm, b = 6·74 cm.

**4** a = 12 m, b = 24 m, c = 16·8 m.

**5** A = 22°, B = 126° 17′, b = 8·63 m.

**6** A = 44° 22′, a = 19·5 cm, c = 25·3 cm.

**7** A = 103° 50′, b = 18·7 cm, c = 27·3 cm.

**8** B = 122° 5′, C = 36° 43′, a = 15·7 cm.

**9** a = 2·1 m, b = 3·2 m, c = 1·2 m.

**10** B = 109° 14′, a = 149 m, b = 163 m.

**11** From a lighthouse on the quay one buoy is 5 km away on a bearing N 50° E and another is 2 km away on a bearing of N 60° W. How far apart are the buoys?

**12** Slip is standing 5 metres from the batsman's wicket at an angle of 125° to the pitch. How far is he from the bowler's wicket? (The wickets are 20 m apart.)

**13** Two boards, one 5 m and the other 6 m long, are standing up with their top edges together in such a way that the angle between the boards is 36°. How far apart are the bottom edges of the boards, and what angle does the longer one make with the floor?

**14** Two buoys marking a harbour mouth are 200 m apart. A tug is 850 m from one buoy and 950 m from the other. Within what angle must the tug steam if it is to pass between the buoys?

**15** X and Y are observation points one kilometre apart, Y being due east of X. The bearing of an enemy position is 023° from X and 015° from Y. How far from X is the position?

**16** A man can travel from A to B by a direct straight road at 10 km h⁻¹, or at 12 km h⁻¹ if he goes along two sides $\overline{AX}$ and $\overline{XB}$ of the △AXB, AX being 5 km and XB 4 km, and $A\hat{X}B$ 116°. Which route is the quicker, and by how long?

**17** A yacht sails 4 km on a bearing of 038° and then 5 km on a bearing of 067°. How far is she finally from the starting-point, and what is her bearing from this point?

**18** Find $A\hat{B}C$ and AC in the quadrilateral ABCD (Fig. 44), all lengths given being in cm.

**19** At a hole 300 m long a golfer hits his ball 200 m at an angle of 33° to the correct line. If he is lucky enough to find his ball, how far will it be from the hole? [*Hint:* work with 2 and 3 as units rather than 200 and 300, as in worked Example 5.]

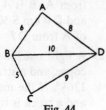

Fig. 44

**20** A triangular field has two sides 50 m and 60 m long, and the angle between these sides is 96°. How long is the third side?

**21** A man prospecting for oil in the desert drives 42 km on a bearing of 032° and then 28 km on a bearing of 154°. How far is he then from his base, and what is his bearing from it?

**22** The sides of a parallelogram are 3 cm and 5 cm, and include an angle of 144°. Find the diagonals of the parallelogram.

**23** A and B are two points 5 km apart, the bearing of A from B being 052°. It is required to fix a third point X, which is known to be exactly 10 km from B and on a bearing of 152° from A. How far is X from A and what is the bearing of B from X?

**24** Two ships leave port at the same time, one steaming at 5 km h⁻¹ on a bearing of 046°, and the other at 9 km h⁻¹ on a bearing of 127°. How far apart are the ships after 2 hours?

**25** A search-party in the bush travels 21 km from its base on a bearing of 032° and then 45 km on a bearing of 287° to a water-hole. How far is the base and what is its bearing from the water-hole?

**26** The sides of a parallelogram are 9·1 cm and 13 cm, and one of the diagonals is 19·5 cm. Use the cosine formula to find the length of the other diagonal.

**27** A stalker is 350 m away from a deer and wants to get closer before he shoots. As there is a deep bog in the direct line between him and the deer he crawls for 200 m at an angle of 8° to this line before he finds a suitable position for a shot. How far is he then from the deer?

**28** A yacht sails round a quadrangular course ABCD, starting from A. B is 4 km due east of A, C 3 km due south of B, and D 4 km S 50° W from C. What is the distance and bearing of A from D?

**29** A light machine-gun is placed 3 500 m due south of a small copse, and a straight road runs from the copse on a bearing of $136\frac{1}{2}°$. If the maximum effective range of the gun is 2 500 m, and a truck is travelling down the road at 64 km h⁻¹, for how many seconds will the truck be within range of the gun?

**30** Searchlights at points 1 570 m apart are directed in such a way that the angle between their beams is always 42°. What is the distance from either light of the furthest point which is picked out by the converging beams?

# Chapter 10

# *Ratio*

If three numbers $a$, $b$, $c$ are in the ratio $8 : 3 : 6$,

i.e. if $\quad a : b : c = 8 : 3 : 6$,

$$\text{then} \quad \frac{a}{8} = \frac{b}{3} = \frac{c}{6}.$$

Also $\quad \dfrac{a}{b} = \dfrac{8}{3}, \ \dfrac{b}{c} = \dfrac{3}{6} = \dfrac{1}{2}, \ \dfrac{c}{a} = \dfrac{6}{8} = \dfrac{3}{4}.$

**Example 1** *Three numbers $a$, $b$, $c$ are in the ratio $6 : 4 : 5$. Find the value of* $\dfrac{3a - b}{4b + c}.$

If $\quad a : b : c = 6 : 4 : 5$, then $\dfrac{a}{6} = \dfrac{b}{4} = \dfrac{c}{5}.$

Let $\quad \dfrac{a}{6} = \dfrac{b}{4} = \dfrac{c}{5} = m.$

Then $\quad a = 6m, \ b = 4m, \ c = 5m$

$$\therefore \ \frac{3a - b}{4b + c} = \frac{18m - 4m}{16m + 5m} = \frac{14m}{21m} = \frac{2}{3}.$$

**Example 2** *Divide $x$ tonnes into two parts in the ratio $u : v$.*

Let the parts be $ku$ tonnes and $kv$ tonnes.

Then $\quad ku + kv = x$

$$\therefore \ k(u + v) = x$$

$$\therefore \ k = \frac{x}{u + v}$$

$\therefore$ the parts are $\dfrac{xu}{u + v}$ tonnes and $\dfrac{xv}{u + v}$ tonnes.

**Example 3** *If* $p : q = 4 : 3$ *and* $q : r = 5 : 7$, *find* $p : q : r$.

$$\frac{p}{4} = \frac{q}{3} \quad \text{and} \quad \frac{q}{5} = \frac{r}{7}.$$

$q$ occurs in both statements.

$\therefore$ make the fraction containing $q$ the same each time.
Then

$$\frac{p}{20} = \frac{q}{15} \quad \text{and} \quad \frac{q}{15} = \frac{r}{21} \quad [15 \text{ is the L.C.M. of 3 and 5}]$$

$$\therefore \frac{p}{20} = \frac{q}{15} = \frac{r}{21}$$

$$\therefore p : q : r = 20 : 15 : 21.$$

**Example 4** *Find the ratio* $x : y$ *if* $10x^2 - 9xy + 2y^2 = 0$.

$$10x^2 - 9xy + 2y^2 = 0$$
$$\therefore (2x - y)(5x - 2y) = 0$$
$$\therefore 2x = y \quad \text{or} \quad 5x = 2y$$

$$\therefore \frac{x}{y} = \frac{1}{2} \quad \text{or} \quad \frac{x}{y} = \frac{2}{5}$$

i.e. $x : y = 1 : 2 \quad \text{or} \quad 2 : 5$.

*Alternatively,* $\qquad 10x^2 - 9xy + 2y^2 = 0$

$\therefore$ dividing both sides by $y^2$,

$$10\frac{x^2}{y^2} - 9\frac{x}{y} + 2 = 0$$

$$\therefore 10\left(\frac{x}{y}\right)^2 - 9\left(\frac{x}{y}\right) + 2 = 0$$

$$\therefore \left[2\left(\frac{x}{y}\right) - 1\right]\left[5\left(\frac{x}{y}\right) - 2\right] = 0$$

$$\therefore \frac{x}{y} = \frac{1}{2} \quad \text{or} \quad \frac{2}{5}$$

i.e. $x : y = 1 : 2 \quad \text{or} \quad 2 : 5$.

**Exercise 10a**

If $\dfrac{a}{3} = \dfrac{b}{5}$, evaluate

**1** $\dfrac{2a}{3b}$  **2** $\dfrac{a^2}{b^2}$  **3** $\dfrac{a+b}{2a+b}$

If $m : n = 5 : 2$, evaluate

**4** $m : 5n$  **5** $m^3 : n^3$  **6** $m - 2n : m + n$

If $u : v = 4 : 3$, evaluate

**7** $2u - v : u + 2v$  **8** $5u - 4v : 3u$

**9** $u^2 - uv : uv + v^2$

Find the value of the ratio $c : d$ if

**10** $3c = 5d$  **11** $5c + 3d = 5d - 2c$  **12** $16c^2 = 25d^2$

**13** $7c + 2d = c - 2d$  **14** $c$ exceeds $d$ by $25\%$

If $u : v = 3 : 5$, prove that

**15** $u + 3 : v + 5 = 3 : 5$  **16** $u - 3 : v - 5 = 3 : 5$

**17** $2u - 3 : 2v - 5 = 3 : 5$

Find the ratio $x : y$ in the following equations:

**18** $7x - 5y = 0$  **19** $9x^2 - 4y^2 = 0$

**20** $6x^2 - 5xy + y^2 = 0$  **21** $2x^2 - 3xy - 2y^2 = 0$

**22** $8x^2 + 14xy - 15y^2 = 0$

**23** The present ages of a father and his son are in the ratio $7 : 2$, and the son's age is 14. What will be the ratio of their ages in 6 years' time?

**24** The number of girls in a class is increased by $15\%$. In what ratio has the number increased?

**25** If the number of men engaged in digging a trench were to be increased in the ratio $m : n$, how would the time taken be affected?

**26** If $x$ is the first of two numbers which are in the ratio $a : b$, find the second number.

**27** A coil spring is stretched so that its length increases from $m$ cm to $n$ cm. Find the ratio in which its length increases. Find also the ratio of the increase in length to the original length.

**28** A plank is $h$ m long. If a length of $k$ m is cut from it, find the ratio in which the length is reduced.

**29** The ratio of the prices per tonne of coal and coke is $m : n$. If the price of coal increases by 15%, and that of coke by 10%, find the new ratio of their costs.

**30** Find the angles of a triangle if they are in the ratio $5 : 7 : 8$.

**31** Show how to divide £168 between four people so that their shares are in the ratio $3 : 5 : 7 : 9$.

**32** Find the shares received by three people if £$x$ is divided among them in the ratio $a : b : c$.

**33** If $a : b : c = 12 : 15 : 10$, evaluate the ratios $a : b$ and $b : c$.

**34** If $p : q = 3 : 4$ and $q : r = 5 : 6$, find $p : q : r$.

**35** If $a : b = 5 : 6$ and $b : c = 8 : 5$, find $a : b : c$.

**36** If $x : y : z = 8 : 6 : 9$, find the ratios $x : y$ and $y : z$.

**37** If $u : v = 7 : 10$ and $v : w = 15 : 13$, find $u : v : w$.

**38** If $a + b : a + 2b = 5 : 7$, find the ratio $a : b$.

**39** If $x + y : x - y = 4 : 3$, find the ratio $x : y$.

**40** If $m - 2n : 2m + 3n = 3 : 20$, find the ratio $m^2 - n^2 : m^2 + n^2$.

**41** If the side of a square is increased in the ratio $5 : 3$, find the ratio in which the area is increased.

**42** If the length of a rectangle is increased in the ratio $5 : 4$, and the width in the ratio $3 : 2$, find the ratio in which the area is increased.

**43** If the length of a rectangle is increased in the ratio $9 : 4$, and the width is decreased in the ratio $3 : 7$, find whether the area is increased or decreased, and in what ratio.

**44** If the radius of a circle is decreased in the ratio $4 : 5$, find the ratio in which the area is decreased.

**45** A spherical balloon is blown out so that its radius increases in the ratio $3 : 2$. Find the ratio in which the volume is increased.

**46** If the radius of a sphere is increased in the ratio 6 : 5, find the ratio in which its surface area is increased.

**47** Two circular cones are such that the ratio of their heights is 4 : 5, and the ratio of their base radii is 4 : 3. Find the ratio of their volumes.

**48** The heights of two circular cylinders are in the ratio 3 : 2, and their base radii are in the ratio 8 : 9. Find the ratio of their volumes.

**49** Find the ratio of the heights of two circular cylinders of equal volume, if the radii of their bases are in the ratio $a : b$.

**50** The areas of two triangles are in the ratio $a : b$, and their bases are in the ratio $c : d$. Find the ratio of their heights.

**51** Given that $\dfrac{a}{b} = \dfrac{4}{3}$, $\dfrac{c}{d} = \dfrac{5}{6}$ and $\dfrac{a+c}{b+d} = \dfrac{5}{4}$, find $\dfrac{2a+c}{b+2d}$.

**52** If $m : n = 2 : 3$, $u : v = 4 : 5$ and $m - u : n + v = 2 : 5$, find the ratio $m + 10u : 2n - 5v$.

**53** Two men each buy a hat and coat. The ratio of the costs of the hats is 7 : 9, and that of the coats is 5 : 8. The money which the first man spends is two-thirds of that which the second man spends. Find the ratio of the combined costs of the two hats to that of the two coats.

**54** Two men have incomes in the ratio 5 : 3, and their expenditures are in the ratio 8 : 5. If their savings are in the ratio 4 : 3, find the ratio of their combined incomes to their combined expenditures.

**55** The masses of two jugs are in the ratio 4 : 5. The masses of the amounts of milk that they can contain are in the ratio 2 : 3. When both jugs are full of milk their masses are in the ratio 3 : 4. Find the ratio of the mass of the smaller jug half full to that of the larger jug completely full.

**Internal and external division of a line**

Consider a line $\overline{AB}$ of length 42 cm. If P is a point on $\overline{AB}$, between A and B, dividing $\overline{AB}$ in the ratio 5 : 2,

$$\text{then} \quad \frac{AP}{PB} = \frac{5}{2}.$$

Hence    AP = $\frac{5}{7}$ of AB = $\frac{5}{7}$ of 42 cm = 30 cm,

and    PB = $\frac{2}{7}$ of AB = $\frac{2}{7}$ of 42 cm = 12 cm.

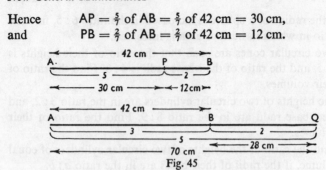

Fig. 45

There is also a point Q, lying on $\overline{AB}$ produced, such that $\frac{AQ}{BQ} = \frac{5}{2}$.

Q is said to divide $\overline{AB}$ **externally** in the ratio 5 : 2, and P divides $\overline{AB}$ **internally**.

If distances measured to the right are taken to be positive, and those to the left negative,

then    $\dfrac{AP}{PB} = \dfrac{+5}{+2} = +\dfrac{5}{2}$    and    $\dfrac{AQ}{QB} = \dfrac{+5}{-2} = -\dfrac{5}{2}$.

Hence Q is said to **divide $\overline{AB}$ in the ratio** −5 : 2.

Notice that    $\dfrac{AP}{PB} = -\dfrac{AQ}{QB}$.

In Fig. 45, since BQ = $\frac{2}{5}$ of AQ,

then    AB = $\frac{3}{5}$ of AQ.

∴    AQ = $\frac{5}{3}$ of AB = $\frac{5}{3}$ of 42 cm = 70 cm

and    BQ = $\frac{2}{3}$ of AB = $\frac{2}{3}$ of 42 cm = 28 cm.

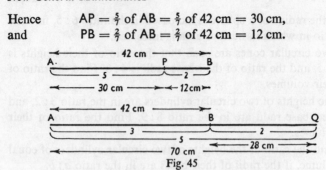

Fig. 46

Notice also (Fig. 46) that if R and S divide $\overline{AB}$ in the ratios 2 : 5 and −2 : 5 respectively, then R is nearer to A than to B, and S lies on $\overline{BA}$ produced.

**Exercise 10b**

**1** A line $\overline{AB}$, 22 cm long, is divided by a point P in the ratio 8 : 3. Find AP and PB.

**2** A line $\overline{XY}$, 6·3 cm long, is divided by a point H in the ratio 3 : 4. Find XH and HY.

**3** A line $\overline{HK}$, 14 cm long, is divided by a point A so that $\dfrac{HA}{AK} = \dfrac{5}{3}$. Find HA and AK.

**4** A line $\overline{AB}$, 20 cm long, is divided by a point Q in the ratio $-8 : 3$. Find AQ and BQ.

**5** A line $\overline{XY}$, 2·4 cm long, is divided by a point K in the ratio $-4 : 7$. Find KX and KY.

**6** A line $\overline{HK}$, 11 cm long, is divided by a point B so that $\dfrac{HB}{BK} = -\dfrac{9}{5}$. Find HB and KB.

**7** A line $\overline{AB}$, 15 cm long, is divided internally and externally by the points P and Q in the same numerical ratio of 3 : 2. Find AP, PB, AQ, BQ.

**8** A line $\overline{HK}$, 25 cm long, is divided by a point A in the ratio 3 : 7, and by a point B in the ratio $-3 : 7$. Find HA, AK, BH, BK.

**9** A line $\overline{XY}$, 3·6 cm long, is divided internally and externally by the points H and K in the same numerical ratio of 5 : 7. Find HK.

**10** A line $\overline{PQ}$, 2·1 cm long, is divided by a point X so that $\dfrac{PX}{XQ} = \dfrac{4}{3}$, and by a point Y so that $\dfrac{PY}{YQ} = -\dfrac{4}{3}$. Find XY.

**11** P, Q are points on $\overline{AB}$ and $\overline{AB}$ produced such that $\dfrac{AP}{PB} = -\dfrac{AQ}{QB} = \dfrac{5}{3}$. If AB = 24 cm, and O is the mid-point of $\overline{AB}$, calculate OA, OP, OQ.

Hence show that OP × OQ = OA².

**12** A line $\overline{\text{AB}}$, $x$ cm long, is divided internally at P and externally at Q in the same numerical ratio of $m : n$, where $m > n$. Find AP, PB, AQ, BQ.

**13** A line $\overline{\text{AB}}$, $x$ cm long, is divided by the points P and Q so that $\dfrac{\text{AP}}{\text{PB}} = \dfrac{m}{n}$ and $\dfrac{\text{AQ}}{\text{QB}} = -\dfrac{m}{n}$, where $m > n$. If O is the mid-point of $\overline{\text{AB}}$, calculate OP and OQ, and hence prove that

$$\text{OP} \times \text{OQ} = \text{OA}^2.$$

**14** A line $\overline{\text{AB}}$ is divided internally at P and externally at Q in the same numerical ratio, so that $\dfrac{\text{AP}}{\text{PB}} = -\dfrac{\text{AQ}}{\text{QB}}$. Prove that A and B divide $\overline{\text{PQ}}$ in the same numerical ratio.

# Chapter 11

# *Similar triangles*

### Theorem 19

**A line drawn parallel to one side of a triangle divides the other two sides in the same ratio.**

**Given** points X, Y on the sides $\overline{AB}$, $\overline{AC}$ respectively of a △ABC such that $\overline{XY} \parallel \overline{BC}$.

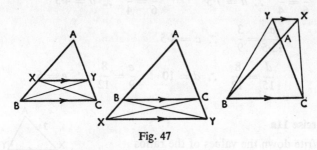

**Fig. 47**

**To prove** AX : XB = AY : YC.

**Construction** Join $\overline{CX}$ and $\overline{BY}$.

**Proof**
$$\frac{AX}{XB} = \frac{\triangle AXY}{\triangle BXY} \quad \triangle s \text{ of same ht., from Y to } \overline{AB}$$

$$= \frac{\triangle AXY}{\triangle CXY} \quad \begin{array}{l} \triangle BXY = \triangle CXY; \text{ same base } \overline{XY}, \\ \text{same} \parallel s \ \overline{XY} \text{ and } \overline{BC} \end{array}$$

$$= \frac{AY}{YC} \quad \triangle s \text{ of same ht., from X to } \overline{AC}$$

$$\therefore AX : XB = AY : YC.$$

Q.E.D.

△AXY is the enlargement of △ABC in the ratio AX : AB, centre A.

The converse of this theorem is also true: namely that if AX : XB = AY : YC, then $\overline{XY} \parallel \overline{BC}$.

81

*New General Mathematics*

**Example 1** *Find a, b, c, d, e in Figs. 48 and 49.*

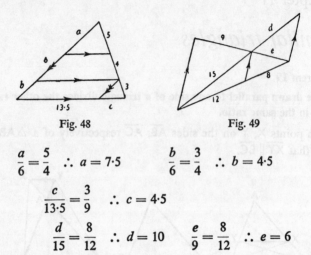

Fig. 48                     Fig. 49

$\dfrac{a}{6} = \dfrac{5}{4}$ ∴ $a = 7.5$         $\dfrac{b}{6} = \dfrac{3}{4}$ ∴ $b = 4.5$

$\dfrac{c}{13.5} = \dfrac{3}{9}$ ∴ $c = 4.5$

$\dfrac{d}{15} = \dfrac{8}{12}$ ∴ $d = 10$      $\dfrac{e}{9} = \dfrac{8}{12}$ ∴ $e = 6$

## Exercise 11a

**1** Write down the values of the ratios
AY : YC, AY : AC, YC : AC
in Fig. 50.

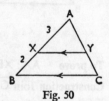

Fig. 50

**2** Write down the values of the ratio $x : y$ in Fig. 51.

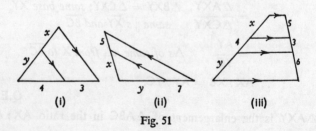

(i)          (ii)          (iii)

Fig. 51

**3** Deduce $x$ and $y$ in Fig. 51 (iii).

**4** Find *a*, *b*, *c*, *d*, *e*, in Fig. 52.

**5** Deduce that $\overrightarrow{XY} \parallel \overrightarrow{AB}$ in Fig. 52 (iii).

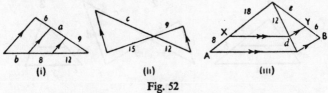

Fig. 52

**6** Find *p*, *q* and the ratio *x* : *y* in Fig. 53.

In Book 2, Chapter 16, some numerical work on similar △s was done. It was then shown that two △s are similar (i.e. of the same shape) if the ∠s of one are respectively equal to the ∠s of the other and that, if this is the case, then the corresponding sides of the two △s are proportional to one another.

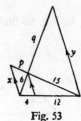

Fig. 53

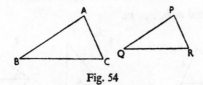

Fig. 54

The conditions under which △s ABC and PQR are similar are summarised below:

(i) If any two pairs of ∠s are equal (e.g. $\widehat{B} = \widehat{Q}$ and $\widehat{C} = \widehat{R}$, when it necessarily follows that $\widehat{A} = \widehat{P}$).

(ii) If the sides are in proportion, viz. $\dfrac{AB}{PQ} = \dfrac{BC}{QR} = \dfrac{CA}{RP}$.

(iii) If one pair of ∠s is equal, and the sides about those ∠s are in proportion—e.g. $\widehat{A} = \widehat{P}$ and $\dfrac{AB}{PQ} = \dfrac{AC}{PR}$.

Formal proofs of these theorems follow after Exercise 11b.

## New General Mathematics

### Exercise 11b (Revision)

In Fig. 55 find $a$, $b$, $c$, $d$ and the ratio $x : y$.

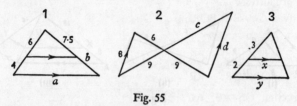

Fig. 55

In Fig. 56 find the ratios $p : q$, $r : s$, $m : n$.

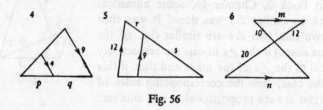

Fig. 56

In Fig. 57 find $a$, $b$, ... $m$.

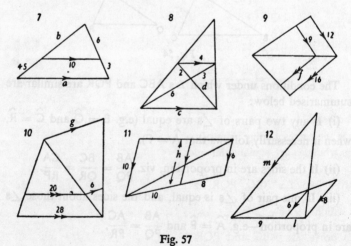

Fig. 57

**Theorem 20**

If two triangles are equiangular, then their corresponding sides are in proportion.

Given two △s ABC, PQR in
which $\hat{A} = \hat{P}$, $\hat{B} = \hat{Q}$, $\hat{C} = \hat{R}$.

To prove $\dfrac{AB}{PQ} = \dfrac{BC}{QR} = \dfrac{CA}{RP}$.

Construction On $\overline{AB}$, $\overline{AC}$ respectively cut off AX = PQ, AY = PR. Join $\overline{XY}$.

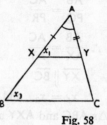

Fig. 58

**Proof**  △AXY ≡ △PQR   *SAS*

△AXY is the displacement of △PQR through $\overrightarrow{PA}$.

$$\therefore\ x_1 = x_2$$
$$= x_3 \qquad \text{given}$$
$$\therefore\ \overline{XY} \parallel \overline{BC} \qquad \text{corr. } \angle s \text{ equal}$$
$$\therefore\ \frac{AB}{AX} = \frac{AC}{AY}$$
$$\therefore\ \frac{AB}{PQ} = \frac{AC}{PR} \qquad \begin{array}{l} AX = PQ, AY = PR; \\ \textit{construction} \end{array}$$

Similarly $\dfrac{AB}{PQ} = \dfrac{BC}{QR}$

$$\therefore\ \frac{AB}{PQ} = \frac{BC}{QR} = \frac{CA}{RP}.$$

Q.E.D.

**Theorem 21**

If the corresponding sides of two triangles are in proportion, then the triangles are equiangular and similar.

Given two △s ABC, PQR in
which $\dfrac{AB}{PQ} = \dfrac{BC}{QR} = \dfrac{CA}{RP}$.

To prove △s ABC and PQR equiangular and similar.

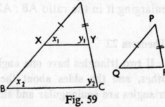

Fig. 59

85

**Construction** On $\overline{AB}$, $\overline{AC}$ respectively cut off $AX = PQ$, $AY = PR$. Join $\overline{XY}$.

**Proof**

$$\frac{AB}{PQ} = \frac{AC}{PR} \qquad \textit{given}$$

$$\therefore \frac{AB}{AX} = \frac{AC}{AY} \qquad \begin{array}{l} AX = PQ, \, AY = PR; \\ \textit{construction} \end{array}$$

$$\therefore \overline{XY} \parallel \overline{BC}$$

$$\therefore x_1 = x_2 \quad \text{and} \quad y_1 = y_2 \qquad \textit{corr.} \angle s$$

$$\therefore \triangle s \text{ ABC and AXY are equiangular and similar.}$$

$\triangle ABC$ is the enlargement of $\triangle AXY$ in the ratio $AB : AX$, centre A.

$$\therefore \frac{BC}{XY} = \frac{AB}{AX}$$

$$= \frac{AB}{PQ} \qquad AX = PQ; \textit{construction}$$

$$= \frac{BC}{QR} \qquad \textit{given}$$

$$\therefore XY = QR$$

$$\therefore \triangle AXY \equiv \triangle PQR \qquad SSS$$

$\triangle PQR$ is the displacement of $\triangle AXY$ through $\overrightarrow{AP}$.

But $\triangle s$ ABC and AXY are equiangular and similar,

$\therefore \triangle s$ ABC and PQR are equiangular and similar.

**Q.E.D.**

$\triangle ABC$ is the result of displacing $\triangle PQR$ through $\overrightarrow{PA}$ and then enlarging it in the ratio $AB : AX$, centre A.

**Theorem 22**

If two triangles have one angle of one equal to one angle of the other, and the sides about these angles in proportion, then the triangles are equiangular and similar.

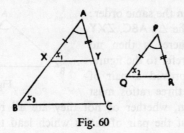

**Fig. 60**

**Given** two △s ABC, PQR in which $\widehat{A} = \widehat{P}$ and $\dfrac{AB}{PQ} = \dfrac{AC}{PR}$.

**To prove** △s ABC and PQR equiangular and similar.

**Construction** On $\overline{AB}$, $\overline{AC}$ respectively cut off AX = PQ, AY = PR. Join $\overline{XY}$.

**Proof**   △AXY ≡ △PQR         *SAS*

△AXY is the displacement of △PQR through $\overrightarrow{PA}$.

$$\therefore x_1 = x_2.$$

But    $\dfrac{AB}{PQ} = \dfrac{AC}{PR}$                *given*

$$\therefore \dfrac{AB}{AX} = \dfrac{AC}{AY} \qquad\qquad AX = PQ,\ AY = PR;$$
*construction*

$$\therefore \overline{XY} \parallel \overline{BC}$$

$$\therefore x_1 = x_3 \qquad\qquad\qquad corr. \angle s$$

$$\therefore \widehat{B} = \widehat{Q}, \text{ and similarly } \widehat{C} = \widehat{R}$$

∴ △s ABC and PQR are equiangular and similar.

Q.E.D.

*N.B.* In working 'riders' the following points must be re-membered:

(i) Equal angles must be marked in the same way or with the same letter ($x_1$, $x_2$; etc.).

(ii) When naming pairs of similar △s the corresponding letters

must be placed in the same order;
e.g. in Fig. 61, the △s ABC, ZXY
are similar. There is then no
further need to refer to the figure.

(iii) Having proved a pair of
△s similar, all three ratios must

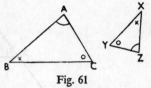

Fig. 61

be written down, whether or not they are all required in the
answer. Pick out the pair of ratios which lead to the required
result.

### Exercise 11c

In Fig. 62 find the lengths $a, b, \ldots k$.

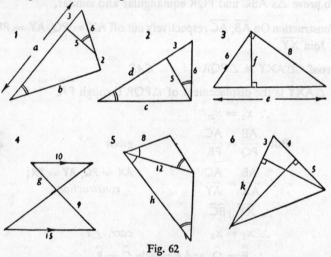

Fig. 62

7  $\overline{XY}$ and $\overline{PQ}$ are two chords of a circle XPYQ which intersect at A inside the circle. Prove that the △s PAX, QAY
are similar and that PA : YA = XP : QY, and also that
PA × AQ = YA × AX.

8  X is a point outside a circle ABQP, and $\overline{XAB}$, $\overline{XPQ}$ are
straight lines. Prove that the △s XAP, XBQ are similar and
that $\dfrac{AP}{BQ} = \dfrac{AX}{QX}$.

88

9 $\overline{XT}$ is the tangent from X to a circle PQT, and $\overline{XPQ}$ is a secant. Prove that the △s XTP, XTQ are similar and that XT : XQ = TP : TQ.

10 ABC is any △, and a line $\overline{PQ}$ cuts $\overline{AB}$ at P, $\overline{AC}$ at Q so that $A\hat{Q}P = \hat{B}$. Prove that the △s APQ, ABC are similar, and hence that AP × BC = AC × PQ.

11 $\overline{AB}$, $\overline{DC}$ are the ‖ sides in a trapezium ABCD, and the diagonals cut at X. Prove that AB × CX = CD × AX.

12 ABC is a △ right-angled at A, and $\overline{AD}$ is an altitude of the △. Prove that the △s ABD and ABC are similar, and hence that $BA^2 = BC × BD$. Without showing the actual proofs, state which pairs of △s are necessary to prove $CA^2 = - × -$ and $DA^2 = - × -$, and fill up the blanks.

13 ABCD is a ‖gm. A straight line through D cuts $\overline{BC}$ at X, and $\overline{AB}$ produced at Y. Prove that $\dfrac{BX}{BY} = \dfrac{CX}{AB}$. [*Hint.* AB = CD.]

14 $\overline{AB}$ is a diameter of a circle ABC. From any point X on $\overline{AC}$ produced a line is drawn at right angles to $\overline{AB}$ produced, cutting it at Y. Prove that AB × AY = AC × AX.

15 ABCD is a rhombus. A straight line through C cuts $\overline{AD}$ produced at P, and $\overline{AB}$ produced at Q. If DP = ½AB, prove that BQ = 2AB.

16 ABC is any △ and $\overline{BE}$, $\overline{CF}$ are altitudes intersecting at H. Prove that (i) $\dfrac{AB}{BE} = \dfrac{AC}{CF}$, (ii) $\dfrac{BH}{CH} = \dfrac{BF}{CE}$. Complete the equation HB × HE = - × -.

17 Two circles intersect at A and B. The tangent at A to one circle cuts the other at C, and the tangent at A to the second circle cuts the first at D. Prove that $BA^2 = BC × BD$.

18 ABC is a △ inscribed in a circle. $\overline{AD}$ is a diameter of the circle, and $\overline{AP}$ is an altitude of the △. Prove that $\dfrac{AB}{BD} = \dfrac{AP}{PC}$, and complete the equation $\dfrac{PC}{CA} = -$.

IV—D

**19** Two circles ABPR, ABSQ cut at A and B. $\overline{PAQ}$ and $\overline{RAS}$ are straight lines (Fig. 63). Prove that $BP \times BS = BQ \times BR$.

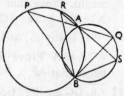

**20** Two circles cut at A and B. The tangent at A to the first circle cuts the second at C; the tangent at B to the second cuts the first at D. Prove that $BA^2 = AD \times BC$.

Fig. 63

**21** Y is any point on the diagonal $\overline{BD}$ of a quadrilateral ABCD. Lines through Y ∥ to $\overline{DA}$ and $\overline{DC}$ respectively cut $\overline{AB}$ and $\overline{BC}$ respectively at X and Z. Prove $\overline{XZ} \parallel \overline{AC}$.

**22** The tangent at A to a circle ABC cuts $\overline{BC}$ produced at T. A line through C parallel to $\overline{BA}$ cuts $\overline{AT}$ at P. Prove that $TC^2 = TA \times TP$, and show also that $\overline{CT}$ is the tangent at C to the circle APC.

**23** Two circles ABX, ABY intersect at A and B, and $\overline{AX}$, $\overline{AY}$ are equally inclined to $\overline{AB}$ and on opposite sides of $\overline{AB}$ (Fig. 64). $\overline{XB}$ and $\overline{YB}$ produced cut the circles again in P and Q respectively. Prove that $BX \times BP = BY \times BQ$.

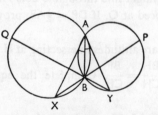

Fig. 64

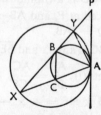

Fig. 65

**24** Two circles touch internally at A (Fig. 65). P is a point on the common tangent at A to the circles. $\overline{PYBX}$ is a straight line touching the smaller circle at B, and $\overline{ACX}$ is also a straight line. Prove that $AB^2 = AC \times AY$.

**25** ABCD is a cyclic quadrilateral, and X a point on $\overline{BD}$ such that $D\hat{A}X = B\hat{A}C$.

Prove (i) BC × AD = AC × DX, (ii) AB × CD = AC × BX. Deduce that BC × AD + AB × CD = AC × BD. [This is known as **Ptolemy's Theorem.**]

## Rectangle properties of a circle
### Theorem 23

If two chords of a circle intersect at a point inside the circle, then the product of the two parts of one chord is equal to the product of the two parts of the other chord.

**Given** $\overline{AB}$, $\overline{CD}$ two chords of a circle ACBD intersecting at R.

**To prove** AR × RB = CR × RD.

**Construction** Join $\overline{AD}$ and $\overline{CB}$.

**Proof** In △s ARD, CRB

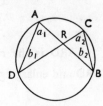

Fig. 66

$$a_1 = a_2 \qquad \textit{same seg. BD}$$
$$b_1 = b_2 \qquad \text{,,} \quad \text{,,} \quad \textit{AC}$$
∴ 3rd ∠s are equal
∴ △s ARD, CRB are similar

△ARD is the result of reflecting △CRB in the bisector of A$\hat{R}$C and enlarging it in the ratio RA : RC, centre R.

$$\therefore \frac{AR}{CR} = \frac{RD}{RB}\left(= \frac{DA}{BC}\right)$$
$$\therefore AR \times RB = CR \times RD.$$
·Q.E.D.

*N.B.* 'To prove' will generally show which △s have to be proved similar. In this theorem the lines AR, RB, CR and RD are involved, therefore two △s are needed which include between them all these four lines. These △s could be ARD and CRB *or* ARC and DRB, and in fact either pair will suffice.

### Theorem 24

If two secants of a circle meet at a point outside the circle, then the product of the two parts of one secant (measured from this

91

point) is equal to the product of
the two parts of the other secant
(measured from the same point).

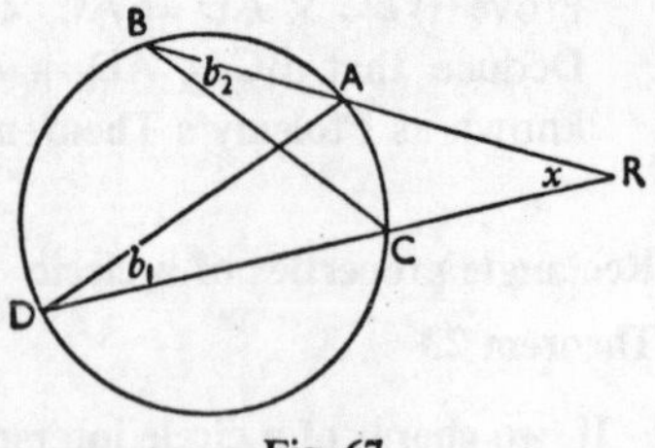

**Given** $\overline{\text{RAB}}$, $\overline{\text{RCD}}$ two secants
of a circle ABDC.

**To prove** RA $\times$ RB = RC $\times$ RD.

**Construction** Join $\overline{\text{AD}}$ and $\overline{\text{CB}}$.

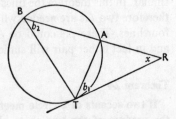

Fig. 67

**Proof** In △s ARD, CRB

$b_1 = b_2$      *same seg.* AC

$x$ is common

∴ 3rd ∠s are equal

∴ △s ARD, CRB are similar

△ARD is the result of reflecting △CRB in the bisector of
B$\hat{\text{R}}$D and enlarging it in the ratio RD : RB, centre R.

$$\therefore \frac{\text{AR}}{\text{CR}} = \frac{\text{RD}}{\text{RB}}\left( = \frac{\text{DA}}{\text{BC}}\right)$$

$$\therefore \text{RA} \times \text{RB} = \text{RC} \times \text{RD}.$$

Q.E.D.

**Theorem 25**

If a secant and a tangent to a circle meet at a point, then the
product of the two parts of the secant (measured from this point) is
equal to the square of the tangent.

**Given** $\overline{\text{RAB}}$ a secant of a circle BAT, and $\overline{\text{RT}}$ a tangent to the circle.

**To prove** RA $\times$ RB = RT$^2$.

**Construction** Join $\overline{\text{TA}}$ and $\overline{\text{TB}}$.

**Proof** In △s RAT, RTB

$b_1 = b_2$      *alt. seg.*

$x$ is common

∴ 3rd ∠s are equal

∴ △s RAT, RTB are similar

Fig. 68

92

$\triangle$ RTB is the result of reflecting $\triangle$ RAT in the bisector of B$\hat{R}$T and enlarging it in the ratio RB : RT, centre R.

$$\therefore \frac{RA}{RT}\left(= \frac{AT}{TB}\right) = \frac{TR}{BR}$$

$$\therefore RA \times RB = RT^2.$$

Q.E.D.

*N.B.* This result can be deduced immediately from Theorem 24 by considering the case in which the two points C and D are so close together that they merge into a single point T, so that RC and RD both become RT, and RC $\times$ RD becomes RT$^2$.

**Summary**

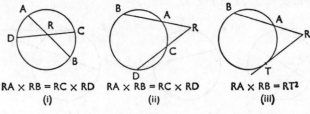

| RA × RB = RC × RD | RA × RB = RC × RD | RA × RB = RT² |
|:-:|:-:|:-:|
| (i) | (ii) | (iii) |

Fig. 69

Note particularly that, in all these results, R occurs in every length; i.e. **all measurements are taken from R.** It is especially important to remember this in numerical problems.

**Example 2** *Find a and b in Fig.* 70.

From Fig. 69 (iii),     $3(7 + a) = 6^2$
$$\therefore 7 + a = 12$$
$$\therefore a = 5.$$

From Fig. 69 (i),     $b \times 3 = 4 \times 5$
$$\therefore b = \frac{20}{3} = 6\frac{2}{3}.$$
*Ans.* $a = 5, b = 6\frac{2}{3}.$

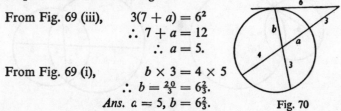

Fig. 70

**Example 3** *Find c in Fig. 71.*

From Fig. 69 (ii),     $c(c + 6) = 5 \times 8$

$$\therefore c^2 + 6c - 40 = 0$$
$$\therefore (c - 4)(c + 10) = 0$$
$$\therefore c = 4 \quad \text{or} \quad -10.$$
*Ans.* $c = 4$.

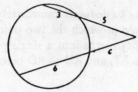

Fig. 71

**Exercise 11d**

Find $a, b, \ldots r$ in Fig. 72.

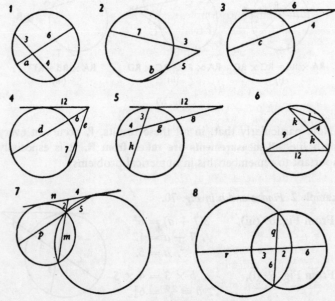

Fig. 72

**9** A brick arch is in the form of an arc of a circle 3 m high in the middle, and 12 m wide. What is the radius of the circle?

**10** An isosceles △ with sides 20, 20 and 24 cm is inscribed in a circle. Find the radius of the circle.

**11** A two-metre plank rests, with one end on the ground, over a semicircular mound one metre in diameter, so that the end on the ground is 80 cm away from the nearest point on the mound. What length of the plank protrudes beyond the mound, and how high is its tip above the ground? (Fig. 73).

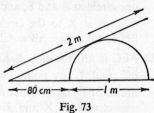

Fig. 73

**12** The mouth of a railway tunnel is a major segment of a five-metre diameter circle bounded by a chord of length four metres. What is the height of the tunnel?

In all the following examples use the 'rectangle properties of the circle', and *not* 'similar triangles'.

**13** In a △ABC, P and Q are points on $\overline{AB}$, $\overline{AC}$ respectively such that $A\hat{Q}P = \hat{B}$. Prove that AP × AB = AQ × AC.

**14** Two circles cut at A and B, and X is any point on $\overline{BA}$ produced. Tangents $\overline{XP}$ and $\overline{XQ}$ are drawn from X to the circles. Prove that XP = XQ.

**15** The tangent at C to a circle ABC cuts $\overline{BA}$ produced at P. D is a point on $\overline{BC}$ produced such that PD = PC. Prove that the circle ABD touches $\overline{PD}$ at D.

**16** ABC is an isosceles △ having AB = AC. A circle through C touches $\overline{AB}$ at A and cuts $\overline{BC}$ (or $\overline{BC}$ produced) at D. Prove that AC² = BC × BD.

**17** Prove that the common chord of two intersecting circles bisects the common tangents.

**18** $\overline{XAB}$ is a secant of a circle TAB, and $\overline{XT}$ is a tangent to the circle. If AB = 3AX, prove that XT = 2XA.

95

**19** $\overline{XAB}$ and $\overline{XCD}$ are secants of a circle ABDC. If XA = XC, prove that AB = CD.

**20** $\overline{BE}$ and $\overline{CF}$ are altitudes of a △ABC, and they intersect at H. Prove BH × HE = CH × HF.

**21** Two circles touch externally at X. A straight line $\overline{ABCD}$ cuts one circle at A and B, and the other at C and D. The common tangent at X to the circles cuts $\overline{ABCD}$ at M. Prove that, if BM = MC, then AB = CD.

**22** ABC is an isosceles △ having AB = AC. P is any point on $\overline{BC}$, and Y any point on $\overline{AP}$. The circles BPY and CPY cut $\overline{AB}$ and $\overline{AC}$ respectively at X and Z (Fig. 74). Prove $\overline{XZ} \parallel \overline{BC}$.

**23** Any circle having O as centre is drawn to pass through two fixed points A and B. X is any point on $\overline{AB}$; $\overline{OX}$ is joined; and a chord $\overline{PXQ}$ of the circle is drawn at right angles to $\overline{OX}$. Prove that the length of this chord is always the same, whatever the radius of the circle.

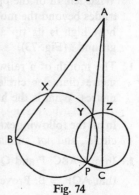

Fig. 74

**24** $\overline{PQ}$ is a common tangent to two circles which intersect at A and B. X is a point on $\overline{PQ}$ produced such that QX = PQ, and $\overline{XA}$ cuts the circles again at R and S, $\overline{XRAS}$ being a straight line. Prove that SR = 3RX.

**25** Two circles ABQP and CBQR cut at B and Q, and $\overline{XABC}$, $\overline{XPQR}$ are straight lines. Prove $\overline{AP} \parallel \overline{CR}$ (without using the line $\overline{BQ}$).

**The ratio of the areas of similar triangles**

In Book 3, Chapter 6, it was shown that the ratio of the areas of similar figures is equal to the ratio of the squares of corresponding lengths. Theorem 26, which follows, provides a geometrical proof for similar triangles.

**Theorem 26**

The areas of similar triangles are in the ratio of the squares of corresponding sides.

**Given** similar △s ABC and PQR.

**To prove** $\dfrac{\triangle ABC}{\triangle PQR} = \dfrac{BC^2}{QR^2}.$

**Construction** Draw the altitudes $\overline{AD}$ and $\overline{PN}$.

Fig. 75

**Proof** In the △s ABD, PQN

$$x_1 = x_2$$
$$y_1 = y_2 = 90°$$

△s ABC, PQR *similar*

*construction*

∴ 3rd ∠s are equal

∴ △s ABD, PQN are similar

△ABD is the result of displacing △PQN through $\overrightarrow{ND}$ and enlarging it in the ratio DA : NP, centre D.

$$\therefore \frac{AD}{PN} = \frac{AB}{PQ}$$

$$= \frac{BC}{QR}$$

△s ABC, PQR *similar*

$$\therefore \frac{\triangle ABC}{\triangle PQR} = \frac{\frac{1}{2}BC \times AD}{\frac{1}{2}QR \times PN}$$

$$= \frac{BC}{QR} \times \frac{AD}{PN}$$

$$= \frac{BC}{QR} \times \frac{BC}{QR}$$

$$= \frac{BC^2}{QR^2}.$$

Q.E.D.

In Book 3, Chapter 28, it was shown that an enlargement in the ratio $r : 1$ with centre the origin can be performed by the matrix operator $\begin{pmatrix} r & 0 \\ 0 & r \end{pmatrix}$. The determinant of this matrix is $r^2$ which is the multiple by which the area of the object is increased by this transformation.

**Example 4** *Find the co-ordinates of the vertices of the similar triangle whose area is 9 times the area of the triangle whose vertices are at* $\begin{pmatrix} 0 \\ 0 \end{pmatrix}$, $\begin{pmatrix} 2 \\ 4 \end{pmatrix}$ *and* $\begin{pmatrix} -1 \\ 3 \end{pmatrix}$, *the centre of enlargement being* $\begin{pmatrix} 0 \\ 0 \end{pmatrix}$.

The ratio of the areas is $9:1$

$\therefore$ the ratio of the lengths is $3:1$

$$\text{The operator is } \begin{pmatrix} 3 & 0 \\ 0 & 3 \end{pmatrix},$$

$$\begin{pmatrix} 0 \\ 0 \end{pmatrix} \text{ is mapped into } \begin{pmatrix} 0 \\ 0 \end{pmatrix},$$

$$\begin{pmatrix} 2 \\ 4 \end{pmatrix} \text{ is mapped into } \begin{pmatrix} 3 & 0 \\ 0 & 3 \end{pmatrix}\begin{pmatrix} 2 \\ 4 \end{pmatrix} = \begin{pmatrix} 6 \\ 12 \end{pmatrix},$$

$$\begin{pmatrix} -1 \\ 3 \end{pmatrix} \text{ is mapped into } \begin{pmatrix} 3 & 0 \\ 0 & 3 \end{pmatrix}\begin{pmatrix} -1 \\ 3 \end{pmatrix} = \begin{pmatrix} -3 \\ 9 \end{pmatrix}.$$

$\therefore$ the required co-ordinates are $\begin{pmatrix} 0 \\ 0 \end{pmatrix}$, $\begin{pmatrix} 6 \\ 12 \end{pmatrix}$, $\begin{pmatrix} -3 \\ 9 \end{pmatrix}$.

**Exercise 11e**

1 In Fig. 76 AX : XB $= 2:3$, and $\overline{XY} \parallel \overline{BC}$.
Write down the ratios
 (i) XY : BC
 (ii) $\triangle$ AXY : $\triangle$ ABC
 (iii) $\triangle$ AXY : trap. XYCB.

Fig. 76

2 If, in Fig. 76, using the data of no. 1, $\overline{BY}$ is joined, what is
 (i) the ratio of the areas of $\triangle$s AXY and BXY?
 (ii) the ratio of the areas of $\triangle$s BXY and BYC?

3 If, in Fig. 76, AX : XB $= 1:2$, what fraction is $\triangle$ AXY of $\triangle$ ABC, and what is the ratio of the areas of $\triangle$ AXY and the quadrilateral XYCB?

**4** In Fig. 76 AX = 6 cm and XB = 3 cm. Find the ratio of the areas of △AXY and the quadrilateral XYCB.

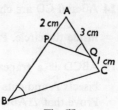

**5** In Fig. 77 A$\widehat{Q}$P = $\widehat{B}$. Find PB, and the ratio △APQ : △ABC.

Fig. 77

**6** In Fig. 78 (i) find the ratio of the areas A : B : C.

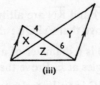

(i)      (ii)      (iii)

Fig. 78

**7** In Fig. 78 (ii) find the ratio of the areas P : Q : R.

**8** „ „ 78 (iii) „ „ „ „ „ „ X : Y : Z.

**9** In a circle ABCD chords $\overline{AC}$, $\overline{BD}$ cut at X inside the circle. AX = 3 cm, XC = 8 cm, DX = 4 cm. Find the ratios of the areas (i) △AXD : △BXC; (ii) △AXB : △CXD.

**10** A line parallel to one side of a triangle divides it into a triangle and a quadrilateral with areas in the ratio 9 : 16. In what ratio does the line divide the other two sides of the triangle?

**11** Two lines drawn parallel to one side of a triangle, as in Fig. 78 (ii), divide it into areas P, Q, R in the ratio 4 : 5 : 16. In what ratio do the lines divide the sides of the triangle?

**12** ABC is a triangle, and X a point on $\overline{AB}$ such that AX : XB = 3 : 5. $\overline{XY}$ is drawn parallel to $\overline{BC}$ to cut $\overline{AC}$ in Y. Find the ratio △AXY : △BCY.

**13** ABC is a triangle right-angled at A, and $\overline{AD}$ is an altitude of the triangle. Prove that the △s ABD, ACD and ABC are similar; that their areas are in the ratio $AB^2 : AC^2 : BC^2$; and hence that $BC^2 = AB^2 + AC^2$.

99

**14** $\overline{AB}$ and $\overline{CD}$ are chords of a circle which intersect at a point P inside the circle. Prove that $\dfrac{\triangle APC}{\triangle BPD} = \dfrac{AC^2}{BD^2}$.

**15** ABCD is a trapezium in which $\overline{AB}$ is parallel to $\overline{DC}$. $\overline{AC}$ bisects $\hat{A}$ and cuts $\overline{BD}$ at O.
Prove that $\triangle ABO : \triangle CDO = AB^2 : AD^2$.

**16** $\overline{ADX}$ and $\overline{BCX}$ are two straight lines, and $B\hat{A}C = B\hat{D}C$.
Prove that $\triangle ABX : \triangle CDX = AB^2 : CD^2$.

**17** $\overline{QM}$ and $\overline{RN}$ are altitudes in a $\triangle PQR$.
Prove that $\triangle PQR : \triangle PMN = PQ^2 : PM^2$.

**18** $\overline{AB}$ is a diameter of a circle, and a chord $\overline{CD}$ cuts $\overline{AB}$ at right angles at E. Prove that $AC^2 : BC^2 = AE : BE$.

**19** ABC is an isosceles triangle right-angled at C, and equilateral triangles are drawn on the sides $\overline{AB}$ and $\overline{AC}$. Prove that the area of the first of these $\triangle$s is twice that of the second.

**20** $\overline{ABCD}$ is a straight line, and P a point outside it such that $P\hat{B}A = P\hat{C}D = A\hat{P}D$.
Prove that $\triangle ABP : \triangle DCP = AB^2 : BP^2$.

**21** AXYZ, ARQP are two circles which intersect at A. $\overline{XAP}$, $\overline{YAQ}$, $\overline{ZAR}$ are straight lines.
Prove that $\triangle XYZ : \triangle PQR = XZ^2 : PR^2$.

**22** P and Q are points on the equal sides $\overline{AB}$ and $\overline{AC}$ respectively of an isosceles triangle ABC. D is a point on $\overline{AB}$ (produced if necessary) such that $A\hat{C}D = A\hat{P}Q$.
Prove $\triangle APQ : \triangle ACD = AP^2 : AB^2$.

**23** D is a point on the side $\overline{AB}$ of a triangle ABC such that $A\hat{C}D = A\hat{B}C$. Prove that $CD^2 : CB^2 = AD : AB$.

**24** ABCD is a trapezium in which $\overline{AB} \parallel \overline{DC}$ and $A\hat{D}B = \hat{C}$.
Prove that $AD^2 : BC^2 = AB : CD$.

**25** $\overline{TA}$ is the tangent at A to a circle ABC, and $\overline{TBC}$ is a straight line. Prove that $AB^2 : AC^2 = TB : TC$.

**26** Use the operator $\begin{pmatrix} 2 & 0 \\ 0 & 2 \end{pmatrix}$ to enlarge the triangle whose vertices are $\begin{pmatrix} 0 \\ 0 \end{pmatrix}$, $\begin{pmatrix} 3 \\ -1 \end{pmatrix}$ and $\begin{pmatrix} 5 \\ 7 \end{pmatrix}$. What is the ratio of the areas of the triangles?

**27** What matrix has the effect of enlarging in the ratio 10 : 1 with centre the origin? What is its determinant?

**28** Enlarge the triangle whose vertices are $\begin{pmatrix} 1 \\ -1 \end{pmatrix}$, $\begin{pmatrix} 3 \\ 1 \end{pmatrix}$ and $\begin{pmatrix} 4 \\ -2 \end{pmatrix}$ in the ratio 2 : 1 with centre $\begin{pmatrix} 1 \\ -1 \end{pmatrix}$. What is the ratio of the areas of the triangles?

**29** Two similar triangles are such that one has an area 25 times the other and has vertices $\begin{pmatrix} 10 \\ 0 \end{pmatrix}$, $\begin{pmatrix} 0 \\ 0 \end{pmatrix}$ and $\begin{pmatrix} 5 \\ 15 \end{pmatrix}$. Find the set of co-ordinates of the vertices of the smaller triangle (centre of enlargement at the origin).

**30** A triangle has vertices $\begin{pmatrix} 2 \\ 1 \end{pmatrix}$, $\begin{pmatrix} 3 \\ -2 \end{pmatrix}$ and $\begin{pmatrix} 4 \\ -1 \end{pmatrix}$. A similar triangle has 4 times the area. Find the co-ordinates of its vertices, the centre of enlargement being $\begin{pmatrix} 2 \\ 1 \end{pmatrix}$.

# Chapter 12

# *Functional notation*
# *Remainder theorem*

## Relations

An algebraic equation implies a **relation** between the variables involved. There are four types of relation between two variables as shown by the following examples:

(i) $y = 2x + 3$ is a **one-to-one** relation as for any value of $x$ there is only one value of $y$, and for any value of $y$ there is only one value of $x$,

(ii) $y = 4x^2$ is a **many-to-one** relation as there are several values of $x$ (two in this case) for any one value of $y$,

(iii) $y^4 = 16x$ is a **one-to-many** relation as there are several values of $y$ for any value of $x$,

(iv) $y^2 = x^6$ is a **many-to-many** relation as there is more than one value of $y$ for any value of $x$, and more than one value of $x$ for any value of $y$. Figure 79 illustrates some of the values in this relation.

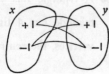

Fig. 79

## Functional notation

A many-to-one relation is called a **function**.

As a one-to-one relation, often called a **one-to-one correspondence**, is a special case of a many-to-one relation it is also a function.

Any algebraic expression which involves the variable $x$ (and no other variable) is a **function of $x$**, and its value depends on the value of $x$. The symbol used is $f(x)$, which is read as 'function of $x$'; $f(2)$ means 'the same expression with 2 written instead of $x$', $f(-1)$ means 'the same expression with $-1$ written instead of $x$', and so on.

Thus if

$$f(x) \equiv x^3 - 2x^2 + 3x - 4,$$

then

$$f(2) = 2^3 - 2 \times 2^2 + 3 \times 2 - 4 = 8 - 8 + 6 - 4 = 2$$
$$f(-1) = (-1)^3 - 2 \times (-1)^2 + 3 \times (-1) - 4$$
$$= -1 - 2 - 3 - 4 = -10$$
$$f(p) = p^3 - 2p^2 + 3p - 4$$
$$f(x + 1) = (x + 1)^3 - 2(x + 1)^2 + 3(x + 1) - 4$$
$$= x^3 + 3x^2 + 3x + 1 - 2x^2 - 4x - 2 + 3x + 3 - 4$$
$$= x^3 + x^2 + 2x - 2.$$

**Example 1** *If* $f(x) \equiv \dfrac{3(x - 2)}{x^2 + 3x + 2}$, *find* $f(0)$, $f(2)$, $f(-3)$, $f(x + 2)$.

$$f(0) = \frac{3(-2)}{2} = -3$$

$$f(2) = \frac{3 \times 0}{4 + 6 + 2} = \frac{0}{12} = 0$$

$$f(-3) = \frac{3(-3 - 2)}{9 - 9 + 2} = \frac{3(-5)}{2} = -\frac{15}{2}$$

$$f(x + 2) = \frac{3(x + 2 - 2)}{(x + 2)^2 + 3(x + 2) + 2} = \frac{3x}{x^2 + 7x + 12}$$

In some cases the use of factors makes the working easier. For example, in Example 1,

$$f(x) \equiv \frac{3(x - 2)}{x^2 + 3x + 2}$$

$$\equiv \frac{3(x - 2)}{(x + 1)(x + 2)}$$

$$\therefore f(0) = \frac{3(-2)}{1 \times 2} = -3$$

$$f(2) = \frac{3 \times 0}{3 \times 4} = 0$$

103

$$f(-3) = \frac{3(-5)}{(-2)(-1)} = -\frac{15}{2}$$

$$f(x+2) = \frac{3(\overline{x+2}-2)}{(x+2+1)(\overline{x+2}+2)} = \frac{3x}{(x+3)(x+4)}$$

## Exercise 12a

**1** State which type of relation is expressed by the following equations:

(i) $y = 3x$

(ii) $y = x^2 - x$

(iii) $y^2 = 4x$

(iv) $2y^2 = 4x - x^2$

(v) $5y = 4x^2$

(vi) $y - y^2 = x$

(vii) $2y + y^2 = 4x + 5x^2$

(viii) $y^3 = 6x - x^2$

(ix) $y = 4x + x^3$

(x) $y^2 - y = 8x$

**2** If $f(x) = x^2$, find the values of

(i) $f(0)$

(ii) $f(1)$

(iii) $f(3)$

(iv) $f(-2)$

(v) $f(-3)$

(vi) $f(y)$

(vii) $f(x+1)$

(viii) $f(2x)$

(ix) $f(-2z)$

(x) $f(x+h)$

**3** If $f(x) = 4x^2 - 1$, find the values of

(i) $f(0)$   (ii) $f(1)$   (iii) $f(\frac{1}{2})$   (iv) $f(-2)$   (v) $f\left(\frac{1}{x}\right)$

**4** If $f(x) = 2^x$, find the values of

(i) $f(1)$   (ii) $f(3)$   (iii) $f(-1)$   (iv) $f(0)$   (v) $f(-2)$

**5** If $f(x) = \dfrac{x^2 - x - 6}{2x - 5}$, find the values of

(i) $f(0)$   (ii) $f(1)$   (iii) $f(2)$   (iv) $f(-2)$   (v) $f(3)$

**6** Write down and simplify the values of $f(x + 1)$ for the following functions:

(i) $f(x) = x - 1$

(ii) $f(x) = x^2 - 1$

(iii) $f(x) = x^2 + 3x - 4$

(iv) $f(x) = x^3$

(v) $f(x) = \dfrac{2x}{x^2 + 2x + 1}$

**7** Evaluate $\dfrac{f(x + h) - f(x)}{h}$ for each of the following functions:

(i) $f(x) = x$     (ii) $f(x) = x^2$     (iii) $f(x) = x^3$

(iv) $f(x) = \dfrac{1}{x}$     (v) $f(x) = 2x^2 - x$

## Remainder theorem

When 109 is divided by 7, the *quotient* is 15, and the *remainder* is 4. Hence $109 = 7 \times 15 + 4$.

Similarly when $x^3 - 2x^2 - 13x + 10$ is divided by $x + 3$:

$$
\begin{array}{r}
x + 3)\overline{x^3 - 2x^2 - 13x + 10}(x^2 - 5x + 2 \\
\underline{x^3 + 3x^2} \qquad\qquad\qquad \\
- 5x^2 - 13x \qquad\quad \\
\underline{- 5x^2 - 15x} \qquad\quad \\
+ 2x + 10 \\
\underline{+ 2x + 6} \\
+ 4
\end{array}
$$

The *quotient is* $x^2 - 5x + 2$ and the *remainder* is 4.

Hence   $x^3 - 2x^2 - 13x + 10 \equiv (x + 3)(x^2 - 5x + 2) + 4$.

This statement is an **identity,** i.e. it is true for any value of $x$.

This suggests a method for finding the remainder without going through the process of division and without finding the quotient; for let the quotient be Q and the remainder R, then

$$x^3 - 2x^2 - 13x + 10 \equiv (x + 3)Q + R.$$

Since this is true for any value of $x$, **let $x$ have the value which makes the divisor zero,**

$$\text{i.e. put } x = -3.$$

Then   $(-3)^3 - 2(-3)^2 - 13(-3) + 10 = 0 \times Q + R$
$$\therefore \; -27 - 18 + 39 + 10 = R$$
$$\therefore \; 4 = R.$$

Hence the remainder is 4.

This may be expressed in another way, using functional notation,

for if   $x^3 - 2x^2 - 13x + 10$ is denoted by $f(x)$

then   $(-3)^3 - 2(-3)^2 - 13(-3) + 10 = f(-3)$.

Hence when $f(x)$ is divided by $x + 3$, the remainder is $f(-3)$.

**Example 2** *Find the remainder when* $2x^3 - 9x^2 + 16x - 18$ *is divided by* $2x - 5$.

Let the quotient be Q and the remainder R.

Then   $2x^3 - 9x^2 + 16x - 18 \equiv (2x - 5)Q + R.$

Put   $x = \frac{5}{2}$ (so that $2x - 5 = 0$).

Then   $2(\frac{5}{2})^3 - 9(\frac{5}{2})^2 + 16(\frac{5}{2}) - 18 = 0 \times Q + R$

$\therefore \frac{125}{4} - \frac{225}{4} + 40 - 18 = R$

$\therefore R = 31\frac{1}{4} - 56\frac{1}{4} + 40 - 18$

$= 71\frac{1}{4} - 74\frac{1}{4}$

$= -3$

$\therefore$ the remainder is $-3$.

Once the reasoning has been understood it will be clear that the working of Example 2 may be further reduced. To find the remainder, it is necessary merely to substitute in the dividend the value of $x$ which makes the divisor zero.

**Example 3** *Find the remainder when* $2x^3 - 3x^2 - 9$ *is divided by* $x - 2$.

If   $x = 2$,   $2x^3 - 3x^2 - 9 = 2 \times 8 - 3 \times 4 - 9$

$= 16 - 12 - 9$

$= -5$

$\therefore$ the remainder is $-5$.

*Alternatively*, using the functional notation,

let   $f(x) \equiv 2x^3 - 3x^2 - 9$

Then $f(2) = 2 \times 8 - 3 \times 4 - 9$
$$= 16 - 12 - 9$$
$$= -5$$

$\therefore$ the remainder is $-5$.

## Exercise 12b

**1** Find the remainder when $x^2 + 2x + 3$ is divided by
   (i) $x - 1$    (ii) $x + 1$    (iii) $x - 2$
   Check by division.

**2** Find the remainder when $2x^2 - 3x + 2$ is divided by
   (i) $x - 1$    (ii) $x - 2$    (iii) $x + 2$
   Check by division.

**3** Find the remainder when $2x^2 - x - 3$ is divided by
   (i) $x + 1$    (ii) $x - 3$    (iii) $x + 3$
   Check by division.

**4** Find the remainder when $3x^3 - 2x^2 - 5x + 3$ is divided by
   (i) $x - 1$    (ii) $x + 1$    (iii) $x + 2$

**5** Find the remainder when $2x^3 - 5x^2 - x + 6$ is divided by
   (i) $x + 1$    (ii) $x - 2$    (iii) $x - 3$

**6** Find the remainder when $4x^3 - 2x^2 + 5x - 3$ is divided by
   (i) $2x - 1$    (ii) $2x - 3$    (iii) $2x + 3$

**7** Find the remainder when $6x^3 + 3x^2 - 7x - 2$ is divided by
   (i) $2x - 3$    (ii) $3x + 1$    (iii) $3x + 2$

## Factorisation

**Example 4** *Verify that $x - 3$ is a factor of $2x^3 - 5x^2 - 5x + 6$.*

If $x - 3$ is a factor, then when $2x^3 - 5x^2 - 5x + 6$ is divided by $x - 3$, the remainder is 0.

If $x = 3$, $2x^3 - 5x^2 - 5x + 6 = 54 - 45 - 15 + 6$
$$= 0$$

$\therefore$ the remainder is 0,
i.e. $x - 3$ is a factor.

**Example 5** *Factorise the expression* $2x^3 + x^2 - 13x + 6.$

If $x = 1,$ $\quad 2x^3 + x^2 - 13x + 6 = 2 + 1 - 13 + 6 \neq 0$
$\therefore x - 1$ is not a factor.

If $x = -1,$ $\quad 2x^3 + x^2 - 13x + 6 = -2 + 1 + 13 + 6 \neq 0$
$\therefore x + 1$ is not a factor.

If $x = 2,$ $\quad 2x^3 + x^2 - 13x + 6 = 16 + 4 - 26 + 6 = 0$
$\therefore x - 2$ is a factor.

$\therefore 2x^3 + x^2 - 13x + 6 = (x - 2)(2x^2 + 5x - 3)$
$\qquad\qquad\qquad\qquad = (x - 2)(x + 3)(2x - 1).$

Notice that when $x - 2$ has been established as a factor, the other factors can be found by inspection.

In Example 6, which follows, functional notation is used. The working is neater, and may always be used provided that the reasoning is fully understood.

**Example 6** *Factorise the expression* $2x^4 - 9x^3 + 13x^2 - 15x + 9.$
Since the absolute term is 9, there is no point in trying the values $x = 2$ or $-2$ or 4 or $-4$, since $(x - 2)$ cannot be a factor, nor can $(x + 2)$ or $(x - 4)$ or $(x + 4)$.

Let $\quad 2x^4 - 9x^3 + 13x^2 - 15x + 9 \equiv f(x).$

Then $\quad f(1) = 2 - 9 + 13 - 15 + 9 = 0$
$\therefore x - 1$ is a factor.

$f(-1) = 2 + 9 + 13 + 15 + 9 \neq 0$
$\therefore x + 1$ is not a factor.

$f(3) = 162 - 243 + 117 - 45 + 9 = 0$
$\therefore x - 3$ is a factor.

$\therefore 2x^4 - 9x^3 + 13x^2 - 15x + 9$
$\qquad\qquad = (x - 1)(2x^3 - 7x^2 + 6x - 9)$
$\qquad\qquad = (x - 1)(x - 3)(2x^2 - x + 3).$

The expression cannot be further factorised.

## Exercise 12c

Factorise the following expressions.

**1** $x^3 + 4x^2 + x - 6$ $\qquad$ **2** $a^3 - 3a - 2$
**3** $d^3 - 3d^2 - 10d + 24$ $\qquad$ **4** $m^3 + 4m^2 - 9m - 36$

**5** $c^3 - 4c^2 - 3c + 18$    **6** $u^3 + 3u^2 + 3u + 2$

**7** $n^3 - n^2 - 3n - 9$    **8** $2y^3 + 3y^2 - 8y + 3$

**9** $2x^3 + x^2 - 15x - 18$    **10** $m^3 - 5m^2 - 22m + 5o$

**11** $n^3 - 3n + 2$    **12** $a^3 + 3a^2 - 4a - 12$

**13** $b^3 - 19b - 30$    **14** $6z^3 - 17z^2 + 4z + 12$

**15** $x^3 - 3x^2 - 45x + 175$    **16** $a^4 - 27a^2 - 14a + 120$

**17** $c^4 - 4c^3 + 8c^2 - 11c + 6$   **18** $d^4 + 5d^3 + 4d^2 - 8d - 8$

**19** $4e^3 - 32e^2 - e + 8$

**20** $n^4 + 6n^3 - 3n^2 - 52n - 60$

**21** $3m^4 + 7m^3 - 24m^2 - 12m + 16$

**22** $2b^3 - 3b^2 - 72b - 35$

**23** $y^4 - 27y^2 + 14y + 120$

**24** $3u^4 - u^3 - 29u^2 + 9u + 18$

**25** $2v^4 + 17v^3 + 23v^2 - 105v - 225$

**26** $w^4 + 14w^3 + 71w^2 + 154w + 120$

**27** $a^4 - 6a^2 + 7a - 6$

**28** $m^4 - 2m^3 - 12m^2 + 40m - 32$

**29** $n^5 - 15n^3 - 10n^2 + 60n + 72$

**30** $6m^4 + m^3 - 7m^2 - 8m - 6$

**Example 7** *If* $x + 2$ *and* $2x - 1$ *are factors of* $2x^3 + hx^2 + kx + 10$, *find h and k, and the other factor.*

Let $2x^3 + hx^2 + kx + 10 \equiv f(x)$.

$x + 2$ is a factor.

$\therefore f(-2) = 0$

$\therefore -16 + 4h - 2k + 10 = 0$

$\qquad\qquad \therefore 4h - 2k = 6$   i.e.   $2h - k = 3$   (i)

$2x - 1$ is a factor.

$\therefore f(\tfrac{1}{2}) = 0$

$\therefore \tfrac{1}{4} + \tfrac{1}{4}h + \tfrac{1}{2}k + 10 = 0$

$\therefore 1 + h + 2k + 40 = 0$   i.e.   $h + 2k = -41$   (ii)

(i) $\times 2$     $4h - 2k = 6$

(ii)      $h + 2k = -41$

Add     $5h \quad\;\; = -35$

$\qquad\qquad\qquad \therefore h = -7$

Subst. in (i) $\quad -14 - k = 3$

$$\therefore k = -17$$

$$\therefore 2x^3 + hx^2 + kx + 10 = 2x^3 - 7x^2 - 17x + 10$$

$$= (x + 2)(2x - 1)(x - 5).$$

The final factor is easily found by inspection, since the product of the three '$x$ terms' is $2x^3$, and the product of the three absolute terms is $+10$.

## Exercise 12d

1 Given that $x - 3$ is a factor of $2x^3 + ax^2 - 5x + 6$, find $a$ and the remaining factor of the expression.

2 When the expression $x^4 - 5x^2 + bx - 4$ is divided by $x + 2$ the remainder is $-4$. Find $b$ and the remainder when the expression is divided by $x - 3$.

3 Given that $x + 3$ is a factor of $x^3 + cx + 6$, find the other two factors.

4 Given that $x^4 + x^3 + ax^2 + bx - 2b$ is exactly divisible by $x + 2$ and by $x - 3$, find $a$ and $b$ and the other two factors.

5 If $ax^3 + bx^2 + x - a$ is exactly divisible by $x + 3$ and by $2x - 1$, find $a$ and $b$ and the other factor.

6 If $ax^4 + bx^3 + 7x + 2b$ is divided by $x - 1$ the remainder is $-2$, and if by $x + 2$ the remainder is 58. Find $a$ and $b$.

7 An expression of the form $ax^2 + bx + c$ is known to be exactly divisible by $x - 3$, and the remainders when it is divided by $x - 1$, $x + 1$ are respectively $-6$, 4. Find the expression.

8 The factors of $ax^3 + bx^2 + cx + 2$ are $x - 1$, $x + 2$, $2x - 1$. Find $a$, $b$ and $c$.

9 Two factors of $ax^3 + bx^2 + cx - 2$ are $x + 1$ and $2x + 1$. The remainder when the expression is divided by $x + 2$ is $-12$. What is the third factor of the expression?

10 A factor of $ax^3 + bx + c$ is $x + 4$. When the expression is divided by $x + 2$ the remainder is 14; also $b = c - a$. Find the other two factors of the expression.

# Chapter 13

# *Vector applications*

A moving object may have more than one velocity at the same time. For example, a liner may be heading due north, but a current flowing from west to east would carry it off course. Again, an aircraft has instruments which indicate to the navigator his speed *relative to the air*, but if he is to keep the aircraft moving in any desired direction *relative to the ground* he must know how the air itself is moving.

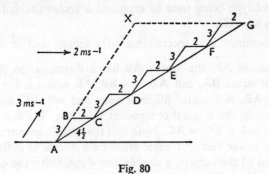

Fig. 80

Suppose a man rows on a river at a speed which in still water would be 3 m s⁻¹, while the river itself flows at 2 m s⁻¹. If he heads along $\overline{AX}$, then after 1 second he has moved 3 m through the water from A to B; but at the same time the point B in the water has moved 2 m to the position C. Hence in the first second the man has moved from A to C.

Similarly in the next second he will move from C to D, and in subsequent seconds will reach the positions E, F, G. By similar triangles it will be seen that $\overline{ACDEFG}$ is a straight line. Hence the line along which the man actually moves is the *straight line* joining A to G.

111

If the equal distances AC, CD, DE etc. are each $4\frac{1}{2}$ m, then in each second the man has moved a distance of $4\frac{1}{2}$ m in the direction $\overrightarrow{AG}$.

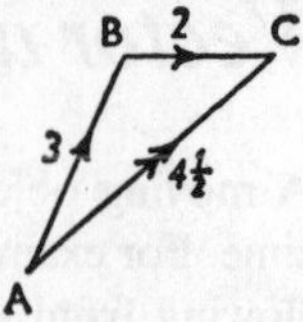

The displacement $\overrightarrow{AC}$ is the vector sum of the displacements $\overrightarrow{AB}$ and $\overrightarrow{BC}$, i.e. $\overrightarrow{AC} = \overrightarrow{AB} + \overrightarrow{BC}$.

Hence the two **component velocities** of 3 m s$^{-1}$ and 2 m s$^{-1}$ may be combined into a single **resultant velocity** of $4\frac{1}{2}$ m s$^{-1}$ in the direction $\overrightarrow{AC}$.

Fig. 81

The resultant velocity is the vector sum of the component velocities.

In $\triangle ABC$ of Fig. 81, **AC** represents the vector sum of **AB** and **BC**, bold type being used to represent a vector (in writing it is usual to use $\underset{\sim}{AB}$).

Displacement is a special case of a vector, and as with the displacement $\overrightarrow{AB}$, the vector **AB** has a direction, so that **AB** does not equal **BA**, but **AB** = −**BA**. AB, which is the magnitude of **AB**, is 3 units, BC is 2 units and **AB**, **BC** are in the directions of the original component velocities. The sum can be stated as **AB** + **BC** = **AC**. Note that the two B's are consecutive, and that in the vector triangle arrows are drawn to indicate the directions of the vectors, a double arrow indicating the direction of the resultant. To go from A to C it is necessary to go either direct, or from A to B and then from B to C (i.e. from A to C via B). If a vector equation is formed first it often makes it easier to draw the triangle correctly.

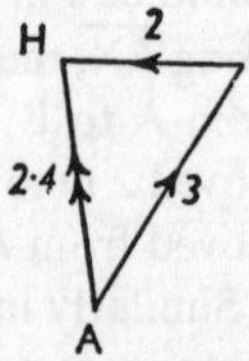

If the velocity of 2 m s$^{-1}$ had been in the opposite direction the vector triangle would have been as in Fig. 82, in which **AH** = **AB** + **BH**, the resultant velocity being represented in magnitude and direction by **AH**. Fig. 81 is called a **triangle of velocities,** but the principles apply to other vectors such as **forces** and **accelerations.**

Fig. 82

Notice that the idea of vectors is quite different from the elementary principles of Euclidean geometry, in which two sides of any triangle are together greater than the third, i.e. AB + BH > AH, where AB, BH and AH are merely *lengths*.

AB is said to be the magnitude or **modulus** of **AB**.

In velocity examples the symbol $_AV_B$ for the velocity of A relative to B is often useful. $_OV_A$ is the velocity of O relative to A, and $_OV_B$ is the velocity of O relative to B. By examining the positions of the letters O, A and B it can be seen that the only way of forming the vector equation is $_OV_B = _OV_A + _AV_B$, i.e. the velocity of O relative to B is the velocity of O relative to A plus the velocity of A relative to B.

**Reminder on bearings.** It is usual to give a bearing by means of a three-digit number, which states the number of degrees of rotation clockwise from due north.

Thus S 20° E, or 20° E of S is given as 160°,
$\qquad$ N 43° E, or 43° E of N ,, $\quad$ ,, $\quad$ ,, 043°,
$\qquad$ N 75° W, or 75° W of N ,, $\quad$ ,, $\quad$ ,, 285°.

**Example 1** *A boat is heading in a direction* 081° *at a speed which in still water would be* $16\,km\,h^{-1}$. *It is carried off course by a current of* $7\,km\,h^{-1}$ *in a direction* 158°. *Find the boat's actual speed and direction.*

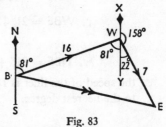

Fig. 83

Let $_BV_W$ represent the velocity of the boat in still water, $_WV_E$ represent the velocity of the water relative to the earth, and $_BV_E$ represent the velocity of the boat relative to the earth. $_BV_E = _BV_W + _WV_E$, from which a rough sketch is drawn, estimating angles and lengths. $\overline{NBS}$ and $\overline{XWY}$ are north-south lines. $N\hat{B}W = 81°$ and $X\hat{W}E = 158°$. Then $\triangle BWE$ is the triangle of velocities.

(i) *By drawing and measurement*

Use a scale of 1 cm to 1 km h⁻¹.

Draw $\triangle BWE$ as in Fig. 83, with BW = 16 cm, WE = 7 cm and angles as shown.

113

By measurement, $BE = 18 \cdot 8$ cm, and $\widehat{NBE} = 102°$

∴ the boat is moving at $18 \cdot 8$ km h$^{-1}$ on a bearing of $102°$.

(ii) *By calculation*

In $\triangle BWE$, using the cosine formula,

$$BE^2 = 16^2 + 7^2 - 2 \times 16 \times 7 \cos 103°$$
$$= 16^2 + 7^2 + 14 \times 16 \cos 77°$$
$$= 256 + 49 + 50 \cdot 4$$
$$= 355 \cdot 4$$

∴ $BE = 18 \cdot 85$.

| No. | Log. |
|---|---|
| 14 | $1 \cdot 146\ 1$ |
| 16 | $1 \cdot 204\ 1$ |
| $\cos 77°$ | $\bar{1} \cdot 352\ 1$ |
| $50 \cdot 39$ | $1 \cdot 702\ 3$ |

Using the sine formula,

$$\frac{\sin \widehat{WBE}}{7} = \frac{\sin 103°}{18 \cdot 85}$$

∴ $\sin \widehat{WBE} = \dfrac{7 \sin 77°}{18 \cdot 85}$

| No. | Log. |
|---|---|
| 7 | $0 \cdot 845\ 1$ |
| $\sin 77°$ | $\bar{1} \cdot 988\ 7$ |
| | $0 \cdot 833\ 8$ |
| $18 \cdot 85$ | $1 \cdot 275\ 4$ |
| $\sin 21° 12'$ | $\bar{1} \cdot 558\ 4$ |

∴ $\widehat{WBE} = 21° 12'$ (*since an obtuse angle is clearly not suitable*)

∴ $\widehat{NBE} = 81° + 21° 12' = 102° 12'$

∴ the speed of the liner is $18 \cdot 8$ km h$^{-1}$ on a bearing of $102°$ to the nearest degree.

**Example 2** *A ferry-boat crosses a river to an exactly opposite point on the far bank. The speed of the boat in still water is $5$ m s$^{-1}$, and the current flows at $2$ m s$^{-1}$. Find the angle to the bank at which the boat must head.*

Let $_BV_W$ represent the velocity of the boat in still water, $_WV_E$ represent the velocity of the current, and $_BV_E$ represent the velocity of the boat relative to the earth.

$_BV_E = _BV_W + _WV_E$, from which a rough sketch is drawn.

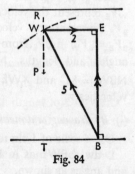

Fig. 84

114

(i) *By drawing and measurement*

Use a scale of 2 cm to 1 m s⁻¹.

Draw $\overline{BE}$ at right angles to the bank, and a line $\overline{PR} \parallel \overline{BE}$ and 4 cm from it. With centre B and radius 10 cm draw an arc to cut $\overline{PR}$ at W.

Then $\triangle BWE$ is the triangle of velocities.

By measurement, $T\hat{B}W = 66°$.

∴ the boat must head upstream at 66° to the bank.

(ii) *By calculation*

$$\cos T\hat{B}W = \cos B\hat{W}E$$
$$= \tfrac{2}{5}$$
$$= 0.400\ 0$$
$$\therefore T\hat{B}W = 66°\ 25'$$

∴ the boat must head upstream at approximately $66\tfrac{1}{2}°$ to the bank.

**Example 3** *In Fig. 85 two strings are being used to raise a mass. A vertical force of 3 newtons is required. The string $\overline{AC}$ is at 30° to the vertical and $\overline{CB}$ is perpendicular to $\overline{AC}$. What forces must be applied to the strings?*

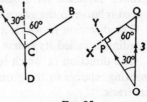

Fig. 85

Let **OP** represent the force in $\overline{AC}$ and **PQ** the force in $\overline{BC}$. The resultant force **OQ** given by **OQ** = **OP** + **PQ** must be 3 newtons vertically. To draw the triangle of forces, first draw $\overline{OQ}$, then $\overline{OP}$ and $\overline{PQ}$ in the appropriate directions.

(i) *By drawing and measurement*

Use a scale of 4 cm to 1 newton.

Draw $\overline{OQ}$ of length 12 cm. Then draw $\overline{OY}$ with $Q\hat{O}Y = 30°$ and $\overline{QX}$ with $O\hat{Q}X = 60°$. These lines meet at P. By measurement $OP = 10.4$ cm and $PQ = 6$ cm.

∴ the force in $\overline{CA}$ is 2·6 newtons and the force in $\overline{CB}$ is 1·5 newtons.

115

*New General Mathematics*

(ii) *By calculation*

$$O\hat{P}Q = 90°$$
$$\therefore \ OP = 3\cos 30°$$
$$= 3 \times 0.866$$
$$= 2.598$$
$$\text{and} \ \ QP = 3\sin 30°$$
$$= 3 \times 0.5$$
$$= 1.5$$

∴ the force in $\overline{CA}$ is 2·6 newtons and the force in $\overline{CB}$ is 1·5 newtons.

### Course, track and drift

The speed which an aircraft would have if the air were still is called its **air-speed** (i.e. speed relative to the air).

The speed of an aircraft over the ground is called its **ground-speed** (i.e. speed relative to the ground).

The direction in which an aircraft is heading is called its **course**.

The direction in which it is actually moving relative to the ground is called its **track**.

The angle between the track and the course is called the **drift**.

Angles are usually given to the nearest degree.

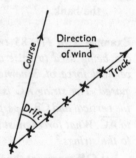

Fig. 86

Notice that although the aircraft is travelling along its *track*, it is pointing in the direction of its *course* (see Fig. 86).

When putting the arrows on the triangle of velocities for an aircraft it is usual to use a single arrow for the

Fig. 87

course, a double arrow for the wind, and a triple arrow for the track. Thus a vector marked with one arrow and a vector marked with two arrows add up to a vector marked with three arrows.

Remember that the **direction of the wind** is usually given as the direction **from** which it is blowing, e.g. a north wind blows *from* the north. Hence if, for example, the direction of the wind is given as 240° it is as in Fig. 88.

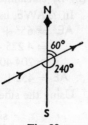

This is in contrast to the way in which the direction of a **current of water** is given. If a current is flowing as in Fig. 88 its direction is given as 060°. A north-easterly current flows **towards** the north-east, and is said to 'set north-east'.

Fig. 88

**Example 4** *An aircraft is flying on a course of 342° with an air-speed of 480 km h⁻¹. The wind is blowing from 043° at 65 km h⁻¹. Find the ground-speed of the aircraft, its track and the drift.*

Let $_AV_W$ represent the air-speed, $_WV_E$ represent the wind-speed and $_AV_E$ represent the ground-speed.

$_AV_E = _AV_W + _WV_E$, from which a rough sketch is drawn. $\overline{NAS}$ is the north-south line, $C\hat{A}W = 18°$ (reflex $C\hat{A}W = 342°$) and $A\hat{C}W = 43°$. $A\hat{W}E = A\hat{C}W + C\hat{A}W = 43° + 18° = 61°$. Then $\triangle AWE$ is the triangle of velocities.

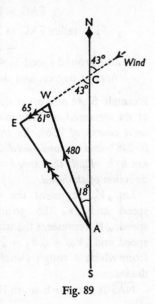

Fig. 89

(i) *By drawing and measurement*

Use a scale of 2 cm to 100 km h⁻¹.

Draw the north-south line $\overline{NAS}$.

Draw $\overline{AW}$ of length 9·6 cm and $\overline{WE}$ of length 1·3 cm with angles as in the figure.

By measurement, $AE = 9·0$ cm and $C\hat{A}E = 25°$ (i.e. reflex $C\hat{A}E = 335°$).

Hence $W\hat{A}E = 7°$.

∴ the ground-speed is 450 km h⁻¹, the track is 335°, and the drift is 7°.

117

(ii) *By calculation*

In $\triangle$AWE, using the cosine formula,

$AE^2 = 65^2 + 480^2 - 2 \times 65 \times 480 \cos 61°$

$= 4\,225 + 230\,400 - 30\,250$

$\eqsim 204\,400$

$\therefore$ AE $= 452 \cdot 1$.

| No. | Log. |
|---|---|
| 130 | 2·113 9 |
| 480 | 2·681 2 |
| cos 61° | $\bar{1}$·685 6 |
| 30 250 | 4·480 7 |

Using the sine formula,

$$\frac{\sin\, E\hat{A}W}{65} = \frac{\sin 61°}{452 \cdot 1}$$

$$\therefore \sin\, E\hat{A}W = \frac{65 \sin 61°}{452 \cdot 1}$$

| No. | Log. |
|---|---|
| 65 | 1·812 9 |
| sin 61° | $\bar{1}$·941 8 |
| | 1·754 7 |
| 452·1 | 2·655 2 |
| sin 7° 13′ | $\bar{1}$·099 5 |

$\therefore$ E$\hat{A}$W $= 7°\ 13'$ (*since an obtuse angle is clearly not suitable*)

$\therefore$ E$\hat{A}$C $= 25°\ 13'$

i.e. reflex E$\hat{A}$C $= 360° - 25°\ 13'$

$= 334°\ 47'$

$\therefore$ the ground-speed is 452 km h$^{-1}$, the track is 335° to the nearest degree, and the drift is 7°.

**Example 5** *An aircraft is flying at an air-speed of 210 km h$^{-1}$ on a course of 256°. Its track is 248° and ground-speed 264 km h$^{-1}$. Find the speed and direction of the wind.*

Let $_AV_W$ represent the air-speed and $_AV_E$ the ground-speed. $_WV_E$ represents the wind-speed and $_AV_W + {}_WV_E = {}_AV_E$, from which a rough sketch is drawn.

$\overline{NAS}$ is the north-south line, S$\hat{A}$W $= 76°$ (reflex N$\hat{A}$W $= 256°$) and S$\hat{A}$E $= 68°$ (reflex N$\hat{A}$E $= 248°$).

Then $\triangle$AWE is the triangle of velocities.

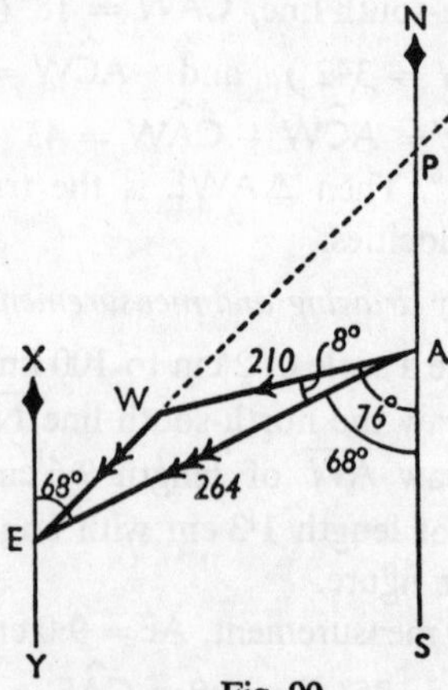

Fig. 90

(i) *By drawing and measurement*

Use a scale of 5 cm to 100 km h⁻¹.

Draw the north-south line $\overline{\text{NAS}}$.

Draw $\overline{\text{AW}}$ and $\overline{\text{AE}}$ so that $S\hat{A}W = 76°$ and $S\hat{A}E = 68°$.

Mark off AW = 10·5 cm (for 210 km h⁻¹) and AE = 13·2 cm (for 264 km h⁻¹).

Join $\overline{\text{WE}}$.

Then $\overline{\text{WE}}$ represents the velocity of the wind in magnitude and direction.

Draw $\overline{\text{XEY}}$, the north-south line at E.

Then $X\hat{E}A = S\hat{A}E = 68°$ (*alt.*).

By measurement WE = 3·15 cm, giving a wind-speed of 63 km h⁻¹, and $W\hat{E}A = 27°$.

∴ $X\hat{E}W = 68° - 27° = 41°$.

Alternatively $\overline{\text{EW}}$ may be produced to cut $\overline{\text{NAS}}$ at P. Then by measurement $N\hat{P}Q$ is found to be 41°.

∴ speed of wind is 63 km h⁻¹ from a direction 041°.

(ii) *By calculation*

In △AWE, using the cosine formula,

$$WE^2 = 210^2 + 264^2 - 2 \times 210 \times 264 \cos 8°$$
$$= 4\,000$$
$$\therefore WE = 63·25.$$

Using the sine formula,

$$\frac{\sin A\hat{E}W}{210} = \frac{\sin 8°}{63·25}$$

$$\therefore \sin A\hat{E}W = \frac{210 \sin 8°}{63·25}$$

$$\therefore A\hat{E}W = 27° \, 32' \text{ (*since an obtuse angle is clearly not suitable*)}$$

$$\therefore X\hat{E}W = 68° - 27° \, 32' = 40° \, 28'$$

∴ speed of wind is 63 km h⁻¹ from a direction 040°.

119

**Example 6** *An aircraft is to have a ground-speed of* 326 km h⁻¹ *on a track of* 186°. *If the speed of the wind is* 58 km h⁻¹ *from a direction* 114° *find the air-speed and course.*

Let $_AV_W$ represent the air-speed, $_AV_E$ represent the ground-speed, and $_WV_E$ represent the wind-speed.

$_AV_W + {_WV_E} = {_AV_E}$, from which a rough sketch is drawn.

$\overline{NAS}$ is the north-south line, $C\hat{A}E = 6°$ (reflex $N\hat{A}E = 186°$) and $A\hat{C}W = 114°$.

Hence $A\hat{E}W = 108°$.

Then $\triangle AEW$ is the triangle of velocities.

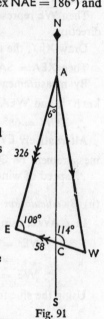

Fig. 91

(i) *By drawing and measurement*

Use a scale of 5 cm to 100 km h⁻¹.

Draw the north-south line $\overline{NAS}$.

Draw AE = 16·3 cm (for 326 km h⁻¹) and WE = 2·9 cm (for 58 km h⁻¹) in the directions given.

By measurement AW = 17·4 cm.

Hence air-speed = 348 km h⁻¹.

Also $W\hat{A}C = 3°$, i.e. $N\hat{A}W = 177°$.

Hence course = 177°.

∴ the air-speed is 348 km h⁻¹ on a course of 177°.

(ii) *By calculation*

In $\triangle AWE$, using the cosine formula,

$$AW^2 = 58^2 + 326^2 - 2 \times 58 \times 326 \cos 108°$$
$$= 58^2 + 326^2 + 116 \times 326 \cos 72°$$
$$\simeq 121\,400$$

∴ AW = 348·5.

Using the sine formula,

$$\frac{\sin W\hat{A}E}{58} = \frac{\sin 108°}{348·5}$$

$$\therefore \ \sin W\widehat{A}E = \frac{58 \sin 72°}{348 \cdot 5}$$

$$\therefore \ W\widehat{A}E = 9° \ 6' \ (\textit{since an obtuse angle is clearly not suitable})$$

$$\therefore \ W\widehat{A}C = 3° \ 6'$$

$$\therefore \ N\widehat{A}W = 176° \ 54'$$

$\therefore$ air-speed is 349 km h$^{-1}$ on a course of 177°.

**Example 7** *An aircraft is to have a track of 310°, and the wind is blowing at 45 km h$^{-1}$ from a direction 075°. If the air-speed is 270 km h$^{-1}$ find the course which the navigator must set.*

Let $_AV_W$ represent the air-speed, $_AV_E$ represent the ground-speed, and $_WV_E$ represent the wind-speed.

$_AV_W + {_WV_E} = {_AV_E}$, from which a rough sketch is drawn.

$\overline{NES}$ is the north-south line, $N\widehat{E}W = 75°$ and $A\widehat{E}S = 50°$ (reflex $X\widehat{A}E = 310°$).

Then $\triangle AWE$ is the triangle of velocities.

(i) *By drawing and measurement*

Use a scale of 5 cm to 100 km h$^{-1}$.

Draw the north-south line $\overline{NES}$.

Draw $\overline{EW}$ so that $N\widehat{E}W = 75°$ and $EW = 2 \cdot 25$ cm (for 45 km h$^{-1}$).

Draw $\overline{EA}$ so that $A\widehat{E}S = 50°$.

With centre W and radius 13·5 cm (for 270 km h$^{-1}$) draw an arc to cut $\overline{EA}$ at A.

Join $\overline{AW}$ and produce to cut $\overline{NES}$ at B.

By measurement $E\widehat{B}A = 42°$, i.e. $X\widehat{A}W = 42°$.

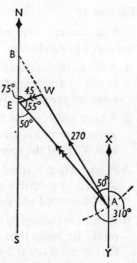

Fig. 92

$\therefore$ reflex $X\hat{A}W = 318°$

$\therefore$ the course required is 318°.

*N.B. In this type of example, start by drawing the line which represents the wind.*

(ii) *By calculation*

In $\triangle AWE$, using the sine formula,

$$\frac{\sin E\hat{A}W}{45} = \frac{\sin 55°}{270}$$

$$\therefore \sin E\hat{A}W = \frac{45 \sin 55°}{270}$$

$\therefore E\hat{A}W = 7° 51'$ (*since an obtuse angle is clearly not suitable*)

$\qquad\qquad = 8°$ to the nearest degree

$\therefore X\hat{A}W = 50° - 8° = 42°$

$\therefore$ reflex $X\hat{A}W = 318°$

$\therefore$ the course required is 318°

## Exercise 13

*In this exercise solve each problem by means of a scale drawing, and check by calculation.*

1 A boat which is headed due west at 15 km h⁻¹ is carried off course by a current of 6 km h⁻¹ which sets south-west. Find the resultant speed and direction of the boat.

2 A boat which would be travelling due east at 16 km h⁻¹ if the water were still is actually moving at 18 km h⁻¹ on a bearing of 079°. Find the speed and direction of the current.

3 A boat which is scheduled to steam due south at 19 km h⁻¹ is affected by a current of 5 km h⁻¹ flowing in a direction 056°. Find the speed and course on which the boat must be set.

4 A swimmer wishes to cross a river to an exactly opposite point on the far bank. If he can swim at 4 km h⁻¹ in still water, and the current flows at 2·4 km h⁻¹, find at what angle to the bank he must head. Find also his speed relative to the bank.

5 A boat whose speed in still water would be $3 \text{ m s}^{-1}$ heads straight across a river, but because of the current it actually travels at an angle of 60° to the bank. Find the speed of the current, and the boat's speed relative to the bank. If the river is 105 m wide, how long would it take to cross it?

6 A motor-launch is scheduled to go from a landing-stage to a harbour which lies due north of it. If the speed of the launch in still water is $28 \text{ km h}^{-1}$, and there is a current of $10 \text{ km h}^{-1}$ which sets due east, find the direction in which the launch must head.

7 A boat which travels at $15 \text{ km h}^{-1}$ in still water is steered on a course of 028°, but is carried off course by a current of $4\frac{1}{2}$ $\text{km h}^{-1}$ in a direction 149°. Find the boat's resultant speed and direction.

8 A man can row a boat on a river at a speed which is three times that of the current. If he wishes to go straight across, find the direction in which he must keep the boat pointing. In what direction must it point if he wishes to cross in the shortest possible time?

9 A boat heads in a direction 208° at a speed of $18 \text{ km h}^{-1}$, but actually travels at $21 \text{ km h}^{-1}$ on a bearing of 217°. Find the speed and direction of the current.

10 A toy plane has an acceleration of $2\cdot5 \text{ m s}^{-2}$. The force of the wind at right angles to the plane gives it an acceleration of $0\cdot5 \text{ m s}^{-2}$. What is the magnitude and direction of the resultant acceleration?

11 Horizontal forces of $5\cdot2$ N and $6\cdot1$ N at 35° to each other are applied to a mass which is lying on a smooth horizontal surface. In what direction will it move?

12 A sledge is pulled by two horizontal forces, one at 20° to the line of motion and the other at 25°. If the first force has a magnitude of $2\cdot3$ N what is the magnitude of the other?

13 A particle of weight 3 N is held by two strings each inclined at 30° to the vertical. What is the tension in each string?

**14** A particle is accelerating at 10 m s$^{-2}$ when it is subjected to a force inclined at 30° to the original line of motion which gives it an extra acceleration of 2 m s$^{-2}$. What is the magnitude and direction of the resultant acceleration?

In each of the following find the ground-speed and track:

**15** Course 194°, air-speed 460 km h$^{-1}$, wind 75 km h$^{-1}$ from 064°.

**16**   ,,    115°, ,,     ,,    440 km h$^{-1}$,  ,,   80 km h$^{-1}$   ,,   077°.

**17**   ,,    298°, ,,     ,,    415 km h$^{-1}$,  ,,   60 km h$^{-1}$    ,,   198°.

**18**   ,,    016°, ,,     ,,    730 km h$^{-1}$,  ,,   100 km h$^{-1}$  ,,   319°.

In each of the following find the speed and direction of the wind:

**19** Course 075°, air-speed 440 km h$^{-1}$, track 081°, ground-speed 490 km h$^{-1}$.

**20** Course 088°, air-speed 410 km h$^{-1}$, track 095°, ground-speed 380 km h$^{-1}$.

**21** Course 105°, air-speed 720 km h$^{-1}$, track 112°, ground-speed 820 km h$^{-1}$.

**22** Course 198°, air-speed 520 km h$^{-1}$, track 204°, ground-speed 490 km h$^{-1}$.

In each of the following find the air-speed and course:

**23** Track 336°, ground-speed 470 km h$^{-1}$; wind 60 km h$^{-1}$ from 217°.

**24** Track 068°, ground-speed 390 km h$^{-1}$, wind 50 km h$^{-1}$ from 130°.

**25** Track 212°, ground-speed 415 km h$^{-1}$, wind 65 km h$^{-1}$ from 146°.

**26** Track 112°, ground-speed 760 km h$^{-1}$, wind 90 km h$^{-1}$ from 237°.

In each of the following find the course:

**27** Track 023°, air-speed 840 km h$^{-1}$, wind 120 km h$^{-1}$ from 250°.

**28** „ 219°, „ „ 740 km h$^{-1}$, „ 140 km h$^{-1}$ „ 282°.

**29** „ 357°, „ „ 820 km h$^{-1}$, „ 80 km h$^{-1}$ „ 112°.

**30** „ 274°, „ „ 540 km h$^{-1}$, „ 90 km h$^{-1}$ „ 227°.

125

# Chapter 14

# *Probability*

Things are sometimes decided on the toss of a coin, the assumption being that it is equally likely to turn up 'heads' or 'tails'. In this case there are two possibilities, of which 'heads' is one and 'tails' is the other, so that the chance that it will be 'heads' is one out of two. Mathematically it is said that the **probability** of a head is $\frac{1}{2}$ and the probability of a tail is $\frac{1}{2}$. The probability of a head or a tail is $\frac{1}{2} + \frac{1}{2} = 1$. An event which is certain has a probability of 1 and an event which will certainly not happen has a probability of 0.

When an unbiased die (singular of dice) is thrown there are six numbers, all equally probable, which can appear. Therefore there is a probability of $\frac{1}{6}$ that any particular number will appear. There are three even numbers occurring in these six. Therefore the probability of getting an even number when throwing a die is given by dividing the number of even scores by the number of possible scores, i.e. the probability is $\frac{3}{6} = \frac{1}{2}$.

In general, if $n$ events are equally probable, the probability of any one of $x$ of them occurring is $\dfrac{x}{n}$ and the probability of it not occurring is $1 - \dfrac{x}{n}$ or $\dfrac{n-x}{n}$.

If two coins are thrown the possible outcomes are two heads, a head and a tail, or two tails; but a head and a tail can appear in two ways—either a head on the first coin and a tail on the second, or a tail on the first and a head on the second. Hence there are four possible results, so that the chance of two heads is one in four, i.e. the probability of two heads is $\frac{1}{4}$, and the probability of a head and a tail is $\frac{2}{4}$, i.e. $\frac{1}{2}$.

The probabilities considered so far are theoretical probabilities based on the assumption that the coin or die is unbiased. Probability can also be based on experimental situations. For example if it is known that out of 1 000 new cars of a particular model 100

126

are faulty on delivery, it can be stated that the probability of getting a faulty car is $\frac{100}{1000} = \frac{1}{10}$. Such probabilities cannot be exact but the larger the sample the more accurate they become.

**Example 1** *On average 1 in 25 of the screws produced by a certain machine is faulty. What is the probability that a screw taken at random made by this machine is good?*

From the given experimental data the probability of a bad screw is $\frac{1}{25}$.

∴ the probability of a good screw is $1 - \frac{1}{25} = \frac{24}{25}$.

*Alternatively*, if 1 in 25 of the screws is bad, 24 in 25 are good.

∴ the probability of a good screw is $\frac{24}{25}$.

**Example 2** *Three coins are thrown. What is the probability of 2 heads and 1 tail?*

There are eight possible results as follows: **HHH**

**HHT HTH THH**

**TTH THT HTT**

**TTT**

Of these, three consist of 2 heads and 1 tail.

∴ the probability of 2 heads and 1 tail is $\frac{3}{8}$.

**Exercise 14a**

1 What is the probability of taking a bad orange out of a bag containing 3 good oranges and 1 bad one?

2 What is the probability of drawing an ace from a pack of 52 cards?

3 What is the probability of picking a white ball out of a bag containing 2 white balls and 3 red ones if one cannot see them?

4 If a letter is chosen at random from the alphabet what is the probability that it is a vowel?

5 The following table shows the numbers in each age group in a school:

| 11 | 12 | 13 | 14 | 15 | 16 | 17 | 18 |
|----|----|----|----|----|----|----|----|
| 42 | 121 | 125 | 131 | 101 | 82 | 53 | 21 |

What is the probability that a pupil chosen at random will be (i) 13, (ii) 13 or less?

6 The result of a football match can be predicted as a home win, draw or away win. What is the probability of predicting the correct outcome without any knowledge of the teams? What is the probability of predicting the correct outcome of 2 such games?

7 A school contains 750 boys and 450 girls. If a pupil is chosen at random what is the probability that a girl is chosen?

8 A lucky dip contains 100 tickets of which 10 have prizes associated with them. What is the probability of getting a prize with one dip?

9 It is known that 1 in 20 of the light bulbs produced by a certain machine is faulty. If one bulb is taken at random from a large number what is the probability of it being a good one?

10 If 2 dice are thrown what is the probability of a total score of (i) 3, (ii) 4, (iii) 6?

## Addition law, mutually exclusive events

It has already been shown that the probability of getting an even score with a die is $\frac{3}{6}$ and this can be considered as the sum of the probabilities of getting a 2, a 4, or a 6, namely $\frac{1}{6} + \frac{1}{6} + \frac{1}{6} = \frac{3}{6}$.

Probabilities can be added provided that the events are **mutually exclusive**, that is to say that one event excludes the possibility of the other; it is impossible to obtain a 4 and a 6 at the same time.

## Multiplication law, statistically independent events

The probability of getting a head with one throw of a coin is $\frac{1}{2}$ and 2 heads with two throws is $\frac{1}{4}$. This conclusion can also be reached by saying that the probability of the first head is $\frac{1}{2}$ and then there are two possible outcomes, a head or a tail, for the second coin, so that the combined probability is $\frac{1}{2}$ of $\frac{1}{2} = \frac{1}{4}$. From this the probability of 2 sixes with two throws of a die is $\frac{1}{6} \times \frac{1}{6} = \frac{1}{36}$. This implies that there are 36 different combinations of numbers with 2 dice, which is true, as for each of the six numbers on one die there are six on the other.

Probabilities can be multiplied if the one event has no effect on the other; the events are said to be **statistically independent.** In the cases considered the way one coin or die turns up has no effect on the way the other does.

When 2 coins are thrown the probability of obtaining at least one head can be calculated in various ways:

(i) It has already been shown that the probability of 1 head and 1 tail is $\frac{1}{2}$ and the probability of 2 heads is $\frac{1}{4}$. As these are mutually exclusive events the probability of 2 heads or 1 head and 1 tail is $\frac{1}{2} + \frac{1}{4} = \frac{3}{4}$.

(ii) The probability of 2 tails is $\frac{1}{4}$, and as the probability of at least 1 head implies everything other than 2 tails the probability is $1 - \frac{1}{4} = \frac{3}{4}$.

(iii) The third method is best illustrated by a Venn diagram. Set A represents the event of obtaining a head on one coin and set B represents the event of obtaining a head on the other coin.

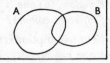

Fig. 93

p{A} means the probability of event A. A ∩ B means heads on both coins and p{A ∩ B} is $\frac{1}{4}$. A ∪ B means at least 1 head and from Fig. 93

$$p\{A \cup B\} = p\{A\} + p\{B\} - p\{A \cap B\}$$
$$= \frac{1}{2} + \frac{1}{2} - \frac{1}{4}$$
$$= \frac{3}{4}$$

In this case this is a long-winded approach but it illustrates the general principles involved. If A and B were mutually exclusive then p{A ∩ B} = 0, which leads to the addition law mentioned above. However when A and B are not mutually exclusive it illustrates that A includes A ∩ B and B also includes A ∩ B.

**Example 3** *A bag contains 6 red marbles and 4 blue marbles. One is drawn from the bag and replaced, then a second one is drawn. What is the probability that (i) they are both blue, (ii) one is blue and one is red?*

There are 10 marbles of which 4 are blue.

∴ the probability of drawing a blue marble is $\frac{4}{10} = \frac{2}{5}$.

The colour drawn second is independent of the colour drawn first.

∴ the probability that both are blue is $\frac{2}{5} \times \frac{2}{5} = \frac{4}{25}$.

The probability of drawing a red marble is $\frac{6}{10} = \frac{3}{5}$.

∴ the probability of drawing first a blue marble, then a red marble, is $\frac{2}{5} \times \frac{3}{5} = \frac{6}{25}$,

and the probability of drawing first a red marble, then a blue marble, is $\frac{3}{5} \times \frac{2}{5} = \frac{6}{25}$.

These are mutually exclusive so that the probability of drawing a red marble and a blue marble when the order does not matter is $\frac{6}{25} + \frac{6}{25} = \frac{12}{25}$.

**Example 4** *A jar contains a large quantity of small coloured sweets. It is known that the ratio of red to yellow to purple sweets in the jar is* 3 : 2 : 1 *and these are the only colours present. If three sweets are taken from the jar at random what is the probability that (i) they are all yellow, (ii) one is yellow and the others are not, (iii) they are all of different colours?*

The assumption is that there are so many sweets that the drawing of one has no effect on the remaining proportion.

The proportion of yellow sweets is $\frac{2}{6} = \frac{1}{3}$.

∴ the probability of a sweet drawn being yellow is $\frac{1}{3}$.

∴ the probability of 3 sweets all being yellow is $\frac{1}{3} \times \frac{1}{3} \times \frac{1}{3} = \frac{1}{27}$.

The probability of a sweet not being yellow is $1 - \frac{1}{3} = \frac{2}{3}$.

∴ the probability of 2 non-yellow sweets, then 1 yellow one, is $\frac{2}{3} \times \frac{2}{3} \times \frac{1}{3} = \frac{4}{27}$,

the probability of a non-yellow sweet, then a yellow sweet, then a non-yellow one, is $\frac{2}{3} \times \frac{1}{3} \times \frac{2}{3} = \frac{4}{27}$,

and the probability of a yellow sweet, then 2 non-yellow ones, is $\frac{1}{3} \times \frac{2}{3} \times \frac{2}{3} = \frac{4}{27}$.

As these three orders are mutually exclusive the probability of 2 non-yellow and 1 yellow sweet in any order is $\frac{4}{27} + \frac{4}{27} + \frac{4}{27} = \frac{12}{27} = \frac{4}{9}$.

The number of ways the three different colours can be chosen is as follows, RYP, RPY, YPR, PYR, YRP, PRY, i.e. 6 ways.

The probability of choosing one of each colour in a particular order is given by $\frac{3}{6} \times \frac{2}{6} \times \frac{1}{6} = \frac{1}{36}$.

The different orders are mutually exclusive so that the probability is the sum of six terms each of which is $\frac{1}{36}$, i.e. the probability is $6 \times \frac{1}{36} = \frac{1}{6}$.

## Exercise 14b

1 When 2 dice are thrown what is the probability of (i) at least one six, (ii) a score of seven?

2 A bag contains 3 white balls and 2 black balls. If one ball is drawn and replaced and then another drawn what is the probability of at least one being white?

3 A card is drawn from a pack and then replaced. A second card is then drawn. What is the probability that (i) they are both black, (ii) at least one is black, (iii) at least one is a king?

4 When 3 coins are thrown what is the probability of (i) 3 heads, (ii) at least one head?

5 If one is equally likely to predict that a match will be a draw, a home win or an away win what is the probability of (i) correctly predicting three results, (ii) correctly predicting at least one out of three?

6 In a certain card game for 4 people the dealer is chosen by each player taking a card from the pack and then replacing it, the dealer being the one who chooses the highest card. On three successive occasions what is the probability of a particular player being dealer (i) each time, (ii) at least once?

7 A certain game is played with a pentagonal top, the sides being marked 1 to 5 and the score on each occasion being the side which rests on the table after the spin. What is the probability of (i) gaining 2 fives in 2 spins, (ii) at least 1 five in 2 spins, (iii) a score of 6 in 2 spins?

8 If the probability of one archer hitting a target is $\frac{1}{2}$ and the probability of another hitting it is $\frac{2}{3}$ for each shot, what is the probability that they both hit it if they each shoot one arrow? What is the probability that at least one hits it?

9 The probability of a seed germinating is $\frac{1}{3}$. If 3 seeds are planted what is the probability that (i) at least one will germinate, (ii) exactly one will germinate?

**10** If the probability of one pupil solving a problem is $\frac{5}{6}$ and of another solving it is $\frac{4}{5}$, what is the probability that (i) at least one will solve it, (ii) one will and one will not?

**11** When 3 dice are thrown, what is the probability of a score of 10?

**12** When 2 dice are thrown, what is the probability of the score being a prime number?

**13** If it is assumed that there are three times as many women in a shopping street as men, what is the probability that the first 3 people one meets are (i) all women, (ii) 2 women and 1 man?

**14** Three integers are chosen at random from 0 to 9. What is the probability that two of them are less than 4 and one is more than 4?

**15** The ratio of red to white to blue sweets in a large bag is $4 : 2 : 3$. Two sweets are chosen at random. What is the probability that (i) they are both blue, (ii) they are of different colours?

**16** In a particular town 4 out of 5 houses have a television set. If 2 houses are visited at random what is the probability that (i) they will both have television, (ii) one has television and the other has not?

**17** Out of every 1 000 boxes produced by a machine 40 have less than 20 matches. What is the probability that if 2 boxes are chosen at random one contains less than 20 matches and the other contains 20 or more?

**18** The ratio in which a vending machine sells coffee with milk and sugar, coffee with milk, coffee with sugar and plain coffee is $5 : 2 : 2 : 1$. What is the probability that when 2 cups are chosen one will be coffee with milk and one plain coffee?

**19** If it is assumed that one in three of the cars on the road is white, what is the probability that out of the first 3 cars one sees on the road 2 will be white?

**20** If it is assumed that half the people in a town are Conservatives, what is the probability that out of 4 people one meets 3 are Conservatives?

### Dependent probability, probability trees

All the examples considered so far have been statistically independent. A simple example of **dependent** probability follows.

**Example ·5** *A bag contains 3 white balls and 2 black balls. Two balls are taken from the bag. What is the probability that (i) both are black, (ii) one is white and one is black?*

The various possibilities can be illustrated by a diagram called **a probability tree** as in Fig. 94. The branches represent the different possibilities at each step, with the associated probabilities.

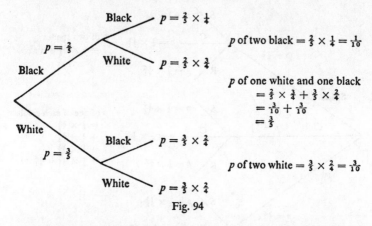

Fig. 94

The first ball to be drawn can be either black or white, and for each possibility there are then the possibilities of black or white for the second ball. Hence the tree starts with 2 branches each of which has 2 further branches. The probability that the first ball is black is $\frac{2}{5}$ and this is independent of the colour of the second ball. There are then 4 balls left of which 1 is black. Thus in 1 case out of 4 when the first ball is black the second is also black, and in 3 cases out of 4 the second is white. As the probability of the first being black is $\frac{2}{5}$, the probability of the first and second being black is $\frac{1}{4}$ of $\frac{2}{5}$, and the probability of the first being black and the second white is $\frac{3}{4}$ of $\frac{2}{5}$. The probability that the first ball is white is $\frac{3}{5}$. There are then 4 balls left of which 2 are black. The probability

133

then of the second being black is $\frac{2}{4}$, so that the probability of white then black is $\frac{1}{2}$ of $\frac{3}{5}$. The cases of white then black and black then white are mutually exclusive, so may be added.

∴ the probability of 2 black is $\frac{2}{5} \times \frac{1}{4} = \frac{1}{10}$,

and the probability of 1 white and 1 black is $\frac{2}{5} \times \frac{3}{4} + \frac{3}{5} \times \frac{1}{2} = \frac{3}{5}$.

Note that the total probability is $\frac{1}{10} + \frac{6}{10} + \frac{3}{10} = 1$.

**Example 6** *If 2 cards are drawn from a pack without replacement what is the probability of* (i) *2 spades,* (ii) *1 black and 1 red?*

It is simplest to consider spades, clubs and red cards.

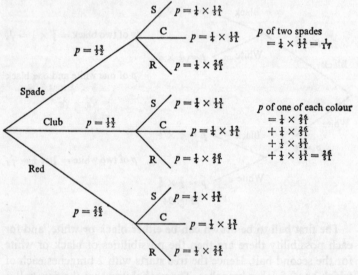

Fig. 95

Probability trees can be used for both dependent and independent probability.

**Exercise 14c**

In each of the following a probability tree is required.

1 A coin is thrown 3 times. What is the probability of (i) 2 heads and 1 tail, (ii) at least 1 head?

**2** If 2 cards are drawn from a pack what is the probability that (i) they are of the same suit, (ii) they are of different suits?

**3** If 2 cards are drawn from a pack what is the probability of (i) 1 being an ace and 1 a king, (ii) both being aces?

**4** A box of peaches contains 4 bad ones and 16 good ones. What is the probability that out of 3 peaches taken from the box (i) they are all good, (ii) 2 are good and 1 is bad?

**5** If it is assumed that children are equally likely to be boys or girls what is the probability that a family of 4 will contain (i) 3 boys and 1 girl, (ii) 2 boys and 2 girls?

**6** A batsman has a probability of $\frac{1}{10}$ of being out on any particular ball, $\frac{1}{5}$ of scoring a 4, $\frac{3}{10}$ of scoring 1, and $\frac{2}{5}$ of not scoring or being out. After 2 balls what is the probability of (i) still being in having scored 4 runs, (ii) having scored 2 runs?

**7** The probability of a boy solving correctly the first question in an examination is $\frac{3}{5}$. If he does it correctly his probability of solving the second is $\frac{4}{5}$, but if he does not his probability of solving the second one is $\frac{2}{5}$. If he solves the second one correctly his probability of solving the third one is $\frac{4}{5}$, but if he does not his probability of solving the third one is $\frac{1}{5}$. What is his probability of getting 2 out of the 3 questions correct?

**8** A bag contains 3 black balls, 4 white balls and 5 red balls. Three balls are removed without replacement. What is the probability of (i) 1 of each colour, (ii) at least 2 red?

**9** If each of 2 players at tennis are equally likely to win a game what is the probability of a particular player winning a set 6–1?

**10** In 5 tosses of a coin what is the probability of 3 heads and 2 tails?

**11** A committee consists of 4 women and 6 men. A subcommittee is formed from it made up of 3 people. What is the probability that (i) they are all men, (ii) 2 of them are men?

**12** A bag contains 20 lupin seeds; 4 of them are for red lupins, 6 for white and 10 for blue. Two seeds are taken at random. What is the probability that they are for different colours?

# Revision examples

**1** Simplify   (i) $\dfrac{\dfrac{3}{2\frac{1}{2}} - \dfrac{3}{7} \text{ of } \dfrac{3}{5}}{5 - \dfrac{1}{3\frac{1}{2}}}$   (ii) $\dfrac{8\cdot4 \times 13\cdot94 \times 0\cdot84}{1\cdot96 \times 3\cdot6 \times 8\cdot2}$

**2**  (i) If $a:b = 3:4$ and $b:c = 8:7$, find the value of $a:b:c$.
   (ii) If $u:v = 5:6$ and $v:w = 9:7$, find the value of $u:v:w$.
   (iii) If $x:y = 3:5$ and $y:z = 6:11$, find the value of $x:y:z$.

**3** The sides of a triangle are 9 cm, 10 cm, 11 cm. Show that the triangle is acute-angled, and calculate the projection of the 9 cm side upon the 10 cm side.

**4** A boy who can swim 100 metres in 80 seconds wants to swim straight across a river flowing at 70 cm s$^{-1}$. At what angle to the bank should he swim?

**5** In $\triangle$ABC, C $= 34°$, $a = 50$ m, $b = 40$ m. Find A, B and $c$.

**6** In Fig. 96, calculate $a$, $b$, $x$, $y$.

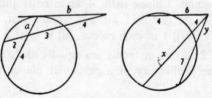

Fig. 96

**7** The cross-section of a lead pipe is a rectangle. If the external dimensions are 10 cm by 8 cm and the walls of the pipe are 5 mm thick, find the volume of lead in a 120-cm length of piping. Find also its mass if the specific gravity of lead is 11·4.

**8** Use the Remainder Theorem to find the factors of
   (i) $2y^3 - 5y^2 - 4y + 3$   (ii) $6z^3 + 7z^2 - 16z - 12$

**9** (i) Solve the equations $x^2 - 3xy = 0$, $x + 2y = 5$.

    (ii) Simplify $\dfrac{(x + y)(x^2 - xy + y^2) - 2y^3}{x - y}$.

**10** Solve the inequalities  (i) $3x - 2 > 4x - 1$

                         (ii) $x^2 + x - 6 \geqslant 0$

## XII

**1** (i) Factorise $24m^2 - 70m + 49$ and $24m^2 - 70m - 49$.

    (ii) Solve $2x + y = 4$, $xy + 6 = 0$.

**2** The heights of two circular cones are in the ratio $8 : 9$, and the radii of their bases are in the ratio $3 : 4$. Find the ratio of their volumes.

**3** Equilateral triangles PQX, PRY are drawn to lie outside $\triangle$PQR. If $\overline{RX}$ cuts $\overline{QY}$ at Z, prove that P, X, Q, Z are concyclic.

**4** In $\triangle$ABC, A $= 81°$, $a = 24\cdot8$ cm, $b = 16\cdot2$ cm. Find B, C and $c$.

**5** If $2x^3 + nx^2 + 5x - 6$ is exactly divisible by $x - 2$, find $n$ and the remaining factor of the expression.

**6** Find the annual income obtained by investing £315 in a 3% stock at $112\frac{1}{2}$.

**7** If 2 cards are drawn from a pack of 52, what is the probability that they are both between 2 and 7?

**8** In the trapezium in Fig. 97 (in which the lengths given are in cm), find $\theta$ and the length of the diagonal AC.

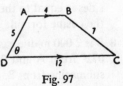

Fig. 97

**9** An aircraft whose air-speed is 400 km h$^{-1}$ has to fly 600 km due north when the wind is blowing from the south-east at 80 km h$^{-1}$. On what bearing should the pilot navigate, and how long will it take him to reach his objective?

**10** ABCD is a parallelogram, and the shorter diagonal $\overline{AC}$ is 12 cm long. The circle ABC cuts $\overline{BD}$ at X, where XD $= 3\frac{1}{2}$ cm. Find BD.

## XIII

1 A man was left £1 000 of 3½% Conversion Loan, which he sold at 84, reinvesting the proceeds in Randfontein £1 shares at 175p. How many shares did he buy? If Randfontein subsequently declared a dividend of 12½%, how did his new income compare with the old?

2 A steamer is heading on a bearing S 63° E at a speed of 30 km h$^{-1}$, and an 8-km h$^{-1}$ tide is setting S 19° W. In what direction is the steamer travelling and at what speed?

3 ABDC is a circle with D the mid-point of the arc BC. $\overline{AD}$ and $\overline{BC}$ intersect at X. Prove that AB × CD = AD × BX.

4 Draw the graph of $y = x^3$ from $x = -3$ to $x = 3$. On the same graph draw $y = 3x - 1$ and shade the area A ∩ B, where A is $\{x, y : y \geqslant x^3\}$ and B is $\{x, y : y \leqslant 3x - 1\}$.

5 Two spherical balls of wax of radii 4 cm and 3 cm respectively are melted and recast to form a single sphere. Find its radius correct to 3 significant figures.

6 Solve to 2 dec. pl. $\dfrac{1}{x - 3} + \dfrac{2}{x - 4} = \dfrac{1}{x - 5}$.

7 Prove that, in any parallelogram, the sum of the squares of the sides is equal to the sum of the squares of the diagonals. (Use the cosine formula.)

8 B is 2 000 m due east of A. A submarine is spotted on bearings 072° from A and 018° from B. Calculate the distance of the submarine from B.

9 By using the Remainder Theorem, factorise
   (i) $2x^3 - x^2 - 15x + 18$
   (ii) $3m^4 - 11m^3 - 12m^2 + 36m - 16$

10 ABC is an equilateral triangle of side 8 cm, and D is a point on $\overline{BC}$ such that AD = 7 cm. *Without using tables*, calculate the lengths of the two parts into which D divides $\overline{BC}$.

## XIV

1 A bag contains 3 blue marbles, 4 white marbles and 3 red marbles. Two marbles are drawn from the bag. Find the probability that

   (i) they are both blue

   (ii) one is red and one is white

   (iii) they are of different colours.

2 Draw on the same diagram the graphs of $x^2 - 3$ and $x + 1$ from $x = -2$ to $x = +3$, taking a 2-cm scale on both axes.

   Use the graph to solve the equation $x^2 - x - 4 = 0$.

3 In Fig. 98, find the length marked $x$, all dimensions given being in cm. (*First find cos* $\theta$, *but do not look out* $\theta$.)

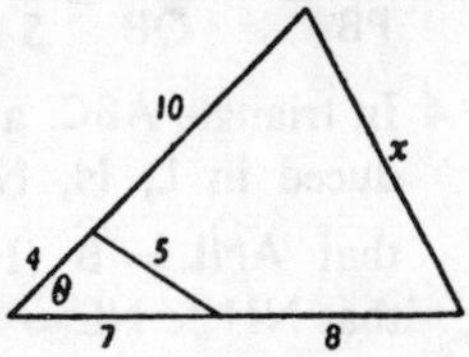

4 If $x^4 - 2x^2 + bx - 5$ is divided by $x + 1$ the remainder is $-8$. Find $b$, and the remainder when the expression is divided by $x - 2$.

5 $V = \pi h(R^2 - r^2)$. (i) Express $r$ in terms of the other letters. (ii) Evaluate $r$ if $V = 896$, $R = 8 \cdot 01$, $h = 10 \cdot 3$, $\log \pi = 0 \cdot 497\ 1$.

Fig. 98

6 The time needed for cooking a turkey is given by the formula $T = \sqrt[3]{5M^2}$, where T is the time in hours and M the mass of the turkey in kg. Find, correct to the nearest minute, the time needed for a turkey of $6 \cdot 8$ kg. Find also the mass of a turkey which would be properly cooked in $4\frac{1}{2}$ hours.

7 Two horizontal forces, inclined to each other at 55°, are applied to a body. If the body moves in a direction at 20° to one force which is of $2 \cdot 3$ N, what is the magnitude of the other force?

8 In Fig. 99, calculate $a$, $b$, $c$.

9 In $\triangle ABC$, $A = 42°\ 17'$, $a = 12 \cdot 41$ cm, $c = 17 \cdot 6$ cm. Find B, C and $b$.

10 The incomes of two men are in the ratio 7 : 5, their expenditures are in the ratio

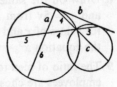

Fig. 99

$5 : 4$, and the ratio of their savings is $5 : 2$. What is the ratio of their combined income to combined expenditure?

## XV

**1** Use the Remainder Theorem to factorise
(i) $m^3 - 13m^2 + 50m - 56$    (ii) $n^3 - 4n^2 + 5n - 2$

**2** A man holds £270 of a $3\frac{1}{2}\%$ stock. He sells at 84 and invests the proceeds in a $4\frac{3}{4}\%$ stock at 108. Find the change in his income.

**3** A line $\overline{AB}$, $4\cdot8$ cm long, is divided by the points P and Q so that $\dfrac{AP}{PB} = -\dfrac{AQ}{QB} = \dfrac{7}{5}$. Find PQ.

**4** In triangle ABC, a line $\overline{LMN}$ cuts the sides $\overline{AB}$, $\overline{AC}$, $\overline{BC}$ produced in L, M, N respectively, so that $A\hat{M}L = \hat{B}$ (Fig. 100). Prove that $NM \times NL = NB \times NC$.

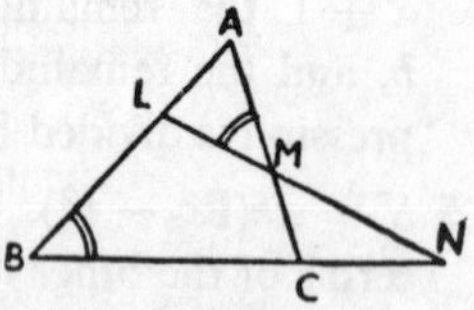

Fig. 100

**5** Two yachts A and B leave harbour at the same time, A sailing due east at 14 km h$^{-1}$, and B on a bearing of $140°\ 22'$ at 10 km h$^{-1}$. Find how far apart the yachts are after one hour. Find also the bearing then of B from A.

**6** Solve the equations $x - y = 3$, $3x^2 - xy - 2y^2 = 7$.

**7** A man wants to buy 100 m of galvanised iron wire of diameter 4 mm, but finds that it is sold by the kg. What mass of wire must he buy, if the specific gravity of iron is $7\cdot79$? (He cannot buy a fraction of a kg.)

**8** Draw on the same diagram the graphs of $y = x^3 - 3x + 1$ and $y = 5x$ from $x = -3$ to $x = +3$, taking a 2-cm scale for values of $x$ and 2 cm = 5 units for values of $y$. Hence solve the equation $x^3 - 8x + 1 = 0$.

**9** The ratio of men to women in a large factory is $4 : 1$. If two employees are chosen at random what is the probability that at least one is a man?

**10** Find the angles of a triangle having sides 5 cm, 6 cm and 10 cm. Work out the angles in turn by cosine formula, and check by finding their sum.

## XVI

**1** A concrete block 30 cm high is in the form of a frustum of a right circular cone, the diameters of the top and bottom of the frustum being respectively 32 cm and 48 cm. Taking $\log \pi = 0.497\,1$, find the volume of concrete in $cm^3$, and also the mass of the block in kg if concrete has a specific gravity of 2.

**2** A ferry steams on a bearing of S 71° W at 25 km $h^{-1}$. If the tide is running at 6 km $h^{-1}$ in a direction S 35° E, what course and speed must the captain set?

**3** Solve the inequalities (i) $(x - 3)(4 - x) > 0$
(ii) $6x^2 + x \geqslant 1$

**4** In Fig. 101, calculate $x, y, z$.

**5** If $m : n = 7 : 6$, $u : v = 2 : 3$ and $m - u : n + v = 1 : 2$, find the value of the ratio $2m - u : n - v$.

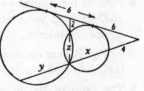

**6** In $\triangle ABC$, A = 128° 17′, C = 30° 7′, $c = 15.6$ cm. Find B, $a$ and $b$.

Fig. 101

**7** Solve the equations $2x + y = 1$, $x^2 + y^2 = 34$.

**8** A car which is travelling at 104 km $h^{-1}$ is 297 m behind another which is travelling at 71 km $h^{-1}$ in the same direction. Find the time that elapses before the faster car overtakes the slower.

**9** Given that $x + 2$ is a factor of $x^3 + kx - 6$, find the other two factors.

**10** In a quadrilateral ABCD, AB = AD = 10 cm, BC = 6 cm, CD = 5 cm, AC = 9 cm. Find $B\hat{C}D$ and BD.

## XVII

**1** In $\triangle ABC$, $C = 42° 17'$, $a = 9·6$ m, $c = 11·4$ m. Find A, B and $b$.

**2** By using the Remainder Theorem, factorise
(i) $a^3 - 3a^2 - 4a + 12$    (ii) $d^4 + d^3 - 8d^2 - 16d - 8$

**3** A water tank has a base of area 1·5 square metres, and is filled through a pipe of diameter 4 cm. Taking $\pi$ to be $3\frac{1}{7}$, find the time taken to fill the tank to a depth of 132 cm if the water flows through the pipe at 75 cm s$^{-1}$.

**4** (i) Evaluate without using tables (a) $0·124 \times 21·6 \div 5·58$,
(b) $(\cos 60° + \tan 45°) \div \sin^2 60°$.

(ii) What distance in km is represented by a length of 1·3 cm on a map of scale 1 to 200 000?

**5** An aircraft has an air-speed of 900 km h$^{-1}$, and the wind is blowing at 126 km h$^{-1}$ from 108°. What course must be set if the track is to be 250°?

**6** Find to the nearest penny the amount of £642·88 in 2 years at $2\frac{3}{4}\%$ per annum compound interest.

**7** In Fig. 102 use the cosine formula (but no tables) to find $x$.

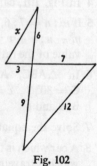

**8** The ratio of the masses of two lorries when empty is $6 : 5$, and of the loads that they can carry $10 : 7$. When fully loaded their masses are in the ratio $13 : 10$. Find the ratio of the mass of the heavier lorry empty to that of the lighter one half full.

Fig. 102

**9** ABCD is a parallelogram, and any line through B cuts $\overline{AD}$, $\overline{AC}$ in P, Q respectively. Prove that $\dfrac{AP}{AD} = \dfrac{AQ}{QC}$.

**10** Solve the equations $x - y = 3$, $3x^2 - xy - 2y = 7$.

# XVIII

1 Construct a trapezium ABCD in which AB = 5 cm, BC = 6 cm, CD = 10 cm, DA = 7 cm, and $\overline{AB}$ is parallel to $\overline{DC}$. Measure AC. By construction and measurement find the area of the trapezium.

2 If 3 dice are thrown find the probability that the total score is less than 6.

3 In Fig. 103 find *a*, *b*, *c*, *d*.

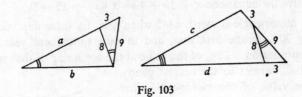

Fig. 103

4 Brisholm is 24·7 km due south of Ambury: a third town, Caddington, lies on bearings of 127° from Ambury and 096° from Brisholm. How far is Caddington from the other two towns?

5 In an examination, 350 candidates were girls and 600 were boys. If 30% of the girls and 40% of the boys passed, find what percentage of the total number of candidates failed.

6 Find the value of the ratio *m* : *n* if

(i) $7m - 5n = 4n - 5m$    (ii) $m^2 - 8mn + 15n^2 = 0$

(iii) $6m^2 - 19mn + 15n^2 = 0$

7 A pupil at a flying-school is instructed to fly his Chipmunk due south to a certain landmark, turn there and come straight back. His air-speed is 300 km h$^{-1}$ and the wind is blowing steadily at 40 km h$^{-1}$ from a direction 322°. What courses should he set for the outward and return flights?

8 ABCD is a parallelogram with AB = 12 cm, AD = 8 cm. The circle ADC bisects $\overline{AB}$, and $\overline{BC}$ produced cuts the circle again at X. Find CX.

143

**9** In a triangle, two sides of 4 cm and 5 cm include an angle of 22° 16′. Find the third side of the triangle.

**10** Given that $x^4 + ax^3 + bx^2 - 9ax - 36$ is exactly divisible by $x - 2$ and by $x + 3$, find $a$ and $b$ and the other two factors.

## XIX

**1** Find the angles of the triangle which has sides of 1·5 cm, 3 cm and 2·4 cm. Use the cosine formula to work out the angles independently, and check by finding their sum.

**2** Solve the equations $x + 3y + 4 = 0$, $4xy + 35 = 0$.

**3** A motor-cycle is worth £145 when new. Its value depreciates by 30% in the first year, and in each subsequent year the depreciation is 22% of the value at the beginning of that year. Find, correct to the nearest penny, the value of the motor-cycle after 3 years.

**4** In Fig. 104, two circles PABY and QABX intersect at A and B, and $\overline{PQ}$ is a common tangent to the circles. $\overline{PAX}$ and $\overline{QAY}$ are straight lines. Prove that $PQ^2 = PY \times QX$.

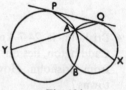

Fig. 104

**5** A line $\overline{AB}$ is 5·6 cm long. The points P and Q divide $\overline{AB}$ internally and externally in the same numerical ratio of 9 : 5. Find PQ.

**6** Use the Remainder Theorem to find the factors of
  (i) $2b^3 + 5b^2 - 68b - 35$
  (ii) $x^4 + x^3 - 51x^2 - 85x + 350$

**7** ABC is an isosceles triangle with AB = AC. P is any point on $\overline{BC}$ produced. Prove that $AP^2 - AB^2 = BP \times CP$. (*Draw altitude $\overline{AM}$.*)

**8** A box of 36 light bulbs contains 3 which are faulty. If 2 are taken from it what is the probability that at least one is faulty?

**9** An inexperienced yachtsman has to reach a marker-buoy 10 km due east of his starting-point, but fails to take into account a

3-km h⁻¹ current setting S 36° W and consequently misses the marker altogether. What is his least distance from the buoy if his speed relative to the water is 8 km h⁻¹?

**10** X, Y and Z are three cigar-makers. X can make 9 while Y makes 8, and Y can make 6 while Z makes 7. How many has each made when their total is 1 659 cigars?

## XX

**1** If $ax^3 + bx^2 - 2ax + 4$ is exactly divisible by $x + 2$ and by $2x - 1$, find $a$ and $b$ and the other factor.

**2** If $\dfrac{c}{d} = \dfrac{5}{3}$, find the value of   (i) $\dfrac{3c}{7d}$   (ii) $\dfrac{c-d}{c+d}$

(iii) $\dfrac{2c-d}{2d}$   (iv) $\dfrac{c^2-d^2}{c^2+d^2}$   (v) $\dfrac{c^2-cd}{cd+2d^2}$

**3** Find, correct to the nearest penny, the compound interest on £210·75 for 18 months at $2\frac{1}{2}\%$ per annum, interest being added half-yearly.

**4** Plot on the same axes from $x = 0$ to $x = 5$ the graphs of $y = \frac{1}{2}x^3$ and $y = 4x + 7$, taking 2 cm as unit on the $x$-axis and 2 mm as unit on the $y$-axis.

Use the graphs to find (i) $\sqrt[3]{80}$,
(ii) a root of $x^3 - 8x - 14 = 0$.

**5** An aircraft flies round a triangular course, the first leg being 20 km on a bearing of 114° 47′, and the second 15 km on a bearing of 230° 27′. How long is the third leg of the course, and on what bearing must the aircraft fly?

**6** Two places are 30 km apart on the main road, but only 16 km by a cross-country route. The short cut is 8 km h⁻¹ slower, but 10 minutes faster, either by bicycle or by car. What are the two speeds (*a*) by bicycle, (*b*) by car?

**7** In Fig. 105, $\overline{PBX}$ and $\overline{QBY}$ are straight lines, and $P\hat{A}B = Q\hat{A}B$.

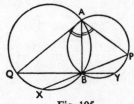

Fig. 105

145

Prove that BX × BP = BY × BQ, and deduce that PQXY is a cyclic quadrilateral.

8 Solve △ABC in which $a = 12.9$ m, $b = 10.3$ m, C $= 29°$ 59′.

9 Find the surface area of a cylindrical can, closed at both ends, of length 3·8 cm and diameter 6·4 cm. (Take $\pi = 3\frac{1}{7}$.)

10 An aircraft's air-speed is 990 km h$^{-1}$ on a bearing of 137°, and its ground-speed 960 km h$^{-1}$ on a bearing of 129°. What are the speed and direction of the wind?

# Chapter 15

# *Areas of triangles, parallelograms, trapeziums and polygons*

**Area of a triangle**

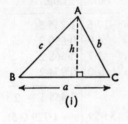

Fig. 106

In Fig. 106 (i) $h = b \sin C$ or $c \sin B$

(ii) $h = b \sin C$ or $c \sin (180° - B)$

$\qquad\qquad = c \sin B$

$$\triangle = \tfrac{1}{2}ah$$

$$\therefore \triangle = \tfrac{1}{2}ab \sin C \text{ or } \tfrac{1}{2}ac \sin B \text{ or } \tfrac{1}{2}bc \sin A$$

This formula is used for finding the area of a triangle in which two sides and the included angle are known.

For triangles in which the three sides are known, **Hero's formula\*** may be used. The rather complicated proof is omitted here, but the formula itself is given and also some worked examples illustrating its use.

$$\triangle = \sqrt{s(s-a)(s-b)(s-c)}, \text{ where } s = \tfrac{1}{2}(a+b+c)$$

---

\* Hero was a mathematician and physicist who studied in Alexandria during the first century B.C. He evolved methods for solving quadratic equations arithmetically, and for the mensuration of regular polygons, but is probably best known for his experimental work with various mechanical devices, including siphons and fountains, pumps of various kinds, penny-in-the-slot-machines, military catapults and the first working steam-engine, models of which are to be found in most school laboratories today.

147

*New General Mathematics*

**Example 1** *Use Hero's formula to find the areas of triangles having sides* (i) 5 cm, 7 cm, 8 cm, (ii) 12·7 cm, 13·9 cm, 8·6 cm.

(i)
$$s = \tfrac{1}{2}(5 + 7 + 8) \text{ cm} = 10 \text{ cm}$$

$$\therefore \triangle = \sqrt{s(s-a)(s-b)(s-c)} = \sqrt{10 \times 5 \times 3 \times 2} \text{ cm}^2$$
$$= \sqrt{300} \text{ cm}^2$$
$$\simeq 17\cdot3 \text{ cm}^2$$

|  |  | No. | Log. |
|---|---|---|---|
| (ii)  $s = \tfrac{1}{2}(12\cdot7 + 13\cdot9 + 8\cdot6) =$ | | 17·6 | 1·245 5 |
| $s - a = 17\cdot6 - 12\cdot7$ | $=$ | 4·9 | 0·690 2 |
| $s - b = 17\cdot6 - 13\cdot9$ | $=$ | 3·7 | 0·568 2 |
| $s - c = 17\cdot6 - 8\cdot6$ | $=$ | 9·0 | 0·954 2 |
|  |  |  | 3·458 1 ÷ 2 |
| $\therefore \triangle \simeq 53\cdot6 \text{ cm}^2$ | | 53·59 | = 1·729 0(5) |

N.B. $s - a + s - b + s - c = 3s - (a + b + c) = 3s - 2s = s$.
In (ii) above, $4\cdot9 + 3\cdot7 + 9\cdot0 = 17\cdot6$, which gives a quick check that the figures are correct.

**Example 2** *Find the areas of the $\triangle$s shown in Fig.* 107.

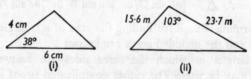

Fig. 107

(i) $\triangle = \tfrac{1}{2} \times 6 \times 4 \times \sin 38° \text{ cm}^2 = 12 \times 0\cdot615\ 7 \text{ cm}^2$
$$= 7\cdot388\ 4 \text{ cm}^2$$
$$\simeq 7\cdot39 \text{ cm}^2$$

(ii) $\triangle = \tfrac{1}{2} \times 23\cdot7 \times 15\cdot6 \times \sin 103° \text{ m}^2$
$= 23\cdot7 \times 7\cdot8 \times \sin 77° \text{ m}^2$
$\simeq 180 \text{ m}^2$

| No. | Log. |
|---|---|
| 23·7 | 1·374 7 |
| 7·8 | 0·892 1 |
| sin 77° | $\overline{1}$·988 7 |
| 180·1 | 2·255 5 |

*Areas of triangles, parallelograms, trapeziums and polygons*

**Exercise 15a**

Use the method of Example 1 to find the areas of the △s whose sides are given in centimetres in nos. 1 to 6.

**1** $a = 7$, $b = 8$, $c = 9$      **2** $a = 5$, $b = 7$, $c = 6$

**3** $a = 4$, $b = 5$, $c = 7$      **4** $a = 4{\cdot}2$, $b = 3{\cdot}3$, $c = 4{\cdot}5$

**5** $a = 3{\cdot}6$, $b = 2{\cdot}8$, $c = 2{\cdot}0$      **6** $a = 1{\cdot}44$, $b = 2{\cdot}16$, $c = 2{\cdot}40$

Use the formulae △ $= \frac{1}{2}bc \sin$ A, etc. to find the areas of the △s in which

**7** $a = 8$ cm, $b = 5$ cm, C $= 40°$

**8** $b = 4$ cm, $c = 3$ cm, A $= 62° \ 13'$

**9** $a = 30$ m, $b = 40$ m, C $= 145°$

**10** $a = 12$ cm, $c = 10$ cm, B $= 98° \ 16'$

**11** $a = 4$ m, $c = 2{\cdot}5$ m, B $= 26° \ 34'$

**12** $b = 3{\cdot}2$ cm, $c = 2{\cdot}7$ cm, A $= 72°$

**13** $a = 13$ cm, $b = 41$ cm, C $= 19° \ 44'$

**14** $a = 36{\cdot}5$ m, $c = 49{\cdot}4$ m, B $= 133° \ 27'$

**Parallelograms**

The parallelogram in Fig. 108, in which $x$ and $y$ are adjacent sides and $\theta$ the angle between them, can be divided by a diagonal into two equal △s, each of which is of area $\frac{1}{2}xy \sin \theta$.

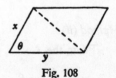

Fig. 108

∴ the area of the ‖gm $= xy \sin \theta$.

If the diagonals of a ‖gm ABCD are of lengths $p$ and $q$ and the angle between the diagonals is $\alpha$ (Fig. 109),

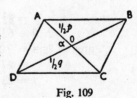

$$\triangle \text{AOD} = \frac{1}{2} \times \frac{1}{2}p \times \frac{1}{2}q \times \sin \alpha$$
$$= \frac{1}{8}pq \sin \alpha.$$

Fig. 109

But the ‖gm consists of four △s equal in area to △ AOD,

∴ the area of the ‖gm $= \frac{1}{2}pq \sin \alpha$.

**Trapeziums and quadrilaterals**

In Book 3, Chapter 2, the area of a **trapezium** was found to be half the product of the sum of the parallel sides and the perpendicular distance between them.

If these dimensions are not known, the area of the trapezium may be found by dividing it into a $\triangle$ and a $\parallel$gm as shown in Fig. 110.

**Example 3** *Find the area of the trapezium in Fig. 110, all the lengths given being in centimetres.*

*Method (i)*

$$\text{Area of } \triangle = \sqrt{11 \times 2 \times 3 \times 6} \text{ cm}^2$$
$$= \sqrt{396} \text{ cm}^2$$
$$= 19 \cdot 90 \text{ cm}^2$$

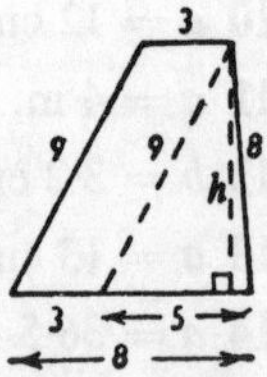

But area of $\triangle = \frac{1}{2}5h$, $\therefore$ $h = \frac{2}{5} \times 19 \cdot 90 = 7 \cdot 96$

$\therefore$ area of $\parallel$gm $= 3h = 23 \cdot 88 \text{ cm}^2$
$\therefore$ area of trapezium $= 43 \cdot 78 \text{ cm}^2$
$\simeq 43 \cdot 8 \text{ cm}^2$

Fig. 110 (i)

*Method (ii)*

From the $\triangle$,

$$\cos \theta = \frac{5^2 + 9^2 - 8^2}{2 \times 5 \times 9}$$

$$= \tfrac{42}{90} = 0 \cdot 466 \, 7$$
$$\therefore \theta = 62° \, 11'.$$
$\therefore$ area of $\parallel$gm $= 9 \times 3 \times \sin 62° \, 11' \text{ cm}^2$
$$= 27 \times 0 \cdot 884 \, 5 \text{ cm}^2$$
$$= 23 \cdot 881 \, 5 \text{ cm}^2$$

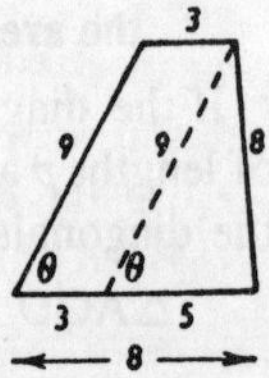

Area of $\triangle = 19 \cdot 90 \text{ cm}^2$
(as in Method (i) above)

Fig. 110 (ii)

$\therefore$ area of trapezium $= 43 \cdot 78 \text{ cm}^2 \simeq 43 \cdot 8 \text{ cm}^2$

**Example 4** *Find the area of the quadrilateral* ABCD *shown in Fig.* 111.

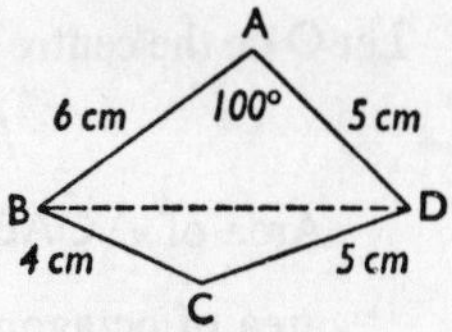

In △ABD,

$$BD^2 = 5^2 + 6^2 - 2 \times 5 \times 6 \cos 100°$$
$$= 25 + 36 + 60 \cos 80°$$
$$= 61 + 10\cdot416$$
$$= 71\cdot416$$

Fig. 111

In △CBD,

$$\cos C = \frac{4^2 + 5^2 - BD^2}{2 \times 4 \times 5}$$

$$= \frac{16 + 25 - 71\cdot416}{40} = \frac{-30\cdot416}{40} = -0\cdot760\,4$$

∴ C = 180° − 40° 30′ = 139° 30′

∴ area of △CBD

$$= \tfrac{1}{2} \times 4 \times 5 \sin C \text{ cm}^2$$
$$= 10 \times 0\cdot649\,4 \text{ cm}^2 = 6\cdot494 \text{ cm}^2$$

Area of △ABD

$$= \tfrac{1}{2} \times 6 \times 5 \sin A \text{ cm}^2$$
$$= 15 \times 0\cdot984\,8 \text{ cm}^2 = 14\cdot772 \text{ cm}^2$$

∴ area of quad. ABCD = 21·266 cm²
$$\simeq 21\cdot3 \text{ cm}^2$$

## Regular polygons

To find the area of a **regular polygon,** join the vertices of the polygon to the centre and consider one of the △s thus formed.

In Example 5, which follows, a regular octagon of side 3 cm is divided into eight equal isosceles △s, each with base 3 cm and vertical angle 45° (360 ÷ 8).

Notice that no working is done in the early stages, all calculations being left until the end of the problem, as also in Example 6.

**Example 5** *Find the area of a regular octagon of side 3 cm.*

Let O be the centre of the octagon, and $\overline{AB}$ one of the sides.

$$h = 1\tfrac{1}{2} \cot 22° \ 30'.$$

Area of $\triangle OAB = \tfrac{1}{2}3h$

$\therefore$ area of octagon $= 8 \times \triangle AOB$
$= 12h \ \text{cm}^2$
$= 18 \cot 22° \ 30' \ \text{cm}^2$
$= 18 \times 2{\cdot}414 \ 2 \ \text{cm}^2$
$\fallingdotseq 43{\cdot}5 \ \text{cm}^2$

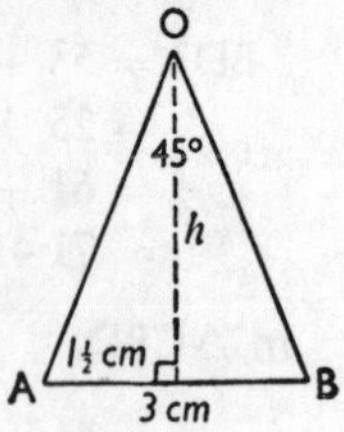

Fig. 112

**Example 6** *Find the area of a regular polygon of 15 sides, inscribed in a circle of radius 4 cm.*

$$A\hat{O}B = \frac{360°}{15} = 24°$$

$\therefore$ area of $\triangle AOB = \tfrac{1}{2} \times 4 \times 4 \times \sin 24° \ \text{cm}^2$
$= 8 \sin 24° \ \text{cm}^2$
$\therefore$ area of polygon $= 15 \times \triangle AOB$
$= 120 \sin 24° \ \text{cm}^2$
$\fallingdotseq 48{\cdot}8 \ \text{cm}^2$

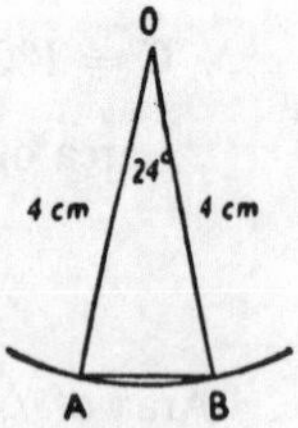

Fig. 113

**To find the area of a regular polygon of *n* sides inscribed in a circle of radius *r*.**

Consider the $\triangle OAB$ formed by two radii $\overline{OA}$, $\overline{OB}$ of the circle, and one side $\overline{AB}$ of the polygon.

Then $\quad A\hat{O}B = \dfrac{360°}{n}$

$\therefore$ area of $\triangle AOB = \tfrac{1}{2}r^2 \sin\left(\dfrac{360°}{n}\right)$

$\therefore$ **area of polygon** $= n \times \triangle AOB$

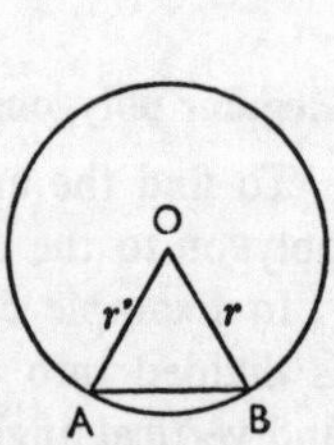

Fig. 114

$$= \tfrac{1}{2}nr^2 \sin\left(\frac{360°}{n}\right).$$

## Exercise 15b

Find the areas of the following figures, all dimensions given being in centimetres.

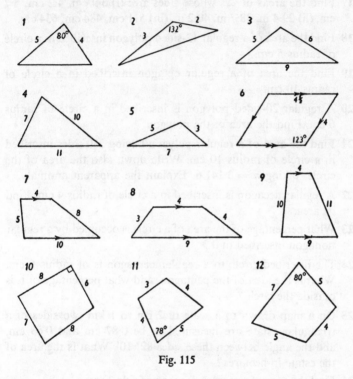

Fig. 115

**13** In △ABC, AB = 5 cm, AC = 6 cm, $\widehat{B}$ = 37°. Find the area of the △. [*Hint:* First find $\widehat{C}$, using the sine formula; then $\widehat{A}$; then the area, using the formula △ = $\frac{1}{2}bc$ sin A.]

**14** Find the area of △PQR in which PQ = 4 cm, PR = 3 cm, $\widehat{R}$ = 75°.

**15** The diagonals of a parallelogram are 10 cm and 12 cm long, and intersect at an angle of 124°. What is the area of the parallelogram?

**16** Two sides of a triangular field are 100 m and 150 m, and the area of the field is half a hectare. What is the angle between the given sides? (Two possible answers.)

**17** Find the areas of △s whose sides are: (i) 3·9 cm, 4·2 cm, 5·7 cm, (ii) 29·4 m, 38·7 m, 40·2 m, (iii) 511 cm, 484 cm, 634 cm.

**18** Find the area of a regular 12-sided polygon inscribed in a circle of radius 5 cm.

**19** Find the area of a regular octagon inscribed in a circle of radius 10 cm.

**20** A regular 20-sided polygon is inscribed in a circle of radius 6 cm. Find the area of the polygon.

**21** Find the area of a regular polygon having 360 sides inscribed in a circle of radius 10 cm. Write down also the area of the circle, taking $\pi = 3·141\ 6$. Explain the apparent anomaly.

**22** A regular decagon is inscribed in a circle of radius 4 cm. Find its area.

**23** What percentage of the area of a circle is occupied by a regular nonagon inscribed in it?

**24** The inscribed circle to a regular pentagon is of radius 5 cm. What is the area of the pentagon, and what percentage of it is outside the circle?

**25** On a map drawn to a scale of 2 cm to 1 km two sides of a triangular estate are measured to be 0·87 cm and 0·63 cm, and the angle between these sides 82° 10′. What is the area of the estate in hectares?

**26** Find the area of a regular decagon of side 2 cm.

**27** Find the area of a regular heptagon of side 10 cm.

**28** A parchment lampshade of the shape shown in Fig. 116 is 20 cm square at the bottom, 12 cm square at the top, and 14 cm deep vertically. What area of parchment is required for the shade, the top and bottom squares being left uncovered?

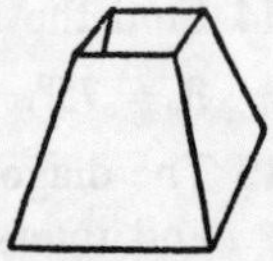

Fig. 116

**29** A marble column 3 m high has a uniform section which is a regular pentagon of side

154

40 cm. If the specific gravity of marble is 2·71, what is the mass of the column?

**30** The sides of a triangular field are measured as 293 m, 386 m and 425 m. Find the area of the field in hectares.

**31** Fig. 117 is a plan of a building estate, the lengths given being in metres. Find the area of the estate in hectares.

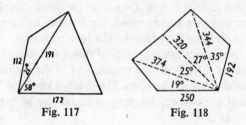

Fig. 117                     Fig. 118

**32** The result of the survey of a school playing-field by a group of boys is shown in Fig. 118, where the lengths are in metres. Find the perimeter of the field in metres, and its area in hectares.

# Chapter 16

# *Variation*

If a heavy rod of uniform section is cut into various pieces, the mass of each piece will be proportional to its length, and the ratio of mass to length will always be the same. Similarly, if a man is bicycling at a steady speed, the distance he covers is proportional to the time for which he has been travelling.

Both of these cases are examples of **direct variation**: in the first the mass varies directly as the length, and in the second the distance varies directly as the time. The symbol used for 'varies as' is $\propto$, so that the two statements just made can be expressed as $M \propto L$ and $D \propto T$.

$M \propto L$ really means that the ratio $\dfrac{M}{L}$ is constant, and it is on this ratio that all subsequent numerical work depends.

**Example 1** *If* $M \propto L$ *and* $M = 6$ *when* $L = 2$, *find the law connecting* $M$ *and* $L$, *and the value of* $L$ *when* $M = 15$.

$$M \propto L, \quad \therefore \frac{M}{L} \text{ is constant (see above).}$$

Let this constant be $k$.

Then $$\frac{M}{L} = k$$

$$\therefore M = kL$$
$$\therefore 6 = k2$$
$$\therefore k = 3$$
$$\therefore M = 3L, \text{ which is the 'law' connecting M and L.}$$

When $$M = 15, \quad 15 = 3L$$
$$\therefore L = 5.$$

*N.B.* $M \propto L$ means that $M = kL$ or $L = \dfrac{1}{k}M$, so that L also varies as M. In general, if $a \propto b$ then $b$ also $\propto a$.

156

If the values of M are plotted against those of L the result is a straight line through the origin, and the same is true for all quantities in direct variation. The law M = 3L is shown as line A in Fig. 119.

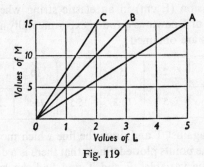

Fig. 119

## Exercise 16a

1 What is the law connecting M and L in Fig. 119 for the lines B and C?

2 In which of the following are the two quantities in italics in direct variation with one another?

   (i) *Number* of pennies in a line and *length* of line.

   (ii) *Number* of bricks in a wall and *area* of wall.

   (iii) *Number* of bricks in a wall and *height* of wall.

   (iv) *Speed* and *distance* when travelling for a fixed time.

   (v) *Time* and *distance* when travelling at a constant speed.

   (vi) *Radius* and *area* of circular discs punched out of a metal sheet.

   (vii) *Number* of people in a household and *cost* of their food.

   (viii) *Area* of grass cut by a mower and *time* mower is working.

   (ix) *Diameter* of a sphere and its *volume*.

   (x) *Age* of a baby and its *mass*.

3 If D ∝ S and D = 140 when S = 35, find the law of the variation, and the value of S when D = 176.

4 $x \propto y$ and $x = 30$ when $y = 12$. Find $x$ when $y = 10$, and $y$ when $x = 14$.

**5** P ∝ Q and P = 4·5 when Q = 12. Find P when Q = 16 and Q when P = 2·4.

**6** A ∝ B and A = $1\frac{7}{8}$ when B = $\frac{5}{6}$. Find A when B = 0·4 and B when A = 7·5.

**7** The extension (E cm) in an elastic string when it is pulled by a force of T newtons is found experimentally and the following results are obtained:

| T | 2 | 5 | 6 | 10 | 12 |
|---|---|---|---|---|---|
| E | 5 | 13·2 | 15·5 | 25·8 | 31·4 |

Plot E against T and draw the line which most nearly goes through the points plotted. Show that there is a direct variation between the variables E and T and find the law connecting them. Read off the probable value of E when T = 7·5 and of T when E = 20.

**8** Two variables A and B are found experimentally to have the following set of values:

| A | 1 | 3 | 6 | 10 | 15 |
|---|---|---|---|---|---|
| B | 6 | 16 | 34 | 55 | 85 |

Show graphically that there is direct variation between A and B: find the law connecting them: read off the value of A when B = 47·6 and of B when A = 12.

**9** The number of dollars ($) obtainable for a number of pounds sterling (£) is given in the following table:

| £ | 2 | 4 | 6 | 8 | 10 |
|---|---|---|---|---|---|
| $ | 4·80 | 9·60 | 14·40 | 19·20 | 24·00 |

Show graphically that $ ∝ £: find the law connecting them: read off the value of $16 in £ and of £7 in dollars.

**10** The height (H cm) of a liquid in a vertical tube and the volume (V cm³) of the liquid are as follows:

| V | 3 | 4 | 6 | 9 | 12 |
|---|---|---|---|---|---|
| H | 2·6 | 3·5 | 5·2 | 7·8 | 10·4 |

Show graphically that H ∝ V: find the law of variation in the form H = *k*V: read off V when H = 7 and H when V = 3·8.

In Fig. 119 it is shown that the graph illustrating direct variation is always a straight line.

If circular discs are punched out of a sheet of metal their areas are proportional to the squares of their radii (A = $\pi$R²), and therefore their masses are also proportional to the squares of the radii, all the discs being of the same thickness.

Hence M varies directly as R², or M ∝ R².

Similarly, since the volumes of spheres are proportional to the cubes of their radii (V = $\frac{4}{3}\pi$R³), V varies directly as R³, or V ∝ R³.

If a car has to travel a certain distance, the greater the average speed the less time it will

take $\left( T = \dfrac{D}{S} \right)$, so that $T \propto \dfrac{1}{S}$, when T is said to

**vary inversely** as S.

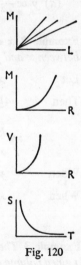

Fig. 120

If sketch graphs are drawn to illustrate these four variations, they will be found to be as in Fig. 120.

### Exercise 16b

**1** Write down the law of variation in each of the following cases, and illustrate the law by a sketch, as in Fig. 120.

(*a*) *Masses* of *lengths* cut off a uniform iron wire.

(*b*) *Masses* of spherical ball-bearings of different *diameters*.

*New General Mathematics*

(c) The *length* and *breadth* of rectangles of the same area.

(d) The *number* of grains of rice in a bag and their total *mass*.

(e) The *diameter* of a circular disc and the *cost* of gilding it.

(f) A circle being divided into a number of equal sectors, the *angle* of each sector and the *number* of sectors.

2 Sketch the following curves, showing both positive and negative values of $x$:

(a) $y \propto x^2$      (b) $y \propto x^3$      (c) $y \propto \dfrac{1}{x}$

(d) $y \propto \dfrac{1}{x^2}$      (e) $y \propto \sqrt{x}$      (f) $y \propto \dfrac{1}{\sqrt{x}}$

**Example 2** $x \propto \sqrt{y}$ *and* $x = 4\frac{1}{2}$ *when* $y = 9$. *Find the relation between x and y. Find also x when* $y = 25$, *and y when* $x = 6$.

Let $\qquad x = k\sqrt{y}$

Then $\qquad 4\frac{1}{2} = k\sqrt{9}$

$\qquad\qquad = 3k$

$\qquad \therefore k = 1\frac{1}{2}$

$\qquad \therefore x = \frac{3}{2}\sqrt{y}$, which is the relation required.

When $\qquad y = 25, \qquad x = \frac{3}{2}\sqrt{25} = 7\frac{1}{2}$

When $\qquad x = 6, \qquad \sqrt{y} = \frac{2}{3}x = \frac{2}{3} \times 6 = 4$

$\qquad\qquad\qquad\qquad \therefore y = 16.$

**Example 3** *The number of spherical shot which can be made from a given volume of lead varies inversely as the cube of the diameter of the shot required. When the diameter is* 0·2 cm *the number of shot is* 270. *How many shot of diameter* 0·3 cm *can be cast from the same volume of lead?*

Let $\qquad N = $ no. of shot, $D = $ diam. in cm.

Then $\qquad N = \dfrac{k}{D^3}$

$\qquad \therefore 270 = \dfrac{k}{0\cdot2^3}$

$$\therefore k = 270 \times 0 \cdot 2^3$$

$$\therefore N = \frac{270 \times 0 \cdot 2^3}{D^3}$$

$$= \frac{270 \times 0 \cdot 2^3}{0 \cdot 3^3} \quad \text{when } D = 0 \cdot 3$$

$$= \frac{270 \times 8}{27} \quad \left[\frac{0 \cdot 2^3}{0 \cdot 3^3} = \left(\frac{0 \cdot 2}{0 \cdot 3}\right)^3 = \left(\frac{2}{3}\right)^3 = \frac{8}{27}\right]$$

$$= 80$$

$$\therefore \text{ number of shot} = 80.$$

In the next example a different method of solution is shown. This alternative method may always be used when the value of the constant $k$ is not required in the answer.

**Example 4** $x \propto y^2$. *How is $x$ affected if the value of $y$ increases by 20%?*

$$\text{Let} \quad x = ky^2 \quad \text{(i)}$$

Let $x$ become $x'$ if $y$ increases to $\frac{120}{100}y$.

$$\text{Then } x' = k\left(\frac{120}{100}y\right)^2 \quad \text{(ii)}$$

Dividing (ii) by (i),

$$\frac{x'}{x} = \frac{k\left(\frac{120}{100}y\right)^2}{ky^2} = \left(\frac{120}{100}\right)^2 = \frac{144}{100}$$

$$\therefore x' = \frac{144}{100}x$$

$$\therefore x \text{ is increased by 44\%.}$$

## Exercise 16c

In each of the following questions, add a sketch to illustrate the variation.

**1** $x \propto y^2$. $x = 45$ when $y = 3$. Find the law: $x$ when $y = 4$: $y$ when $x = 125$.

**2** $A \propto B^3$. $A = 32$ when $B = 4$. Find the law: A when $B = 6$: B when $A = 13 \cdot 5$.

3 P ∝ √Q. P = 10 when Q = 16. Find the law: P when Q = 9: Q when P = $1\frac{7}{8}$.

4 $Z^2$ ∝ Y. Z = 9 when Y = 27. Find the law: Z when Y = 48: Y when Z = 6.

5 V ∝ $D^3$. V = 108 when D = 6. Find the law: V when D = 3: D when V = 2·048.

6 D ∝ √H. D = 6 when H = 24. Find the law: D when H = 150: H when D = $10\frac{1}{2}$.

7 $x$ ∝ $y^2$. How is $x$ affected if $y$ is (i) increased by 10%? (ii) decreased by 10%?

8 $x$ ∝ $\sqrt{y}$. How is $x$ affected if $y$ is increased by 44%?

9 V ∝ $R^3$. What is the percentage increase in V if R increases by 20%?

10 W ∝ $D^2$. What is the percentage decrease in W if D diminishes by 15%?

11 The variables $x$ and $y$ are thought to be connected by a relation of the form $y = kx^2$, and the following set of values for $x$ and $y$ is found experimentally. By plotting $y$ against $x^2$ show that this relation is the correct one, and read off the value of $k$.

| $x$ | 2 | 4 | 6 | 8 | 10 |
|-----|-----|------|----|----|-------|
| $y$ | 5·9 | 24·5 | 53 | 97 | 150·5 |

12 Ball-bearings of various diameters are carefully weighed, and the following results are obtained:

| Diameter (D mm) | 5 | 10 | 15 | 20 |
|-----------------|------|------|-------|-------|
| Mass (M g) | 0·51 | 4·06 | 13·70 | 32·45 |

By plotting M against $D^3$ show that M ∝ $D^3$ and find the approximate mass of a bearing of diameter 12 mm.

**Joint variation**

If metal discs of various diameters and thicknesses are weighed, the masses will depend upon both the area and the thickness of the discs. In fact $M \propto R^2T$, where M is the mass, R the radius and T the thickness of the disc. This is an example of **joint variation,** and it could be said that the mass **varies jointly as** the thickness and the square of the radius.

**Partial variation**

When a large household has to be fed, the cost of feeding depends upon two quite independent factors: first the cost of overheads (e.g. cook's wages, fuel, etc.), which remains the same however many people are in the house; and secondly the cost of the food itself, which is directly proportional to the number of people being fed. Hence it can be said that the cost is **partly constant and partly varies as** the number of people present or, in algebraic form, $C = a + kN$, C being the cost, N the number of people, and $a$ and $k$ both constants.

**Example 5** *The mass of copper wire depends jointly upon its length and the square of its diameter. If 500 m of wire of diameter 3 mm has a mass of 31·5 kg, what will be the mass of 1 km of wire of diameter 2 mm?*

$$\text{Let} \quad M = \text{mass in kg,}$$
$$D = \text{diam. in mm,}$$
$$L = \text{length in m.}$$
$$\text{Then} \quad M = kLD^2.$$
$$\therefore \; 31·5 = k \times 500 \times 3^2 \quad \text{(i)}$$
$$M = k \times 1\,000 \times 2^2 \quad \text{(ii)}$$

Dividing (ii) by (i),

$$\frac{M}{31·5} = \frac{1\,000}{500} \times \left(\frac{2}{3}\right)^2 = 2 \times \frac{4}{9} = \frac{8}{9}$$

$$\therefore \; M = 31·5 \times \frac{8}{9} = 28$$

$$\therefore \; \text{mass} = 28 \text{ kg.}$$

163

*New General Mathematics*

**Example 6** *The resistance to the motion of a car is partly constant and partly varies as the square of the speed. At 40 km h⁻¹ the resistance is 530 N, and at 60 km h⁻¹ it is 730 N. What will be the resistance at 70 km h⁻¹?*

Let $R$ = resistance in newtons,
$V$ = speed in km h⁻¹.
Then $R = a + kV^2$,

where $a$ and $k$ are both constants.

$\therefore\ 530 = a + 1\,600\,k$     (i)
and $\ 730 = a + 3\,600\,k$     (ii)

Subtracting,

$200 = 2\,000\,k$
$\therefore\ k = \frac{1}{10}$

Substituting in (i),

$530 = a + 1\,600 \times \frac{1}{10} = a + 160$
$\therefore\ a = 370$
$\therefore\ R = 370 + \frac{1}{10}V^2$

When $\ V = 70$
$R = 370 + \frac{1}{10} \times 4\,900$
$= 370 + 490$
$= 860$
$\therefore$ resistance $= 860$ N.

**Exercise 16d**

**1** Write down the equation connecting the variables for each of the following statements:

(i) The volume V of a cone varies jointly as its height H and as the square of its base-diameter D.

(ii) The kinetic energy E of a body varies jointly as its mass M and as the square of its velocity V.

(iii) When a beam of length $l$ is loaded with a mass M at its mid-point, the sag $s$ varies jointly as the load and as the cube of the length.

(iv) If a body is being steadily accelerated, the distance $d$

it travels from the start is partly constant and partly varies as the square of the final velocity $v$.

(v) The force of attraction F between two bodies varies as the product of their masses, M and $m$, and inversely as the square of the distance $d$ between them.

(vi) The distance D in which a car can be stopped by its brakes varies partly as the velocity V and partly as the square of the velocity.

**2** $A \propto BC$. When $B = 4$ and $C = 9$, $A = 6$. Find A when $B = 3$ and $C = 10$. Find also C if $A = 20$ and $B = 15$.

What is the effect on A if B is increased by 10% and C diminished by 10%?

**3** $x \propto y^2 z$. When $y = 2$ and $z = 3$, $x = 4\frac{1}{2}$. Find $x$ when $y = 5$ and $z = 4$. Find also $y$ when $x = 21$ and $z = 3\frac{1}{2}$.

What happens to $x$ if $y$ is doubled and $z$ halved?

**4** $p \propto \dfrac{q}{r^2}$. When $q = 5$ and $r = 3$, $p = 3\frac{1}{3}$. Find $p$ when $q = 9$ and $r = 1\cdot2$.

**5** $x$ is partly constant and partly varies as $y$. When $y = 2$, $x = 0$, and when $y = 6$, $x = 20$. Find the law of the variation, and also $x$ when $y = 3$.

**6** $x$ is partly constant and partly varies inversely as $y$. When $y = 3$, $x = 1$, and when $y = 6$, $x = 3$. Find $x$ when $y = 4$.

**7** A varies partly as B and partly as the square root of B. When $B = 4$, $A = 22$, and when $B = 9$, $A = 42$. Find A when $B = 25$.

**8** $x \propto y$ and $y \propto z^3$. How does $x$ vary with $z$?

**9** $x \propto y^2$ and $y \propto z^2$. How does $x$ vary with $z$?

**10** $A \propto BC$ and $B \propto \dfrac{1}{C^2}$. How does A vary with C?

**11** The mass of a cylinder of given material varies jointly as the square of the radius and as the height. If the radius is increased by 20% and the height by 10%, what is the percentage increase in the mass? *(W)*

**12** It is found that when the velocity $(v \, \text{m s}^{-1})$ of a stream of water is determined by a water-pressure gauge recording a height $(h \, \text{cm})$ $h$ varies as the square of $v$. If a speed of $2 \, \text{m s}^{-1}$ causes a height of 7 cm, find the height caused by a speed of $6 \, \text{m s}^{-1}$.

$(C)^*$

**13** The cost of the mass-production of cars is partly constant and partly varies as the number of cars produced. If the total cost of making 40 cars is £18 700 and of making 100 cars is £35 500, find the total cost of making 200 cars. $(C)$

**14** The total cost of making a solid metal sphere is made up of an amount which is independent of the size of the sphere and an amount which varies as the cube of its radius. When the radius of the sphere is 8 cm, its total cost is £4·80; and when the radius is 12 cm the cost is £12·40. Find the total cost of a sphere of radius 10 cm. $(C)^*$

**15** If $z$ varies directly as $\dfrac{x}{y^2}$, and $y$ varies inversely as $x$, and $z = \frac{1}{3}$, $x = 2$, $y = \frac{1}{4}$ are simultaneous values, express (i) $y$ in terms of $x$, (ii) $z$ in terms of $x$.

If the value of $x$ is increased by 10%, find the corresponding increase in the value of $z$. $(OC)$

**16** The mass of a sphere varies as the cube of its radius and also as the specific gravity of the material of which it is made. The specific gravity of gold is 19·25 and of silver 10·5. Find the radius of a sphere of silver equal in mass to three times that of a sphere of gold of radius 2 cm. $(W)$

**17** The resistance (R) to the motion of a car is partly constant and partly varies as the square of the velocity (V). When $V = 50 \, \text{km h}^{-1}$, $R = 370 \, \text{N}$, and when $V = 60 \, \text{km h}^{-1}$, $R = 480 \, \text{N}$. Find V when $R = 760 \, \text{N}$.

Show that, when the car is travelling at V km h$^{-1}$, an increase of 1 km h$^{-1}$ in the speed would cause an increase of $\dfrac{2V + 1}{10}$ newtons in the resistance. $(OC)^*$

**18** The total time taken by a Council meeting consists of a fixed number of minutes (taken on business which does not provoke discussion) added to the time spent on discussion, which varies as the square of the number of members present. With 14 members present the meeting takes 72 minutes, and with 20 members it takes 123 minutes. How long would the meeting take if 18 members were present? *(OC)*

**19** (i) If $y$ varies directly as $x$ and inversely as $z$, and if $x$ varies inversely as $y^2$, prove that $z^2$ varies directly as $x^3$.

(ii) A man finds that part of the expenses of his holiday is constant and that the other part varies jointly as the number of days and the number of people in his party. For 10 days the total cost for 5 people is £146, and for 14 days for 6 people the cost is £231. What would be the cost for 6 people for 20 days?

**20** If a car of mass M tonnes initially travelling at $v$ km h$^{-1}$ is stopped in $x$ metres by a resistance of R newtons, it is known that, when all these quantities vary, the resistance is directly proportional to the mass and the square of the speed and is inversely proportional to the distance. A car of mass 2 tonnes travelling at 50 km h$^{-1}$ is stopped in 20 metres by a resistance of 10 500 N.

(i) Obtain an equation connecting M, $v$, $x$ and R.

(ii) From this formula express $v$ in terms of M, $x$ and R.

(iii) If the maximum resistance which can be brought to bear on a car of mass $3\frac{1}{2}$ tonnes is 26 880 N, what is the greatest speed at which it can be driven if it must be possible to stop it in 35 metres? *(W)\**

Chapter 17

# Right-angled triangle divided into similar triangles

**Theorem 27**

In a right-angled triangle, the perpendicular from the right angle to the hypotenuse divides the triangle into two triangles which are similar to the original triangle, and to each other.

Given the triangle XYZ right-angled at X, and $\overline{XM}$ the perpendicular from X to $\overline{YZ}$.

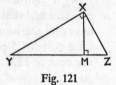

Fig. 121

To prove that △s XYZ, MYX, MXZ are similar.

Proof In △s XYZ, MYX

$$Y\hat{X}Z = Y\hat{M}X \qquad \textit{rt. } \angle s, \textit{ given}$$

$$\hat{Y} \text{ is common}$$

∴ △s XYZ, MYX are equiangular and similar.

△XYZ is the result of reflecting △MYX in the bisector of M$\hat{Y}$X and enlarging it in the ratio YZ : YX, centre Y.
Similarly it may be proved that △s XYZ, MXZ are similar.

△XYZ is the result of reflecting △MXZ in the bisector of M$\hat{Z}$X and enlarging it in the ratio YZ : XZ, centre Z.

∴ △s XYZ, MYX, MXZ are similar.

Q.E.D.

Corollary 1 The square of either of the sides which contain the right angle is equal to the product of the hypotenuse and the segment of the hypotenuse adjacent to that side,

i.e. $XY^2 = YZ \times YM$ and $XZ^2 = YZ \times MZ$.

For since $\triangle$s XYZ, MYX are similar,

$$\frac{XY}{MY} = \frac{YZ}{YX} \left[ = \frac{XZ}{MX} \right]$$

$$\therefore \ XY^2 = YZ \times YM.$$
Similarly $\ XZ^2 = YZ \times MZ.$

Hence XY is a **mean proportional** between YZ and YM,
and XZ „ „ „ „ „ YZ „ MZ.

The proof may also be stated in a trigonometrical form,

for in $\triangle$ XYM, $\cos Y = \dfrac{YM}{YX}$

and in $\triangle$ XYZ, $\cos Y = \dfrac{YX}{YZ}$

$$\therefore \frac{YX}{YZ} = \frac{YM}{YX}$$

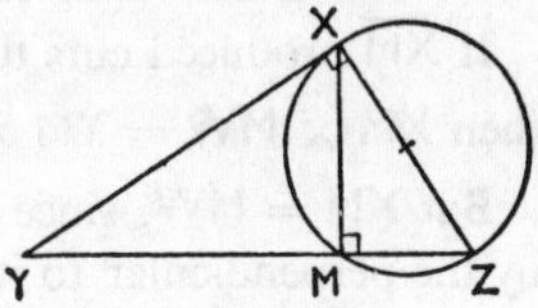

i.e. $XY^2 = YZ \times YM.$

Fig. 122

The result of Corollary 1 is already familiar as applied to a
circle (Theorem 25). Fig. 122 should be self-explanatory.

Corollary 1 leads to a simple proof of Pythagoras' Theorem,

$$\begin{aligned}
\text{for} \quad XY^2 + XZ^2 &= YZ \times YM + YZ \times MZ \\
&= YZ(YM + MZ) \\
&= YZ \times YZ \\
&= YZ^2.
\end{aligned}$$

**Corollary 2** **The square of the perpendicular from the right angle
to the hypotenuse is equal to the product of the segments into which
it divides the hypotenuse,**

i.e. $MX^2 = MY \times MZ.$

For since $\triangle$s MYX, MXZ are similar,

$$\frac{MX}{MZ} = \frac{MY}{MX} \left[ = \frac{YX}{XZ} \right]$$

$$\therefore \ MX^2 = MY \times MZ.$$

169

This result may also be proved trigonometrically as follows:

$$M\hat{Z}X = 90° - M\hat{X}Z = M\hat{X}Y$$

$$\therefore \tan M\hat{Z}X = \tan M\hat{X}Y$$

$$\therefore \frac{MX}{MZ} = \frac{MY}{MX}$$

$$\therefore MX^2 = MY \times MZ.$$

Corollary 2 may also be seen to be true in Fig. 123.

Since $Y\hat{X}Z$ is a right angle, X lies on the circle drawn on $\overline{YZ}$ as diameter.

If $\overline{XM}$ produced cuts the circle at W,
then $XM \times MW = YM \times MZ$.

But $XM = MW$, since a chord is bisected by the perpendicular to it from the centre.

$$\therefore XM^2 = YM \times MZ.$$

Fig. 123

This result may alternatively be stated as:

**MX is a mean proportional between MY and MZ.**

Also a square the length of whose side is MX is equal in area to a rectangle the lengths of whose sides are MY and MZ. This suggests a method for constructing a square equal in area to a given rectangle as in Construction 14 which follows.

**Construction 14**

**To construct a square equal in area to a given rectangle.**

**Given** a rectangle ABCD.

**To construct** a square equal in area to rect. ABCD.

**Construction** Produce $\overline{AB}$ to H, making $BH = BC$.

On $\overline{AH}$ as diameter draw a semicircle.

Produce $\overline{CB}$ to meet the semicircle at P.

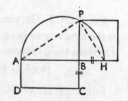

Fig. 124

Then the square with side $\overline{PB}$ is the required square.

**Proof** Join $\overline{PA}$, $\overline{PH}$.

Then $\hat{APH} = 90°$.    $\angle$ *in a semicircle*

$\therefore$ $\triangle APH$ is right-angled at P, and $\overline{PB}$ is the perpendicular from the right angle to the hypotenuse.

$\therefore$ $PB^2 = AB \times BH$

$\cdot$        $= AB \times BC$    *BH = BC by constr.*

$\therefore$ area of square on $\overline{PB}$ = area of rectangle ABCD.

Q.E.F.

Construction 14 could alternatively have been stated as:

**To construct a mean proportional between two given lengths.**

**Summary of results**

In Fig. 125

$$YX^2 = YM \times YZ$$
$$ZX^2 = ZM \times ZY$$
$$MX^2 = MY \times MZ.$$

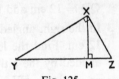

Fig. 125

Notice also that

$$\tfrac{1}{2}XY \times XZ = \text{area of } \triangle XYZ = \tfrac{1}{2}XM \times YZ$$

$$\therefore \ XY \times XZ = XM \times YZ.$$

**Example** $\triangle ABC$ *is such that* $\hat{A} = 90°$, *AB* = 15 *cm*, *AC* = 8 *cm*, *and* $\overline{AD}$ *is an altitude. Calculate* AD, BD, CD.

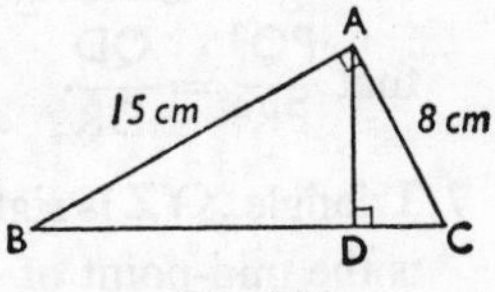

$$BC = \sqrt{15^2 + 8^2} \text{ cm} = 17 \text{ cm}$$

$$AD \times BC = AB \times AC$$

$\therefore$ $AD \times 17 = 15 \times 8$

$\therefore$ $AD = \dfrac{15 \times 8}{17} \text{ cm} = \dfrac{120}{17} \text{ cm} = 7\tfrac{1}{17} \text{ cm}$

$$BA^2 = BD \times BC$$

$\therefore$ $15^2 = BD \times 17$

$\therefore$ $BD = \dfrac{15^2}{17} \text{ cm} = \dfrac{225}{17} \text{ cm} = 13\tfrac{4}{17} \text{ cm}$

Fig. 126

171

$$CA^2 = CD \times CB$$

$$\therefore \quad 8^2 = CD \times 17$$

$$\therefore \quad CD = \frac{8^2}{17} \text{ cm} = \frac{64}{17} \text{ cm} = 3\tfrac{13}{17} \text{ cm}$$

$$\therefore \text{ the lengths are } 7\tfrac{1}{17} \text{ cm, } 13\tfrac{4}{17} \text{ cm, } 3\tfrac{13}{17} \text{ cm.}$$

*Check.* $BD + DC = 13\tfrac{4}{17} \text{ cm} + 3\tfrac{13}{17} \text{ cm} = 17 \text{ cm} = BC.$

## Exercise 17

1 Triangle ABC is right-angled at A, and $\overline{AD}$ is an altitude. If BD = 12 cm and DC = 3 cm, calculate AD.

2 Triangle PQR is right-angled at P, and $\overline{PD}$ is an altitude. If QD = 12 cm and DR = 4 cm, calculate PR.

3 In the right-angled $\triangle XYZ$, XY = 5 cm, YZ = 13 cm. ZX = 12 cm. Find the lengths of the two parts into which $\overline{YZ}$ is divided by the altitude $\overline{XD}$.

4 The altitude $\overline{PM}$ of a right-angled triangle meets the hypotenuse $\overline{QR}$ in M. If QM = 2·7 cm, MR = 1·2 cm, calculate PM, $\hat{Q}$, and the area of $\triangle PQR$.

5 Triangle ABC is right-angled at B, and $\overline{BD}$ is an altitude. If AB = 2BC, prove that AD = 4DC.

6 Triangle PQR is right-angled at P, and $\overline{PD}$ is an altitude. Prove that $\dfrac{PQ^2}{PR^2} = \dfrac{QD}{DR}$.

7 Triangle XYZ is right-angled at X, and $\overline{XN}$ is an altitude. If M is the mid-point of $\overline{YZ}$, prove that $XN^2 = MZ^2 - MN^2$.

8 $\overline{DM}$ is an altitude of $\triangle DEF$, which is right-angled at D. Prove that $DE \times DM = DF \times EM$.

9 Draw a rectangle measuring 8 cm by 3 cm. Construct a square of equal area, and measure one of its sides.

10 $\overline{CD}$ is a diameter of a circle, centre O, and $\overline{CP}$ is a chord. The tangent at D cuts $\overline{CP}$ produced at T.
Prove that $CP \times CT = 4OP^2$.

11 In $\triangle ABC$, $\overline{AD}$ is an altitude and $AB = AC$. Prove that $AB$ is a mean proportional between $AD$ and the diameter of the circumcircle of $\triangle ABC$.

12 Triangle LMN is such that $\hat{L} = 90°$, $\hat{M} = 30°$, $LN = 2$ cm, and $\overline{LX}$ is an altitude. Using surds where necessary (*not decimals*) write down LM, MN, LX, MX, NX. Verify that
$LX^2 = MX \times NX$, $LM^2 = MN \times MX$, $LN^2 = MN \times NX$.

13 In $\triangle DEF$, $\hat{D} = 90°$, $\hat{E} = 27°$, $DE = 4$ cm, and $\overline{DH}$ is an altitude. Calculate DF, DH, EF, EH. Verify that
$EF \times EH = DE^2$.

14 Draw a rectangle measuring 5·4 cm by 2·4 cm. Construct a square equal in area to the rectangle. Measure a diagonal of the square.

15 Draw a triangle with sides 9 cm, 10·6 cm, 5·6 cm. Construct a square equal in area to the triangle. Measure a side of the square.

16 $\overline{AD}$ is an altitude of $\triangle ABC$, which is right-angled at A. If $\overline{DE}$ is an altitude of $\triangle ABD$, prove that $AD^2 = AC \times DE$.

17 Triangle PQR is right-angled at P, and $\overline{PS}$ is an altitude. If $QR = 3PQ$, prove that $SR = 8QS$.

18 Use the results of Corollaries 1 and 2 to construct a line of length $\sqrt{40}$ cm in two different ways. Measure the length of the line.

19 In $\triangle XYZ$, $\hat{X}$ is a right angle and $\overline{XM}$ is an altitude. If $YZ = 5MZ$, prove that $YZ^2 = 5XZ^2$.

20 In $\triangle XYZ$ the perpendicular from X to $\overline{YZ}$ meets YZ in $\overline{M}$. If $XY^2 = YM \times YZ$, prove that $Y\hat{X}Z = 90°$.

21 Triangle ABC is right-angled at A. $\overline{AD}$, $\overline{DE}$, $\overline{DF}$ are the altitudes of $\triangle s$ ABC, ABD, ACD respectively. Prove that the square on $\overline{AE}$ is equal to the rectangle of the two lengths into which $\overline{AC}$ is divided by F.

22 Triangle XYZ is right-angled at X, and $\overline{XM}$ is an altitude. If $XY = 2XZ$, prove that $5XM = 2YZ$.

**23** Inscribe a regular hexagon in a circle of radius 3·6 cm. Construct a square equal in area to the hexagon. Measure a side of the square.

**24** Triangle ABC is right-angled at A, and AB = 4 m, BC = 5 m. If $\overline{AD}$, $\overline{DE}$, $\overline{DF}$ are the altitudes of △s ABC, ABD, ACD respectively, calculate the area of the rectangle AEDF in square metres correct to 3 sig. fig.

**25** Triangle ABC is right-angled at C, and AC = 60 cm, BC = 80 cm. If $\overline{CD}$ is an altitude of △ABC, and $\overline{DE}$ is an altitude of △BCD, calculate BE and EC.

# Chapter 18

# *Bisectors of vertical angle of a triangle*

## Internal and external bisectors of an angle

In Fig. 127, the **internal** bisector of
$B\hat{A}C$ is $\overline{AM}$.

If $\overline{BA}$ is produced to any point P,
and $\overline{AN}$ is drawn to bisect $C\hat{A}P$, then
$\overline{AN}$ is said to be the **external** bisector
of $B\hat{A}C$.

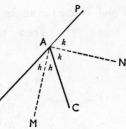

Fig. 127

$$M\hat{A}N = h + k.$$
But $2h + 2k = 180°$, since $\overline{BAP}$ is a straight line.
$$\therefore\ h + k = 90°$$

$$\therefore\ M\hat{A}N \text{ is a right angle.}$$

Hence the internal and external bisectors of an angle are at
right angles to each other.

## Theorem 28

The internal and external bisectors of an angle of a triangle
divide the opposite side internally and externally respectively in the
ratio of the sides which contain the angle.

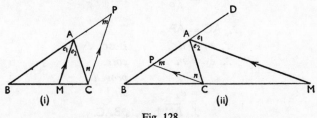

Fig. 128

175

**Given** triangle ABC with $\overline{AM}$ bisecting $\widehat{BAC}$ (i) internally or (ii) externally and cutting (i) $\overline{BC}$ or (ii) $\overline{BC}$ produced in M.

**To prove** that $\dfrac{BA}{AC} = \dfrac{BM}{MC}$.

**Construction** Through C draw a line parallel to $\overline{MA}$, to cut (i) $\overline{BA}$ produced or (ii) $\overline{BA}$ in P.

**Proof** Name the angles $e_1$, $e_2$, $m$, $n$ as in the figures.

$$
\begin{aligned}
\text{Then} \quad m &= e_1 & \textit{corr.} \\
&= e_2 & \textit{given} \\
&= n & \textit{alt.}
\end{aligned}
$$

$\therefore \triangle$ ACP is isosceles, and AC = AP.

$$
\begin{aligned}
\therefore \quad \frac{BA}{AC} &= \frac{BA}{AP} \\
&= \frac{BM}{MC}. & \overline{AM} \parallel \overline{PC}
\end{aligned}
$$

Q.E.D.

The **converse** is also true,

i.e. if $\dfrac{BA}{AC} = \dfrac{BM}{MC}$, then $\overline{AM}$ bisects $\widehat{BAC}$.

For, with the same figures and construction,

$$
\begin{aligned}
\frac{BA}{AC} &= \frac{BM}{MC} & \textit{given} \\[4pt]
&= \frac{BA}{AP} & \overline{AM} \parallel \overline{PC}
\end{aligned}
$$

$$
\begin{aligned}
\therefore \text{ AC} &= \text{AP} \\
\therefore \quad m &= n & \textit{isosc. } \triangle \\
\therefore \quad e_1 &= m & \textit{corr.} \\
&= n & \textit{proved} \\
&= e_2 & \textit{alt.}
\end{aligned}
$$

$\therefore \overline{AM}$ bisects $\widehat{BAC}$.

In Fig. 129, $\overline{AM}$ and $\overline{AN}$ are the internal and external bisectors of $B\hat{A}C$.

$$\therefore \quad \frac{BM}{MC} = \frac{AB}{AC}$$

and

$$\frac{BN}{CN} = \frac{AB}{AC}.$$

Hence

$$\frac{BM}{MC} = \frac{BN}{CN},$$

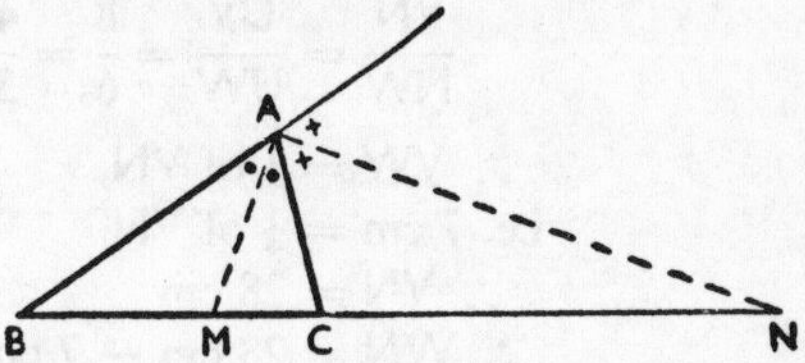

Fig. 129

that is M and N divide $\overline{BC}$ internally and externally in the same numerical ratio.

Notice that M, lying between B and C, divides $\overline{BC}$ in a positive ratio; N, lying on $\overline{BC}$ produced, divides $\overline{BC}$ in a negative ratio. (See p. 78, Chap. 10.)

Hence, to be strictly correct,

$$\frac{BM}{MC} = -\frac{BN}{NC},$$

but the minus sign may be ignored in the working of the present chapter.

**Example** *UVW is a triangle in which the internal and external bisectors of* $V\hat{U}W$ *meet* $\overline{VW}$ *and* $\overline{VW}$ *produced in* M *and* N. *If* $UV = 8\ cm,\ VW = 7\ cm,\ WU = 6\ cm,\ prove\ that$ $\dfrac{MV}{VN} = \dfrac{MW}{WN} = \dfrac{1}{7}.$

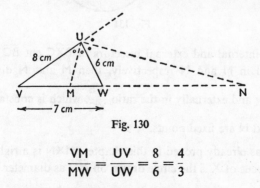

Fig. 130

$$\frac{VM}{MW} = \frac{UV}{UW} = \frac{8}{6} = \frac{4}{3}$$

$$\therefore \ VM = \tfrac{4}{7} \text{ of } VW = \tfrac{4}{7} \text{ of } 7 \text{ cm} = 4 \text{ cm}$$
$$\therefore \ MW = 7 \text{ cm} - 4 \text{ cm} = 3 \text{ cm}$$
$$\frac{VN}{NW} = \frac{UV}{UW} = \frac{8}{6} = \frac{4}{3}$$
$$\therefore \ VW = \tfrac{1}{4} \text{ of } VN,$$
$$\text{i.e. } 7 \text{ cm} = \tfrac{1}{4} \text{ of } VN$$
$$\therefore \ VN = 28 \text{ cm}$$
$$\therefore \ WN = 28 \text{ cm} - 7 \text{ cm} = 21 \text{ cm}$$
$$\therefore \ \frac{MV}{VN} = \frac{4}{28} \text{ and } \frac{MW}{WN} = \frac{3}{21},$$
$$\text{i.e. } \frac{MV}{VN} = \frac{MW}{WN} = \frac{1}{7}.$$

## Circle of Apollonius

In Fig. 131, B and C are fixed points, and X is a point which moves so that the ratio $\dfrac{XB}{XC}$ is constant.

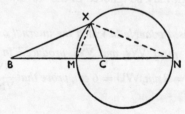

Fig. 131

If the internal and external bisectors of $\text{B}\hat{\text{X}}\text{C}$ cut $\overline{BC}$ and $\overline{BC}$ produced in M and N respectively, then M and N divide $\overline{BC}$ internally and externally in the ratio $\dfrac{XB}{XC}$, which is constant.

$\therefore$ M and N are fixed points.

Also, as already proved in this chapter, $\text{M}\hat{\text{X}}\text{N}$ is a right angle.
$\therefore$ the locus of X is the circle drawn on $\overline{MN}$ as diameter.

**Exercise 18**

1 In $\triangle$ABC, AB = 7 cm, BC = 9 cm, CA = 5 cm, and the bisector of $\hat{A}$ meets $\overline{BC}$ at D. Calculate BD, DC.

2 ABC is a triangle in which AB = 12 cm, BC = 14 cm, CA = 9 cm, and X is a point on $\overline{BC}$ such that BX = 8 cm. Prove that $\overline{AX}$ bisects $\hat{A}$.

3 P, X, Q, Y are four points on a straight line. X and Y divide $\overline{PQ}$ internally and externally in the same numerical ratio. If PX = 6 cm and XQ = 4 cm, calculate QY.

4 Y, A, X, B are four points on a straight line. X and Y divide $\overline{AB}$ internally and externally in the same numerical ratio. If AX = 6 cm and XB = 15 cm, calculate YA.

5 PQR is a triangle in which PQ = 15 cm, QR = 16 cm, RP = 9 cm. The internal and external bisectors of $\hat{P}$ meet $\overline{QR}$ and QR produced at A and B, and the mid-point of $\overline{QR}$ is M. Calculate QA, AR, RB, and show that MA × MB = MR².

6 ABCD is a rhombus, and the side $\overline{AB}$ is trisected at M and N, M being nearer to A than to B. The diagonal $\overline{AC}$ cuts $\overline{DM}$, $\overline{DN}$ at P, Q respectively. Prove that $\dfrac{DP}{PM} = \dfrac{2DQ}{QN}$.

7 A straight line parallel to the side $\overline{QR}$ of $\triangle$PQR meets $\overline{PQ}$, $\overline{PR}$ in X, Y respectively, and M is the mid-point of $\overline{QR}$. Prove that if $\overline{MX}$ bisects $P\hat{M}Q$, then $\overline{MY}$ bisects $P\hat{M}R$.

8 In $\triangle$PQR, PQ = 41 cm, QR = 40 cm, $\hat{R}$ is a right angle, and the bisector of $\hat{P}$ meets $\overline{QR}$ in X. Calculate PX (3 sig. fig.).

9 In $\triangle$LMN, LM = 9 cm, MN = 11 cm, NL = 5 cm, and the internal and external bisectors of $\hat{L}$ meet $\overline{MN}$ and $\overline{MN}$ produced at A and B. Calculate AB in cm, correct to 2 dec. pl.

10 $\overline{CD}$ is a diameter of a circle, and P is a point on the circumference. X, Y are points on $\overline{CD}$, $\overline{CD}$ produced, such that $X\hat{P}D = D\hat{P}Y$. Prove that $\dfrac{CX}{DX} = \dfrac{CY}{DY}$.

*New General Mathematics*

**11** The bisector of $\hat{P}$ of $\triangle PQR$ cuts $\overline{QR}$ in X, and the median $\overline{QM}$ in Y. If $QX : XR = 4 : 3$, find the value of $QY : YM$.

**12** In $\triangle ABC$ the internal and external bisectors of $\hat{A}$ meet $\overline{BC}$ and $\overline{BC}$ produced at P and Q. Prove that B and C divide $\overline{PQ}$ in the same numerical ratio.

**13** D, E are points on the side $\overline{BC}$ of $\triangle ABC$ such that $B\hat{A}D = A\hat{C}B$ and $C\hat{A}E = D\hat{A}E$. Prove that $\dfrac{BD}{BA} = \dfrac{DE}{EC}$

**14** In $\triangle PQR$, $PQ = 8$ cm, $QR = 12$ cm, $RP = 11$ cm. S is a point on $\overline{PR}$ such that $\overline{SQ}$ bisects $\hat{Q}$. T is a point on $\overline{PQ}$ such that $\overline{TS} \parallel \overline{QR}$. Calculate PT.

**15** ABCD is a parallelogram, and E is the mid-point of $\overline{AB}$. The bisectors of $\hat{A}$, $\hat{B}$ meet $\overline{ED}$, $\overline{EC}$ at X, Y respectively. Prove that $\overline{XY}$ is parallel to $\overline{AB}$.

**16** Triangle GHK is right-angled at K, $GH = 85$ cm, $GK = 40$ cm, and the bisector of $\hat{G}$ meets $\overline{HK}$ in M. Calculate the area of $\triangle GHM$.

**17** The straight line $\overline{PRQS}$ is such that $PQ = RS$, and circles drawn on $\overline{PQ}$, $\overline{RS}$ as diameters intersect at A, B. If $\overline{AR}$ bisects $P\hat{A}Q$, prove that $PS \times RQ = PR^2$.

**18** Triangle ABC is right-angled at A, $AB = 45$ cm and $AC = 28$ cm. The bisectors of $\hat{B}$, $\hat{C}$ meet $\overline{AC}$, $\overline{AB}$ in P, Q respectively. Calculate PQ (3 sig. fig.).

**19** In no. 18, if $\overline{BP}$, $\overline{CQ}$ intersect at R, and $\overline{AR}$ produced cuts $\overline{BC}$ at X, calculate BX (3 sig. fig.).

**20** Triangle PQR is right-angled at P, $\overline{PN}$ is an altitude, and the bisector of $\hat{Q}$ meets $\overline{PR}$ at M. Prove that $\dfrac{PM}{PN} = \dfrac{MR}{PR}$.

**21** X, Y are two points on the circumference of a circle of diameter 8 cm such that the length of chord XY is 7·5 cm. Show how to construct two points A, B on the circumference such that $AX = \frac{2}{3}AY$, $BX = \frac{2}{3}BY$. Measure AX, AY, BX, BY.

**22** The quadrilateral PQRS is such that the bisectors of $P\hat{Q}R$ and $P\hat{S}R$ meet on the diagonal $\overline{PR}$. Prove that the bisectors of $Q\hat{P}S$ and $Q\hat{R}S$ meet on $\overline{QS}$.

**23** The sides $\overline{AB}$, $\overline{AC}$ of $\triangle ABC$ are produced to X, Y respectively. If the bisectors of $C\hat{B}X$, $B\hat{C}Y$ meet at Z, prove that $\overline{AZ}$ bisects $B\hat{A}C$.

**24** In $\triangle ABC$, AB = 3 cm, BC = 4 cm, $\hat{B}$ = 60°. The bisector of $\hat{A}$ meets $\overline{BC}$ at D. Calculate DC.

**25** The incentre of $\triangle ABC$ is I, and $\overline{AI}$ produced meets $\overline{BC}$ at D. Prove that $\dfrac{ID}{IA} = \dfrac{BC}{AB + AC}$.

**26** XYZ is a triangle in which XY > XZ. The mid-point of $\overline{YZ}$ is M, and the bisector of $\hat{X}$ meets $\overline{YZ}$ in A. Prove that $\dfrac{XY + XZ}{XY - XZ} = \dfrac{MZ}{MA}$.

**27** $\overline{CD}$ is a diameter of a circle, $\overline{AB}$ is a chord at right angles to $\overline{CD}$, and E is any point on the circumference. If $\overline{DE}$ cuts $\overline{AB}$ at F, prove that $\dfrac{AE}{AF} = \dfrac{BE}{BF}$.

**28** Two circles touch internally at T, and a chord $\overline{AC}$ of the outer circle touches the inner circle at B. Prove that $\dfrac{AB}{BC} = \dfrac{AT}{TC}$.

**29** $\overline{AB}$ is a diameter of a circle, and P is any point on the circumference. The perpendicular from P to $\overline{AB}$ meets $\overline{AB}$ at N, and the tangent at P meets $\overline{AB}$ (produced either way) at T. Prove that $\dfrac{NA}{AT} = \dfrac{NB}{BT}$.

**30** PQR is a triangle in which PQ = 3PR, and the bisector of $\hat{P}$ cuts $\overline{QR}$ at A. If the perpendicular from Q to $\overline{PA}$ meets $\overline{PA}$ produced at N, prove that PA = AN.

181

# Chapter 19

# *Circular measure*

When any system of measurement is found to be inconvenient for
some particular purpose, another system is generally introduced
to overcome the difficulty: for example, the French had no hesita-
tion in introducing a mass called a 'livre' (2 livre = 1 kilogramme)
when they found that the kilogramme, although an essential part
of the metric system, was rather too large for everyday affairs.
Similarly, it is unrealistic to measure distances in space in terms
of kilometres, and the unit used instead is the 'light-year' (a
distance of approximately $9 \cdot 7 \times 10^{12}$ km).

For calculations involving arcs or sectors of
circles, degrees and minutes are clumsy units,
and the **radian** is used instead. A radian is
defined as the angle which is subtended at the
centre of a circle by an arc equal in length to
the radius of the circle (Fig. 132).

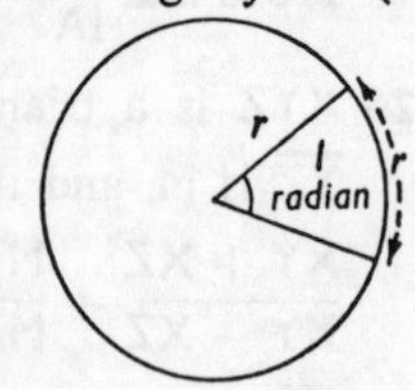

Fig. 132

Since the circumference of a circle of radius $r$ cm is $2\pi r$ cm, it
follows that the angle subtended at the centre by the arc which is
the whole circumference is $2\pi$ radians.

$$\therefore 2\pi \text{ radians} = 360 \text{ degrees.}$$
$$\therefore \pi \text{ rad} = 180°$$
$$\therefore 1 \text{ rad} = \left(\frac{180}{\pi}\right)° \simeq 57° \, 17' \, 45''.$$

*N.B.* Radians are sometimes indicated by $^c$, as degrees are
by °; the $c$ denoting 'circular measure'.

In much trigonometrical work angles are expressed in radians
and not in degrees. For example in a $\triangle$ with angles of 45°, 60°,
75°, adding to 180°, the angles are often written as $\dfrac{\pi}{4}, \dfrac{\pi}{3}, \dfrac{5\pi}{12}$, adding
to $\pi$ rad.

182

**Example 1** *Write down (i) the supplement of* $\frac{2\pi}{5}$, *(ii) the complement*

*of* $\frac{3\pi}{8}$, *(iii) the third angle of a* $\triangle$ *in which two angles are* $\frac{\pi}{6}$ *and* $\frac{2\pi}{9}$.

(i) the supplement of $\frac{2\pi}{5} = \pi - \frac{2\pi}{5} = \frac{3\pi}{5}$

(ii) the complement of $\frac{3\pi}{8} = \frac{\pi}{2} - \frac{3\pi}{8} = \frac{\pi}{8}$

(iii) the 3rd $\angle$ of the $\triangle$ =

$$\pi - \frac{\pi}{6} - \frac{2\pi}{9} = \pi\left(1 - \frac{1}{6} - \frac{2}{9}\right) = \frac{11\pi}{18}.$$

**Example 2** *Express* $80°$ *in radians, and* $1.45$ *rad in degrees and minutes, taking* $\pi = 3.142$ *(or* $\log \pi = 0.497\ 1$).

$$180° = \pi \text{ rad} = 3.142 \text{ rad}$$

$$\therefore\ 80° = \frac{80}{180} \times 3.142 \text{ rad} \eqsim 1.396 \text{ rad}$$

$$\pi \text{ rad} = 180°$$

$$\therefore\ 1.45 \text{ rad} = \frac{1.45}{\pi} \times 180°$$

$$= 83.10°$$

$$\eqsim 83°\ 6'.$$

| No. | Log. |
|---|---|
| 1·45 | 0·161 4 |
| 180 | 2·255 3 |
| | 2·416 7 |
| $\pi$ | 0·497 1 |
| 83·10 | 1·919 6 |

### Use of tables of radians and degrees

The process of turning degrees and minutes into radians is very similar to that of looking up the sine of an angle; e.g. to find the equivalent of $40°\ 16'$ in radians, $40°\ 12' = 0.701\ 6$ rad; $4' = 0.001\ 2$ rad, from the 'differences' table; therefore by addition $40°\ 16' = 0.702\ 8$ rad. Similarly an angle given in radians can be converted into degrees and minutes; e.g. $1.303\ 5$ rad $= 74°\ 41'$, etc.

Angles greater than $90°$ may be subdivided; e.g. $163°\ 25' = 80° + 83°\ 25' = (1.396\ 3 + 1.455\ 9)$ rad $= 2.852\ 2$ rad.

The following additional table will be found useful:

| | |
|---|---|
| 90° = 1·570 8 rad | 1 rad = 57° 18′ |
| 180° = 3·141 6 „ | 2 „ = 114° 36′ |
| 270° = 4·712 4 „ | 3 „ = 171° 53′ |
| 360° = 6·283 2 „ | 4 „ = 229° 11′ |

**Exercise 19a**

*Take* $\pi = 3·142$ *or log* $\pi = 0·497\ 1$.

1 Using $\pi$ rad = 180°, convert into radians as accurately as possible (i) 36° (ii) 27° 36′ (iii) 84° 42′ (iv) 146° 29′ (v) 218° 38′. Check from the radian tables.

2 As in no. 1, convert the following angles in radians into degrees and minutes: (i) 2·5 (ii) 0·530 6 (iii) 1·411 (iv) 3·647 (v) 2·084. Check from the tables.

3 Express in degrees (i) $\dfrac{\pi}{2}$ (ii) $\dfrac{\pi}{5}$ (iii) $\dfrac{\pi}{10}$ (iv) $\dfrac{2\pi}{3}$ (v) $\dfrac{3\pi}{8}$.

4 Express in radians, as fractions of $\pi$, (i) 45° (ii) 30° (iii) 20° (iv) 75° (v) 126°.

5 Write down as fractions of $\pi$ the supplements of

(i) $\dfrac{\pi}{4}$ (ii) $\dfrac{2\pi}{3}$ (iii) $\dfrac{4\pi}{7}$ (iv) $\dfrac{5\pi}{18}$ (v) $\dfrac{3\pi}{17}$.

6 As in no. 5, write down the complements of

(i) $\dfrac{\pi}{4}$ (ii) $\dfrac{\pi}{3}$ (iii) $\dfrac{\pi}{6}$ (iv) $\dfrac{\pi}{8}$ (v) $\dfrac{\pi}{9}$.

7 Write down, in terms of $\pi$, the third angles of $\triangle$s in which two angles are (i) $\dfrac{\pi}{2}, \dfrac{\pi}{3}$ (ii) $\dfrac{\pi}{4}, \dfrac{\pi}{6}$ (iii) $\dfrac{2\pi}{9}, \dfrac{4\pi}{9}$ (iv) $\dfrac{4\pi}{15}, \dfrac{\pi}{3}$ (v) $\dfrac{3\pi}{8}, \dfrac{5\pi}{16}$.

**Length of arc**

Since the length of an arc is directly proportional to the angle subtended by it at the centre, and an arc of length $r$ subtends an angle of 1 rad, it follows that

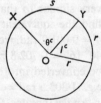

Fig. 133

$$\frac{s}{r} = \frac{\theta}{1} = \theta$$

$$\therefore s = r\theta.$$

### Area of sector

The angle subtended at the centre by the whole circumference is $2\pi$ rad: the angle subtended at the centre by the arc $XY(s)$ is $\theta$ rad.

∴ the area of the sector $XOY$ is $\dfrac{\theta}{2\pi}$ of the area of the whole circle.

∴ the area of the sector $XOY = \dfrac{\theta}{2\pi} \times \pi r^2$

$$= \tfrac{1}{2}r^2\theta.$$

Summary:　　　　　　　$\pi$ **radians** $= 180°$
**Length of arc** $= r\theta$
**Area of sector** $= \tfrac{1}{2}r^2\theta$

The simplicity of these formulae shows the reason for preferring to work in radians rather than in degrees and minutes when calculations involving arcs and sectors are required.

**Example 3** *A sector of a circle is bounded by two radii 6 cm long and an arc of length 5 cm. Find (i) the angle of the sector to the nearest minute, (ii) the area of the sector.*

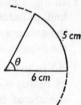

Fig. 134

Let the $\angle$ of the sector be $\theta$.

(i) Then　　　　$5 = 6\theta$　　　　$arc = r\theta$

$$\therefore \; \theta = \frac{5}{6} = 0\cdot833\,3 = 47°\,45'$$

(ii) Area of sector $(= \tfrac{1}{2}r^2\theta)$
$$= \tfrac{1}{2} \times 36 \times \tfrac{5}{6} \text{ cm}^2$$
$$= 15 \text{ cm}^2$$

**Example 4** AB *is a chord of a circle with centre O and radius 4 cm; $A\hat{O}B = 110°$. Calculate (i) the length of the minor arc AXB, (ii) the area of the sector AOBX, (iii) the area of the segment AXB.*

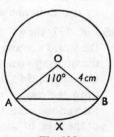

Fig. 135

(i) $\qquad A\hat{O}B = 110° = 2 \times 55° = 1.919\ 8$ rad

$\therefore$ arc AXB $= 4 \times 1.919\ 8$ cm $\qquad arc = r\theta$

$\qquad\qquad = 7.679\ 2$ cm

$\qquad\qquad \simeq 7.68$ cm

(ii) Sector AOBX $= \frac{1}{2} \times 16 \times 1.919\ 8$ cm² $\qquad sector = \frac{1}{2}r^2\theta$

$\qquad\qquad = 15.358\ 4$ cm²

$\qquad\qquad \simeq 15.36$ cm²

(iii) $\qquad \triangle AOB = \frac{1}{2} \times 16 \sin 110°$ cm² $\qquad \triangle = \frac{1}{2}bc \sin A$

$\qquad\qquad = 8 \times 0.939\ 7$ cm²

$\qquad\qquad = 7.517\ 6$ cm²

$\therefore$ area of segment AXB $= (15.358\ 4 - 7.517\ 6)$ cm²

$\qquad\qquad\qquad\qquad\quad = 7.840\ 8$ cm²

$\qquad\qquad\qquad\qquad\quad \simeq 7.84$ cm²

## Exercise 19b

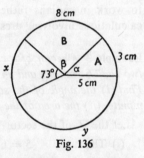
Fig. 136

1 In Fig. 136 find (i) $\alpha$, $\beta$ in degrees and minutes; (ii) the lengths of the arcs $x$ and $y$; (iii) the areas of the sectors A and B.

2 XY is an arc 8 cm long in a circle of radius 6 cm. Find the area of the sector bounded by two radii and the arc XY.

3 In no. 2 calculate the length of the chord $\overline{XY}$.

4 Find the area of a sector of a 14-cm diameter circle bounded by two radii and an arc of length 10 cm.

5 Fig. 137 shows diagrammatically where the world's cheese comes from: 56% from the sterling area, 23% from the western hemisphere, 14% home produced, and 7% from the rest of the world, the areas of the various sectors being these percentages of the area of the whole circle. Calculate in degrees and minutes the angles of the four sectors.

Fig. 137

**6** In Fig. 137 the ratio of the areas of the largest and smallest sectors is 8 : 1. What is the ratio of the lengths of the arcs of these sectors?

**7** The area of a sector of a circle is 3 cm², and the radius of the circle is 4 cm. What is the length of the arc of the sector?

**8** A spider runs round the rim of a circular clock-face 10 cm in diameter at the **angular speed** of 2 radians per second. What is the spider's **linear speed** in cm s⁻¹?

**9** At what angular speed in radians per second is the seconds hand of a watch revolving?

**10** A flywheel turns at 100 revolutions per minute. What is its angular speed in terms of π? If the radius of the wheel is 18 cm, what is the linear speed in cm s⁻¹ of a point on the rim of the wheel?

**11** A bicycle with 48-cm diameter wheels is moving at 3·6 m s⁻¹. At what angular speed in radians per second is the wheel turning? How many revolutions per minute is this, to the nearest whole number?

**12** A curved slot in a link mechanism is shown in Fig. 138. If the slot is 5 mm wide, its shorter curved edge 2 cm long, and the radius of this edge 8 cm, find the area of the slot as a fraction of a square centimetre.

Fig. 138

**13** If $\overline{AB}$ is the chord of a quadrant of an 8-cm diameter circle, find the length of the arc of the quadrant, and also the area of the minor segment cut off by $\overline{AB}$.

**14** A chord subtends an angle of 140° at the centre of a circle of radius 6 cm. Find (i) the length of the chord, (ii) the length of the minor arc cut off by the chord, (iii) the area of the minor segment cut off by the chord.

**15** $\overline{PQ}$ is a chord 8 cm long in a circle of radius 5 cm. Find the length of the minor arc PQ, and also the area of the minor segment PQ.

**16** $\overline{AB}$ is a chord 9 cm long in a circle of radius 5 cm. Find the length of the minor arc AB, and also the area of the minor segment AB.

**17** A triangle with sides 10 cm, 24 cm and 26 cm has centred at each vertex a pulley of radius 2 cm. If an endless string is stretched tightly round all three pulleys, what is its length?

**18** A piece of corrugated iron in section consists of a series of arcs, each 10 cm wide and 2·5 cm deep. If the width of the piece is one metre, how wide would it be if flattened?

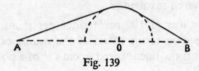

Fig. 139

**19** A railway line from A to B (Fig. 139) consists of two straight portions and a circular arc, the centre of the circle being at O on the line $\overline{AB}$, and its radius 100 m. If AO = 300 m and BO = 200 m, what is the length of the line? (The straight portions are tangents to the arc.)

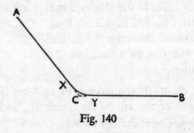

Fig. 140

**20** A tramway running from A to B (Fig. 140) consists of an arc XY of radius 100 m and two tangents $\overline{AX}$ and $\overline{BY}$ to that arc. If the tangents meet at C, and AC = CB = 400 m, and $A\hat{C}B = 130°$, what is the distance of A from B along the tramway?

**21** Two circles, each 5 cm in radius, intersect so that their centres are 8 cm apart. What is the area included in both circles?

**22** A child stands 10 m away from the nearest point of a circular pond 10 m in diameter, and runs by the shortest possible route round the pond and back to the starting point. What is the length of the run?

**23** A cylindrical pipe of diameter 10 cm is secured to a horizontal beam by a tight metal band AXB (Fig. 141), the cylinder being in the middle of the band and the distance AB being 24 cm, measured along the beam. What is the length of band from A to B?

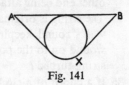

Fig. 141

**24** If the cylinder in no. 23 were replaced by a gutter of semi-circular section of diameter 10 cm, how long would the band be in this case?

**25** The centres of two pulleys of radii 5 cm and 25 cm are 50 cm apart. Find the length of a belt tightly stretched round the outside of both pulleys.

**26** As in no. 25, but with pulleys of radii 5 cm and 20 cm, their centres being 75 cm apart.

**27** If the belt in no. 26 had been crossed between the pulleys, how long would it have been?

**28** Fig. 142 shows a section of a stone bridge, the arc being part of a circle of radius 6 m. What is the area of stonework in this section?

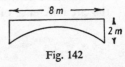

Fig. 142

**29** Find the ratios, in the form $n : 1$, in which (i) the circumference, (ii) the area of a 10-cm diameter circle is divided by a chord 8 cm long. ($n > 1$)

**30** Find in radians per second the angular velocity of a flywheel $d$ cm in diameter if a point on the rim of the wheel is travelling at $v$ cm s$^{-1}$.

**31** $l$ cm of wire is bent into an arc of a circle of radius $r$ cm. Find in radians the angle subtended at the centre of the circle by the arc (in terms of $l$ and $r$).

189

**32** $l$ cm of wire is bent so as to form the boundary of a sector of a circle of radius $r$ cm (i.e. to form two radii and an arc). Express in radians the angle between the radii in terms of $l$ and $r$.

**33** What is the area of the sector in no. 32 in terms of $l$ and $r$?

**34** A tortoise is secured to one end of a thin string $l$ m long, the other end being attached to a cylindrical post of diameter $d$ cm. The string is originally tangential to the post, and the tortoise walks round keeping the string taut until the string is fully wound on to the post. Through what angle in radians has the string turned?

**35** If a chord of a circle subtends an angle $\theta$ at the centre of the circle, and the area of the minor segment cut off by the chord is half the area of the sector defined by the chord, show that $\theta = 2 \sin \theta$.

**36** A circle of radius $x$ cm is inscribed in a sector of a circle of radius $r$ cm and angle $\theta$ (Fig. 143). Show that

$$r = x + x \operatorname{cosec} \frac{\theta}{2}.$$

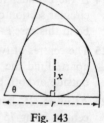

Fig. 143

**37** If, in Fig. 144, the shaded area is equal to the area of the circle, show that the perimeter of the complete figure is equal to twice the circumference of the circle.

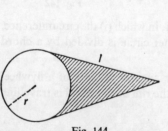

Fig. 144

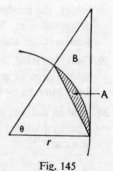

Fig. 145

**38** In Fig. 145 show that the areas A and B are respectively $\frac{1}{2}r^2(\theta - \sin \theta)$ and $\frac{1}{2}r^2(\tan \theta - \theta)$.

Deduce that $\sin \theta < \theta < \tan \theta$.

If $\theta$ is very small, show that $\dfrac{\sin \theta}{\theta}$ and $\dfrac{\tan \theta}{\theta}$ both tend towards

unity.

**39** A chord of a circle which subtends an angle of $\theta$ at the centre of the circle divides the circle into two segments such that the area of one is equal to twice the area of the other. Prove that $\theta - \sin \theta = \frac{2}{3}\pi$.

**40** Solve graphically the equation of no. 39, taking values of $\theta$ $\frac{2}{3}\pi$, $\frac{3}{4}\pi$, $\frac{5}{6}\pi$, $1\frac{1}{12}\pi$, $\pi$. Plot separately the graphs of $\theta - \frac{2}{3}\pi$ and $\sin \theta$, and give the answer in degrees.

# Chapter 20

# *Small circles and great circles*
# *Latitude and longitude*

## Small circles and great circles

In Fig. 146 the surface of a sphere, centre O, is cut by a plane
ABCD. The perpendicular
from O to the plane is $\overline{OM}$,
and P is any point on the
curve in which the plane
cuts the sphere.

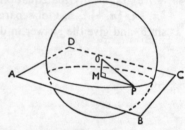

Since $\triangle OMP$ is right-
angled at M,

$$MP^2 = OP^2 - OM^2$$
$$\therefore MP = \sqrt{OP^2 - OM^2}.$$

Fig. 146

But OP is constant, since it is the radius of the sphere, and OM
is also a fixed length.

$$\therefore \text{ MP is constant.}$$
$$\therefore \text{ P lies on a circle centre M.}$$

**∴ a plane cuts a sphere in a circle whose centre is the foot of the
perpendicular from the centre of the sphere to the plane.**

The circle of intersection shown in Fig. 146 is a **small circle.** Its
radius is less than the radius of the sphere, since

$$MP^2 = OP^2 - OM^2, \text{ i.e. } MP^2 < OP^2.$$

If the plane passes through O, then M coincides with O, $\overline{MP}$
coincides with $\overline{OP}$, and the radius of the circle of intersection is
equal to the radius of the sphere. Such a circle is called a **great
circle.** Hence of all the circles which can be drawn on the surface
of the sphere, those with their centres at O are great circles.

## Latitude and longitude

The earth is approximately spherical in shape, and rotates about
its polar axis, which is a straight line joining the North and South

Poles (N and S in Fig. 147), and passing through the centre of the earth (O in Fig. 147).

If the spherical surface is cut by a plane which passes through $\overline{NOS}$, the circle of intersection is a great circle, called a **meridian** (NAS and NBS).

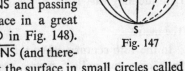

A plane perpendicular to $\overline{NS}$ and passing through O intersects the surface in a great circle called the **equator** (CLD in Fig. 148). Other planes perpendicular to $\overline{NS}$ (and therefore parallel to each other) cut the surface in small circles called **parallels of latitude** (EPF and HQK). The centres of these small circles lie on $\overline{NS}$.

Fig. 147

The position of a point on the surface of the earth is determined by the meridian and the parallel of latitude on which it lies.

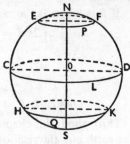

In Fig. 149, NGS is the **Greenwich Meridian**, i.e. the meridian which passes through Greenwich. This is used as the standard from which the positions of other meridians are measured, in degrees east or west. The plane of the meridian NPLS makes with the plane of NGS an angle GOL

Fig. 148

(since $\overline{OG}$ and $\overline{OL}$ are both perpendicular to $\overline{NS}$), and the number of degrees in angle GOL gives the **longitude** of P *east* of Greenwich. The longitude of P is also given by angle RXP, since $\overline{XR}$ and $\overline{XP}$ are both perpendicular to $\overline{NS}$, and angle RXP = angle GOL. Similarly the number of degrees in angle GOM gives the longitude of Q *west* of Greenwich. Longitude may vary from 180° E to 180° W.

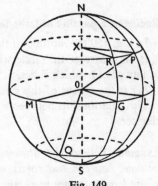

Fig. 149

The **latitude** of a point is measured in degrees north or south of the equator. The latitude of P *north* of the equator is given by the angle LOP, since the plane NPLS is perpendicular to the plane of the equator, MGL. The latitude of P is also given by the angle OPX, since angles OPX and LOP are alternate. Similarly the latitude of Q *south* of the equator is measured by the angle MOQ. Latitude may vary from 90° N to 90° S.

### The metre

In the 18th century, when the Metric System began to take its final form, ten million metres was defined as the measure of a quadrant of the earth's circumference on the meridian passing through Paris.

If $R$ is taken as the radius of the earth, then

$$\tfrac{1}{4} \text{ of } 2\pi R = 10^7 \text{ metres}$$

$$\therefore R = \frac{2 \times 10^7}{\pi} \text{ metres}$$

$$= 6 \cdot 366 \times 10^6 \text{ m} \simeq 6\,370 \text{ km}$$

$$\text{and} \quad 2\pi R = 4 \times 10^7 \text{ m} = 4 \times 10^4 \text{ km}.$$

Throughout this chapter $R$ will be taken to denote the radius of the earth and the relation

$$2\pi R = 4 \times 10^4 \text{ km}$$

will be used.

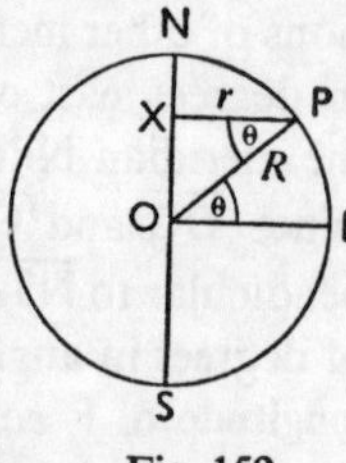

### Radius of a parallel of latitude

In Fig. 150 the latitude of the point P is $\theta$, and X is the centre of the circle which is the parallel of latitude on which P lies.

Fig. 150

If $r$ is the radius of this circle, then $r = R \cos \theta$.

This relationship between $r$ and $R$ will be used throughout this chapter.

**Example 1** *Find the distance, measured along the parallel of latitude, between two points whose latitudes are both 56° N, and whose longitudes are respectively 23° E and 17° W.*

In Fig. 151, A is the point lat. 56° N, long. 23° E; B is the point lat. 56° N, long. 17° W. C, lying on the polar axis $\overline{NS}$, is the centre

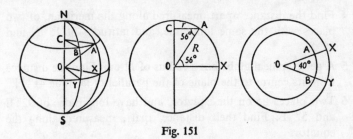

Fig. 151

of the parallel of latitude through A and B. O is the centre of the earth, and the meridians through A and B meet the equator in X and Y respectively.

$$r = R \cos 56°$$

∴ the circumference of the parallel of latitude through A and B

$$= 2\pi r$$
$$= 2\pi R \cos 56°$$

The difference between the longitudes of A and B (i.e. $\stackrel{\frown}{ACB}$ or $\stackrel{\frown}{XOY}$) = 23° + 17° = 40°

$$\therefore \text{ arc } AB = \frac{40}{360} \text{ of } 2\pi R \cos 56°$$
$$= \tfrac{1}{9} \times 4 \times 10^4 \cos 56° \text{ km}$$
$$= \tfrac{4}{9} \times 10^4 \times 0.559 \, 2 \text{ km}$$
$$\simeq 2 \, 490 \text{ km}$$

## Exercise 20a

*Take* $2\pi R = 4 \times 10^4$ *km,* $\pi$ *as* 3·142, *log* $\pi$ *as* 0·497 1.

1 On a geographical globe of radius 18 cm, find the radius of the circle formed by the parallel of latitude 56° S.

2 On a globe of radius 60 cm, find in cm the length of the parallel of latitude 67° N.

3 Two places lie on the same meridian, and have latitudes of 15° N and 36° N. Find their distance apart measured along the meridian.

4 Find the distance apart, measured along the meridian, of two places with the same longitude, and latitudes of 15° N and 36° S.

5 A geographical globe has a radius of 11 cm. Find the distance from its centre to the plane of the parallel of latitude 41° N.

6 Two places lie on the equator, and have longitudes of 92° E and 57° E. Find their distance apart, measured along the equator.

7 Two places, with longitudes of 152° E and 171° W, both lie on the equator. Find their distance apart, measured along the equator.

8 Two places have the same longitude and are 264 km apart, measured along the meridian. Find the difference between their latitudes.

9 Find the distance of a place with latitude 68° S from the axis of the earth.

10 Find the length of the parallel of latitude 42° N.

11 Find the distance apart, measured along the parallel of latitude, of two places which both have latitude 63° N, and whose longitudes differ by 1° (3 sig. fig.).

12 Find the distance, measured along the parallel of latitude, between two places with the same latitude of 18° S, and with longitudes of 96° E and 57° E.

13 Find the distance, measured along a meridian, of the South Pole from any point on the parallel of latitude 65° S.

14 Find the length of the Tropic of Capricorn (lat. 23° 30′ S).

15 Two places with the same latitude of 77° N have longitudes of 154° E and 142° W. Find their distance apart, measured along the parallel of latitude (nearest km).

16 Find the latitude at which each degree of longitude represents a distance of 50 km measured along the parallel of latitude.

**17** Oslo and Gotha have the same longitude of 10° 43′ E, and their latitudes are 59° 54′ N and 50° 56′ N respectively. Find the distance between them (nearest km).

**18** Venice is at 45° 25′ N, 12° 24′ E; Rome is at 41° 53′ N, 12° 25′ E. Find their distance apart (nearest km).

**19** Find the parallel of latitude along which a journey of 166 km makes a change of 4° in longitude (nearest degree).

**20** Havana and Canton lie on the same parallel of latitude 23° N, and their longitudes are respectively 82° 15′ W and 113° 15′ E. Find their distance apart, measured along the parallel of latitude.

**21** A place X is at 70° S, 90° E; Y is at 70° S, 90° W. Find the distance from X to Y (i) along a great circle, (ii) along the parallel of latitude.

**22** Find the distance between Brindisi, 40° 39′ N, 18° 2′ E, and Stockholm, 59° 20′ N, 18° 3′ E.

**23** Find the distance, measured along the parallel of latitude, from Aberdeen, 57° 26′ N, 2° 5′ W, to Göteburg, 57° 26′ N, 11° 59′ E (nearest km).

**24** The position of a place A is 38° N, 73° E; B is at 38° N, 107° W. Find the distance from A to B (i) along the parallel of latitude, (ii) along a great circle (3 sig. fig.).

## Longitude and time

The earth rotates from west to east. Hence a point on its surface which lies on a meridian which is to the east of the meridian through a second point will reach a given time by the sun before the second point.

Since the earth rotates once, i.e. through 360°, in 24 hours, a difference of 1 hour is caused by a difference in longitude of $\frac{360°}{24} = 15°$; and a difference in longitude of 1° makes a difference in time of $\frac{24}{360} \times 60$ minutes = 4 minutes.

For example, the longitudes of Haifa and Lucknow are 35° E and 81° E respectively.

*New General Mathematics*

Difference in longitude $= 46°$.

$\therefore$ difference in time $= \frac{46}{360}$ of 24 hours

$$= \frac{46}{15} \text{ hours}$$

$$= 3 \text{ h } 4 \text{ min}$$

Hence when it is noon in Haifa the time would be 15.04 in Lucknow, if the clocks in those places were set to agree with the sun.

To avoid confusion, clock times are arranged to be the same in specified areas. For example in Great Britain all clock times are the same as at Greenwich (based on Greenwich Mean Time, or G.M.T.).

The longitudes of Harwich and Fishguard are respectively 1° 16′ E and 4° 56′ W.

$$\text{Difference} = 6° 12′ = 6\tfrac{1}{5}°$$

$\therefore$ difference in time $= \dfrac{6\tfrac{1}{5}}{360}$ of 24 hours

$$= \frac{6\tfrac{1}{5}}{15} \times 60 \text{ minutes}$$

$$= 24\tfrac{4}{5} \text{ minutes.}$$

$\therefore$ sunset would be about 25 minutes earlier in Harwich than in Fishguard.

In Europe there is Central European Time, one hour ahead of G.M.T., and Eastern European Time, two hours ahead of G.M.T. In U.S.A. there are five time divisions, namely Atlantic, Eastern, Central, Mountain and Pacific, each an hour different from the next.

### The nautical mile

The **nautical mile** is defined as the length of arc of a great circle on the earth's surface which subtends an angle of 1′ at the centre of the earth.

From this definition the circumference of the earth

$$= 360 \times 60 \text{ nautical miles}$$
$$= 21\,600 \qquad \text{,,} \qquad \text{,,}$$
$$\therefore 21\,600 \text{ nautical miles} = 2\pi R = 4 \times 10^4 \text{ km}$$
$$\therefore 1 \text{ nautical mile} = \frac{40\,000}{21\,600} \text{ km} = 1\cdot 852 \text{ km}.$$

A speed of one nautical mile per hour is called one **knot,** and this unit of speed is used by mariners and also by airmen.

The knot is so called because a knotted cord was used to determine the speed of a sailing ship: the 'log' was thrown overboard with the cord attached to it, and a speed of 6 knots was registered when 6 knots in one minute passed through the fingers of the sailor taking the observation.

### Shortest route between two points

In Fig. 152 (i), A and B are any two points on the earth's surface. AXB is the great circle passing through A and B, and AYB is any

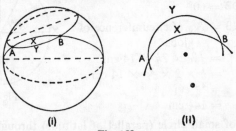

Fig. 152

small circle through A and B. The radius of the great circle is equal to the radius of the earth, and the radius of the small circle is less. It is clear in Fig. 152 (ii) that the route along the circle with the greater radius is shorter than the route along the circle with the smaller radius.

Hence the shortest route between two points on the surface of the earth is along the great circle which passes through both points.

This explains an apparent paradox which arises when considering the route taken by a vessel steaming between two ports which,

*New General Mathematics*

for example, have the same latitude and are on opposite sides of the Atlantic Ocean. On a map drawn on a projection such as Mercator's, in which the parallels of latitude appear as straight lines parallel to the equator, the shortest route seems to be along a straight line, i.e. along the parallel of latitude. In fact the shortest route lies north of this line in the northern hemisphere, and south of it in the southern hemisphere.

**Example 2** *A geographical globe has a radius of 14 cm, and* A *and* B *are two points on its surface.* A *has lat.* 60° N *and long.* 90° W. B *has lat.* 60° N *and long.* 90° E. *A piece of string stretches from* A *to* B, *passing over the North Pole. Another piece of string is placed along the parallel of latitude from* A *to* B. *Find the lengths of the two pieces of string, taking* π *to be* $\frac{22}{7}$.

In Fig. 153, X and Y are points on the equator, and O is the centre of the earth.

$$X\hat{O}A = Y\hat{O}B = 60°$$

∴ $A\hat{O}B = 60°$

∴ arc ANB = $\frac{60}{360}$ of circumference of globe

$= \frac{60}{360} \times 2\pi \times 14$ cm

$= \frac{1}{6} \times 2 \times \frac{22}{7} \times 14$ cm

$= \frac{44}{3}$ cm

$= 14\frac{2}{3}$ cm

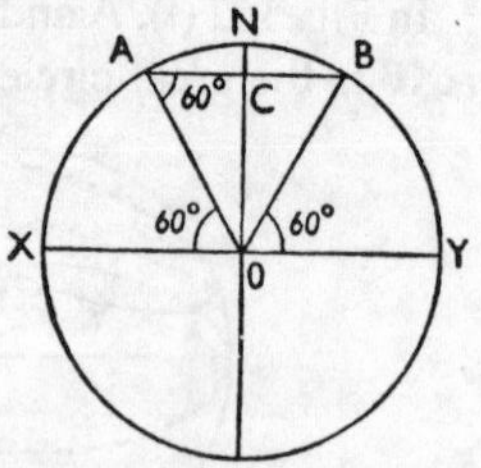

Fig. 153

Radius of small circle (parallel of latitude) through A and B is AC

$= AO \cos 60°$ cm

$= 14 \times \frac{1}{2}$ cm

$= 7$ cm

Distance from A to B along the parallel of latitude

$=$ half the circumference of this small circle

$= \frac{1}{2}$ of $2\pi \times 7$ cm

$= 22$ cm

∴ the lengths of the pieces of string are $14\frac{2}{3}$ cm and 22 cm.

**Example 3** P *and* Q *are two points on the earth's surface;* P *is the point* 48° N, 15° E, *and* Q *is* 48° N, 95° E. *Find their distance apart*

(i) *in km measured along the parallel of latitude*
(ii) *in km measured along a great circle*
(iii) *in nautical miles measured along a great circle.*

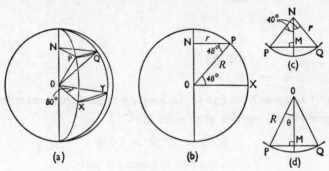

Fig. 154

(i) Distance from P to Q along parallel of latitude

$$= \text{arc PQ in Fig. 154 (c)}$$

$$= \tfrac{80}{360} \text{ of } 2\pi r$$

$$= \tfrac{2}{9} \times 2\pi R \cos 48°$$

$$= \tfrac{2}{9} \times 4 \times 10^4 \cos 48° \text{ km}$$

$$= \tfrac{8}{9} \times 10^4 \cos 48° \text{ km}$$

$$\simeq 5\,950 \text{ km}$$

| | No. | Log. |
|---|---|---|
| | $8 \times 10^4$ | 4·903 1 |
| | $\cos 48°$ | $\bar{1}$·825 5 |
| | | 4·728 6 |
| | 9 | 0·954 2 |
| | 5 948 | 3·774 4 |

(ii) From Fig. 154 (c) $\text{PM} = r \sin 40° = R \cos 48° \sin 40°$

     „    „    „ (d) $\text{PM} = R \sin \theta$

$\therefore \ \sin \theta = \cos 48° \sin 40°$

$\therefore \qquad \theta = 25° 28'$

$\therefore \ \text{P}\widehat{\text{O}}\text{Q} = 2\theta = 50° 56' = 50.93°$

| | No. | Log. |
|---|---|---|
| | $\cos 48°$ | $\bar{1}$·825 5 |
| | $\sin 40°$ | $\bar{1}$·808 1 |
| | $\sin 25° 28'$ | $\bar{1}$·633 6 |

∴ arc PQ on great circle (Fig. 154 (d))

$$= \frac{50 \cdot 93}{360} \text{ of } 2\pi R$$

$$= \frac{50 \cdot 93}{360} \times 4 \times 10^4 \text{ km}$$

$$= \frac{50 \cdot 93}{9} \times 10^3 \text{ km}$$

$$= 5\ 659 \text{ km}$$

$$\simeq 5\ 660 \text{ km}$$

(iii) Distance from P to Q along a great circle, in nautical miles, is given by the number of minutes in $P\widehat{O}Q$.

$$P\widehat{O}Q = 50° 56' = 3\ 056'$$

∴ distance = 3 056 nautical miles.

∴ the required distances are approximately

(i) 5 950 km,

(ii) 5 660 km,

(iii) 3 060 nautical miles.

*N.B.* (ii) can be derived from (iii) by using 1 nautical mile = 1·852 km

e.g.    3 056 nautical miles = 3 056 × 1·852 km

$$\simeq 5\ 660 \text{ km}$$

but the method first used is generally simpler.

| No. | Log. |
| --- | --- |
| 3 056 | 3·485 2 |
| 1·852 | 0·267 7 |
| 5 661 | 3·752 9 |

### Exercise 20b

*Take* $2\pi R = 4 \times 10^4$ *km, π as* 3·142 (*unless otherwise instructed*), *log π as* 0·497 1. *Where appropriate give distances correct to* 3 *significant figures.*

1 Find the difference in latitude of two places which are 130 nautical miles apart, and which have the same longitude.

2 Find in nautical miles the distance between two places which lie on the equator, and have longitudes of 56° W and 29° W.

**3** Find the difference between the longitudes of two places which lie on the equator, and are 320 nautical miles apart.

**4** Two places, A and B, are 210 nautical miles apart, and A is due south of B. If the latitude of A is 47° 50′ S, find the latitude of B.

Find the difference in local time of two places whose longitudes are

**5** 113° 56′ E and 48° 44′ E (nearest minute).

**6** 57° 13′ W   „   81° 36′ E ( „   „   ).

**7** 53° 36′ W   „   55° 26′ W ( „   second).

**8** 1° 5′ E   „   1° 7′ W ( „   „   ).

**9** 47° 51′ W   „   65° 27′ E ( „   minute).

**10** 63° 19′ E   „   146° 23′ W ( „   „   ).

**11** Two places lying on the equator have longitudes of 162° E and 169° W. Find the distance between them in nautical miles.

**12** Find in nautical miles the distance, measured along a meridian, of the South Pole from any point on the parallel of latitude 58° S.

**13** A place P is due north of a place Q, and they are 590 nautical miles apart. If the latitude of P is 3° 20′ N, find the latitude of Q.

**14** A vessel leaves Cape Verde, latitude 15° 45′ N, and steams due south for 50 hours at 25 knots. What is then its latitude?

**15** The longitudes of Oxford and Llandaff are respectively 1° 15′ W and 3° 14′ W. If the sun sets at 19.16 G.M.T. at Oxford, at what time is sunset at Llandaff (nearest minute)?

For the following pairs of places, find the difference in local time. Find also, to the nearest km, their distance apart measured along the parallel of latitude.

**16** Waterford 52° 14′ N, 7° 6′ W; Cambridge 52° 14′ N, 0° 7′ E.

**17** Yarmouth 52° 36′ N, 1° 43′ E; Wolverhampton 52° 36′ N, 2° 7′ W.

**18** Belfast 54° 35′ N, 5° 56′ W; Stockton 54° 35′ N, 1° 18′ W.

**19** A, B are two points on the equator, and their longitudes differ by 78° 26'. Find
  (i) the difference between local times at A and B (nearest minute)
  (ii) the distance AB measured along the equator in km
  (iii) the distance AB measured along the equator in nautical miles.

**20** X, Y are two points with the same longitude, and latitudes which differ by 56° 12'. Find
  (i) the distance XY measured along the meridian in km
  (ii) the distance XY measured along the meridian in nautical miles.

**21** A, B are two points on the earth's surface, O is the centre of the earth, and AÔB = 64° 36'. Find the distance from A to B along a great circle (i) in km, (ii) in nautical miles.

**22** O is the centre of the earth, P and Q are two points on the surface, and PÔQ = 82° 48'. Find
  (i) the distance PQ measured along a great circle in km
  (ii) the distance PQ measured along a great circle in nautical miles.

**23** P and Q are two points on a geographical globe of radius $17\frac{1}{2}$ cm. P is the point 63° 18' N, 97° 30' E; Q is the point 63° 18' N, 82° 30' W. Taking $\pi$ to be $\frac{22}{7}$, find in cm correct to 3 sig. fig.
  (i) the length of the chord PQ
  (ii) the distance from P to Q along a great circle
  (iii) the distance from P to Q along the parallel of latitude.

**24** On a geographical globe of radius 21 cm, A and B are two points on the parallel of latitude 30° S. Their longitudes are 50° W and 130° E respectively. A piece of thread is stretched over the South Pole and joins A to B. Find the length of the thread. If the thread is now stretched along the parallel of latitude 30° S running east from A, with one end at A, find to the nearest half-degree the longitude of the point reached by the other end of the thread. (Take $\pi = \frac{22}{7}$.)

25 Colombo is at 6° 54′ N, 79° 49′ E. Georgetown is at 6° 54′ N, 58° 11′ W. Find the difference in local time of these two places and also their distance apart in km by the shortest possible route on the earth's surface.

26 P and Q are two places with the same latitude 63° N, and with longitudes 140° W and 150° E respectively. Find the distance from P to Q measured along the parallel of latitude. Find also their distance apart measured along a great circle. (Both answers in km.)

27 Two points X and Y lie on the same parallel of latitude 44° S, and their longitudes are respectively 90° E and 130° E. Find in km the shortest distance from X to Y measured on the surface of the earth. Find also the same distance in nautical miles.

28 A is the point 72° N, 20° W; B is the point 72° N, 80° W. Find in km the distance from A to B measured (i) along the parallel of latitude, (ii) along a great circle. Find also the distance along a great circle in nautical miles.

29 The position of Bergen is 60° N, 5° E; Cape Chidley, Labrador, is 60° N, 65° W. Find the difference in local time between these two places. Find also in km the distance between them (i) by parallel of latitude, (ii) by great circle. How many nautical miles would it be by great circle?

30 Sydney and Valparaiso have the same latitude 33° 30′ S, and their longitudes are respectively 151° 8′ E and 71° 38′ W. Find their distance apart

  (i) measured along a great circle (km)

  (ii)    „      „   „ „    „    (nautical miles)

  (iii)    „       „    the parallel of latitude (km).

# Chapter 21

# *Harder trigonometrical problems*

**Example 1** *From a point A the elevation of the top of a mountain is 35° 18', and from a point B 2 000 m nearer the mountain in a straight line from A the elevation is 62° 5'. Find the height to 3 sig. fig.*

From Fig. 155

$$2\,000 + x = h \cot 35°\,18' = 1{\cdot}412\,4h$$
$$x = h \cot 62°\ \ 5' = 0{\cdot}529\,9h$$
$$\therefore\ \ \overline{2\,000} \qquad\qquad\qquad = \overline{0{\cdot}882\,5h}$$
$$\therefore\ \ h = \frac{2\,000}{0{\cdot}882\,5}$$
$$\therefore\ \text{height} \simeq 2\,270 \text{ m}$$

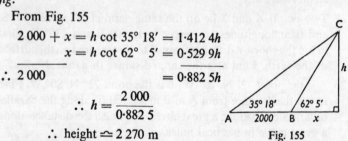

Fig. 155

*Alternative method.*

In $\triangle$ABC,

$$A\widehat{C}B = 62°\,5' - 35°\,18' = 26°\,47',\ BC = h \operatorname{cosec} 62°\,5'$$

$\therefore$ by sine formula

$$\frac{h \operatorname{cosec} 62°\,5'}{\sin 35°\,18'} = \frac{2\,000}{\sin 26°\,47'}$$
$$\therefore\ h = 2\,000 \sin 35°\,18' \sin 62°\,5' \operatorname{cosec} 26°\,47'$$
$$= 2\,266$$
$$\therefore\ \text{height} \simeq 2\,270 \text{ m}$$

| No. | Log. |
|---|---|
| 2 000 | 3·301 0 |
| sin 35° 18' | $\bar{1}$·761 8 |
| sin 62°  5' | $\bar{1}$·946 2 |
| cosec 26° 47' | 0·346 2 |
| 2 266 | 3·355 2 |

**Example 2** *From a point A due west of a wireless-mast the elevation of the top of the mast is 34°, and from a point B due south of the mast the elevation is 28½°. If the distance AB is 750 m what is the height of the mast?*

Let the height of mast be $h$ m.

Then $AD = h \cot 34°$ m,

$BD = h \cot 28\frac{1}{2}°$ m,

$AB = 750$ m and $A\hat{D}B = 90°$.

$\therefore\ 750^2 = (h \cot 34°)^2 + (h \cot 28\frac{1}{2}°)^2$

$= h^2[1 \cdot 482\ 6^2 + 1 \cdot 841\ 8^2]$

$= h^2[2 \cdot 197 + 3 \cdot 393]$

$= h^2 \times 5 \cdot 590$

$\therefore\ h^2 = \dfrac{750^2}{5 \cdot 590}$

$\therefore\ h = 317 \cdot 3$

$\therefore$ height $\simeq 317$ m

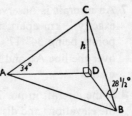

Fig. 156

| No. | Log. |
|---|---|
| $750^2$ | $2 \cdot 875\ 1 \times 2$ |
|  | $= 5 \cdot 750\ 2$ |
| $5 \cdot 590$ | $0 \cdot 747\ 4$ |
|  | $5 \cdot 002\ 8 \div 2$ |
| $317 \cdot 3$ | $= 2 \cdot 501\ 4$ |

## Exercise 21

In Fig. 157 find to 3 sig. fig. the lengths marked $h$, all dimensions being in metres.

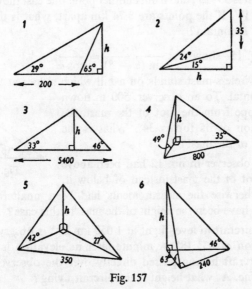

Fig. 157

**7** An aircraft is observed from two points A and B which are exactly 2 km apart, the elevation of the aircraft from these points being 34° 17′ and 51° 34′. If the aircraft is vertically over the line $\overline{AB}$ and is between A and B, what is its height in metres?

**8** If the aircraft in no. 7 had been vertically over $\overline{AB}$ produced, the elevations and distance AB being unaltered, what would its height have been then?

**9** A ship steaming due East at 20 km h⁻¹ is observed by a coast-guard on the beach to be on a bearing N 67° W; a quarter of an hour later her bearing is N 9° W. What is the shortest distance between the ship and the coastguard?

**10** From a point on the top of a cliff two buoys 880 m apart are visible, one being NE and the other NW of the point. If the angles of depression of the buoys are respectively 24° 15′ and 30° 23′, find the height of the cliff in metres.

**11** From a point due north of a mountain the elevation of its summit is 35° 23′, and from another point due east the elevation is 41° 17′. If the points are 3·74 km apart, what is the height of the mountain?

**12** In Fig. 158 show that $\dfrac{h}{\sin(\alpha - \beta)} = \dfrac{x}{\cos \alpha}$.

A wireless-mast stands on a hill which slopes at 9° to the horizontal. To an observer 500 m down the slope from the foot of the mast, the elevation of its top is 34°. What is the height of the mast?

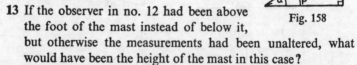

Fig. 158

**13** If the observer in no. 12 had been above the foot of the mast instead of below it, but otherwise the measurements had been unaltered, what would have been the height of the mast in this case?

**14** A jet aircraft in level flight at 1 050 km h⁻¹ is observed at an elevation of 63° 18′. A minute later its elevation is 38° 34′, the aircraft having passed directly over the observer during this time. At what height is the aircraft flying?

**15** The angle of elevation of the top of a cathedral spire due north of the observer is 22° 18': if the observer walks 150 m due west the elevation is then 17° 32'. What is the height of the spire?

**16** From a boat due east of a 100-metre cliff the top of the cliff is at an angle of elevation 30° 34'. What will be the angle of elevation when the boat has moved 200 m due south from its present position?

**17** A boy scout estimates that the angle of elevation of the top of a church spire is 34°, while the reflection of the top of the spire in a lake between him and the spire is at an angle of depression of 38°. Assuming that the scout's eye is 1·5 m above the ground, calculate the height of the spire.

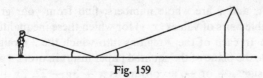

Fig. 159

**18** From the top of a 300-metre radio mast two farmhouses can be seen, both of them at an angle of depression of 35°. If the bearing of one of the farmhouses from the tower is due north and of the other 73° east of north, how far apart are the farmhouses?

**19** An aircraft is flying due west at a constant height and at a speed of 750 km h⁻¹. When first spotted it is due east of an observer and at an elevation of 63°: half a minute later it is due west and at an elevation of 28°. What is its height?

**20** From A, a point on level ground due north of a mountain, the elevation of the top of the mountain is 64°: from B, due west of the mountain and at the same level as A, the elevation is 28°. What is the bearing of A from B?

If A and B are 3 km apart, how high is the mountain (in metres, to 3 sig. fig.)?

# Revision examples

1 Find the factors of the expression $3x^2 + 16x + 21$, and hence find the two prime factors of the number 31 621. (C)

2 On the same sheet of graph paper and with the same axes and scales draw the graphs of the straight lines
$x + 3y - 22 = 0$, $2x + y - 10 = 0$ and $x - y = 0$
for *positive values* of $x$ and $y$.

(Choose a conveniently large scale, but the three intersections of the lines should appear on your graph.)

(i) Shade in the region within which $x + 3y - 22 < 0$, $2x + y - 10 > 0$ and $x - y < 0$.

If $x$ and $y$ are whole numbers, find from your graph the possible pairs of values $(x, y)$ for which these inequalities hold.

(ii) In each of the 7 regions into which the 3 straight lines divide the plane of the squared paper insert in order a sequence of 3 signs, $+$ or $-$, according as $x + 3y - 22$, $2x + y - 10$ and $x - y$ are each positive or negative (e.g. the region given in section (i) will be $- + -$). State the one sequence of signs that you have not used and say what you can deduce about the possible values of $x$ and $y$ which satisfy the corresponding three inequalities. (O)

3 Prove that equiangular triangles have their corresponding sides in the same proportion.

XYZK is a rectangle having $XY = a$ cm and $YZ = b$ cm. If P is the mid-point of $\overline{YZ}$, show that the perpendicular distance

of K from $\overline{XP}$ is $\dfrac{2ab}{\sqrt{4a^2 + b^2}}$ cm. (L)*

4 The centre of a circle of radius 9 cm is O, and P is a point 12 cm from O. A line $\overline{PAB}$ meets the circle in A and B and makes an angle of 29° with $\overline{PO}$. Calculate (i) the angle OBA, (ii) the length of the chord AB in centimetres, correct to three significant figures. (N)*

5 The volume of metal in a tube is given in cubic centimetres by the formula $V = \pi a\{R^2 - (R - t)^2\}$, where $a$ cm is the length, R cm the outside radius, $t$ cm the thickness of the metal. Find the value of V when $a = 8\cdot6$, R $= 2\cdot75$, $t = 0\cdot8$, $\pi = 3\cdot142$, giving your answer to three significant figures.

Use the same formula to express R in terms of $\pi$, V, $t$ and $a$.
(*OC*)*

6 Prove that the angle subtended by an arc of a circle at the centre is double the angle subtended by the same arc at any point on the remainder of the circumference.

A, B, C and D are points on a circle whose centre is O. $\overline{AB}$ and $\overline{DC}$ are produced to meet beyond B and C at X. $\overline{AC}$ and $\overline{BD}$ meet inside the circle at Y. Prove that $A\hat{X}D + A\hat{Y}D = A\hat{O}D$.
(*W*)

7 (i) A square field has an area of $2\frac{1}{2}$ hectares. What is the length of a side in metres, to the nearest metre?

(ii) Find the area contained between two concentric circles whose radii are $4\cdot8$ cm and $3\cdot8$ cm, taking $\pi = 3\frac{1}{7}$. (*L*)*

8 A ship leaves a port P which lies in latitude 20° N. It sails due east through 30° of longitude and then due south to Q, which lies on the equator. Calculate the distance it has travelled. (Take the circumference of the earth to be 40 000 km.)

On the return journey it sails due west through 30° of longitude and then due north back to P. Show that the difference in length between the outward and return journeys is approximately 201 kilometres.

Using this value of 201 km and taking 1 knot to be $1\cdot852$ km h$^{-1}$, calculate the difference in time between the two journeys, assuming that on each journey the ship sails at an average speed of 25 knots.
(*C*)*

9 Two years ago my age was $4\frac{1}{2}$ times that of my son. Six years ago my age was twice the square of his age. Find his present age.
(*N*)

**10** A pyramid, on a square base of side 10 cm, is 12 cm in height. Calculate

   (i) its total surface area

   (ii) the length of a slant edge

   (iii) the inclination of a face to the base.     (*OC*)

## XXII

**1** The price of an article in a shop window is marked as £23·40 plus £3·90 purchase tax. Express the purchase tax as a percentage of the untaxed price.

Another article is marked £35·70 (including purchase tax). What is the amount of the tax on the second article if the purchase tax is charged at the same rate as on the first article?

What would be the new cash price of the first article if the untaxed price rose by 15 per cent and the rate of tax were $8\frac{1}{3}$ per cent?     (*W*)*

**2** In the quadrilateral ABCD, $\overline{BA}$ is parallel to $\overline{CD}$ and AB + CD = BC. The bisector of angle ABC meets $\overline{AD}$ at X, and $\overline{CD}$ produced at E. Prove that (i) BX = XE, (ii) $\overline{CX}$ bisects angle BCD, (iii) angle BXC = 90°.     (*N*)

**3** (i) Express as a single fraction in its simplest form

$$\frac{x + 2y}{20} - \frac{3x - 2y}{12} - (y - x).$$

   (ii) Simplify $6(a - b)^2 \div 4(b^3 - a^3)$.     (*C*)

**4** Prove the formula $\dfrac{a}{\sin A} = \dfrac{b}{\sin B} = \dfrac{c}{\sin C}$ for an obtuse-angled triangle.

If A = 30°, $a$ = 5·6 cm, $c$ = 7·4 cm, find the value of sin C. What two values of C does this give?     (*W*)*

**5** Prove that the angles between a chord of a circle and the tangent at one extremity of the chord are equal to the angles in the alternate segments.

ABCD is a cyclic quadrilateral, and $\overline{AB}$ and $\overline{DC}$ are produced to meet at P. A circle is drawn to circumscribe the triangle PAC, and $\overline{PQ}$ is drawn parallel to $\overline{DB}$. Prove that $\overline{PQ}$ is a tangent to the circle PAC. (*L*)

**6** A bag contains 5 balls of which 3 are red and 2 are white.

(i) If a ball is drawn at random what is the probability that it will be red?

(ii) A ball is drawn and not replaced and a second ball is drawn. What is the probability that both are red?

(iii) A ball is drawn and replaced and a second ball is drawn. What is the probability that both are red?

(iv) If 3 drawings are made in succession, *without replacement*, what are the probabilities that (i) all are red, (ii) at least one is white? (*O*)

**7** A man takes 3 h 18 min. longer to walk a distance of 24 km than a boy takes to cycle the same distance. The average speed of the cyclist is 11 km h$^{-1}$ more than that of the man. Find the speed of the man. (*OC*)*

**8** If the angle BAC of triangle ABC is bisected and the bisector cuts the side $\overline{BC}$ in D, prove that $\dfrac{AB}{AC} = \dfrac{BD}{DC}$.

E is the middle point of the side $\overline{AC}$ of triangle ABC. The internal bisector of the angle BAC cuts $\overline{BE}$ in Q. $\overline{BK}$ is drawn parallel to $\overline{QC}$ meeting $\overline{AC}$ produced in K.

Prove that CK = AB. (*O*)

**9** A thin hemispherical bowl is suspended from a point by three strings, each 60 cm long, attached to three points on the rim of the bowl at the vertices of an equilateral triangle. The angle between each pair of strings is 90°. **Either** by drawing and measurement, **or** by calculation, find the diameter of the bowl. (*OC*)*

**10** Draw the graph of $2 + 4x - 3x^2$ between $x = -2$ and $x = +3$. By drawing a further graph, find as accurately as you can the values of $x$ for which $2 + 4x - 3x^2$ is greater than $-1\frac{1}{2} + 2x$. Obtain also the value of $x$ for which $2 + 4x - 3x^2$ is a maximum, giving your answer as accurately as your graph will allow. (*L*)

## XXIII

**1** ABC is an acute-angled triangle. D is the foot of the perpendicular from A to $\overline{BC}$; P is the foot of the perpendicular from D to $\overline{AB}$; Q is the foot of the perpendicular from D to $\overline{AC}$. Prove that (i) the points A, P, D, Q are concyclic, (ii) angle APQ = angle ACB, (iii) the points P, Q, C, B are concyclic.

(*OC*)

**2** If $bc + 1 = c^2$ and $a = \dfrac{1}{b} - \dfrac{1}{bc}$, express (i) $b$ in terms of $c$,

(ii) $a$ in terms of $c$ in its simplest form. (*C*)

**3** (i) If $R = \begin{pmatrix} 2 & 2 \\ 1 & 3 \end{pmatrix}$ determine $R^2$ and the inverse of R.

(ii) If $A = \begin{pmatrix} 0 & 1 \\ 1 & 0 \end{pmatrix}$, $B = \begin{pmatrix} 2 & 0 \\ 0 & 2 \end{pmatrix}$ and $C = AB$ evaluate the matrix C. Does $BA = C$?

The line segment $\overline{PQ}$, where the co-ordinates of P and Q are given by the column matrices $\begin{pmatrix} 2 \\ 1 \end{pmatrix}$, $\begin{pmatrix} 4 \\ 2 \end{pmatrix}$ respectively, is transformed by this matrix C into the line segment $\overline{P'Q'}$. Show that the transformation consists of a reflection in a line and a stretch. State the equation of the line of reflection and the magnitude of the stretch.

Write down a matrix D which would effect a reflection in $y = -x$ and a stretch of magnitude $k$. (*O*)

**4** From the top T of a tower $\overline{PT}$ the angle of elevation of the top S of a wireless mast $\overline{QS}$ is 30°. The tower is 30 m high and the distance PQ is 50 m. O is a point on the ground 50 m from P such that angle OPQ is 80°. Find the height QS, the distance OQ, and the angle of elevation of S from O. (*N*)*

**5** Prove that the ratio of the areas of similar triangles is equal to the square of the ratio of corresponding sides.

ABC is a triangle right-angled at B, and $\overline{BD}$ is the perpendicular from B to $\overline{AC}$. Prove that $\dfrac{AB^2}{BC^2} = \dfrac{AD}{DC}$. (*W*)

**6** (i) A farmer sold a horse at a gain of 20 per cent on the original cost. If he had received £15 less, he would have lost 10 per cent on the transaction. Find the original cost of the horse.

(ii) A rectangular steel safe, including the door, is made of steel 5 cm thick, the external dimensions of the safe being 120 cm by 120 cm by 50 cm. If the specific gravity of steel is 7·83, find the mass of the safe in tonnes (correct to two places of decimals). (L)*

**7** (a) Find, correct to two places of decimals, the roots of the equation $3x^2 - 11x + 3 = 0$.

(b) Solve the simultaneous equations $x^2 + xy - 10 = 0$, $4y - 3x = 6$. (N)

**8** P and Q are two points on a geographical globe of diameter 50 cm. They both lie on the parallel of latitude 50° N. P has longitude 90° W and Q has longitude 90° E. A piece of string, AB, has one end A on P; the other end B just reaches Q when the string is stretched over the North pole. Calculate the length of the string.

If, instead, the string, with the end A still on P, is laid along the parallel 50° N running East from P, calculate the longitude of the point reached by the end B. (O)*

**9** Define a tangent to a circle.

Prove that the two tangents drawn to a circle from an external point are equal in length.

A quadrilateral PQRS is circumscribed about a circle whose centre is O.

Prove that (i) PQ + RS = PS + RQ,

(ii) $P\hat{O}Q + R\hat{O}S = 180°$. (L)

**10** On a certain aerodrome the number of minutes elapsing between the time of landing of an aircraft and the time when it is ready to fly again is noted for 100 aircraft, the distribution being as shown:

| Time (minutes) | 4– | 8– | 12– | 16– | 20– | 24– | 28–32 |
|---|---|---|---|---|---|---|---|
| No. of aircraft | 1 | 7 | 26 | 38 | 22 | 5 | 1 |

Draw a histogram for this distribution. State the modal class and the percentage of aircraft taking longer than 20 min for recovery. (*MEI*)

## XXIV

1 (i) A man sells an article for £1·26 at a loss of $12\frac{1}{2}$ per cent on the cost price. What was the cost price of the article?

(ii) A man has a gross income of £1400 on which he pays tax at the average rate of 15p in the pound. If his gross income increases by 15 per cent and the rate of tax increases to an average of 20 p in the pound, what is the percentage gain or loss of net income? (*L*)

2 $\overline{AB}$ is a diameter of a circle. A chord $\overline{AP}$ produced meets the tangent at B at T. The tangent at P meets $\overline{BT}$ at R. $\overline{BL}$ is drawn parallel to $\overline{AP}$ to meet $\overline{PR}$ at L. Prove that (i) PR = RT, (ii) BL = PT. (*N*)

3 A road sign is a vertical equilateral triangle with its base parallel to the ground. When the sun is directly behind the triangle and at an altitude of 75°, the shadow cast on the ground is an isosceles triangle. Calculate the size of one of the base angles of this triangle. (*OC*)

4 If the fares on a certain line were raised $\frac{1}{2}$p per kilometre, the distance a passenger could travel for £2·40 would be 16 km less than at present. Find the present cost of travel per km.
(*C*)*

5 The cost of silver-plating articles of a given shape is the sum of two parts, of which one is constant, whatever the size of the article, and the other varies as the square of the height of each article. It costs $18\frac{1}{2}$p to plate one of these articles 10 cm high and 56p to plate one 20 cm high. What will it cost to plate one 14 cm high, and how high will articles be which cost 24p each to plate? (*O*)*

6 Prove that the internal bisector of an angle of a triangle divides the opposite side in the ratio of the sides which contain the angle.

ABC is a triangle with M the mid-point of $\overline{BC}$. X and Z are points in $\overline{AB}$ and $\overline{AC}$ such that $\overline{XM}$ and $\overline{ZM}$ bisect the angles AMB and AMC respectively. Prove that $\overline{XZ}$ is parallel to $\overline{BC}$.

(*W*)

7 A regular decagon (ten-sided figure) is inscribed in a circle of radius 6 cm. Calculate with the help of your tables

  (i) the length of one side of the decagon
  (ii) the length of the perpendicular from the centre of the circle to one side
  (iii) the area of the decagon.

(Give each of your results to 3 significant figures.)    (*OC*)*

8 Draw the graph of $y = 2x^2 - 7x - 3$ for values of $x$ from $-1$ to 4, taking 2 cm as the unit for $x$ and 1 cm as the unit for $y$.

  Using the same axes and the same scales draw the graph of $y = -x$. Use your graphs to find approximate roots of the equations

  (*a*) $2x^2 - 7x - 3 = 0$,  (*b*) $2x^2 - 6x - 3 = 0$.    (*N*)*

9 Prove that the straight line joining the mid-points of two sides of a triangle is parallel to the third side and equal to half of it.

  ABCD is a quadrilateral and E, F, G and H are respectively the mid-points of $\overline{AB}$, $\overline{AC}$, $\overline{CD}$ and $\overline{BD}$. Prove that EFGH is a parallelogram.    (*L*)

10 In a certain year the income tax paid by a married man with one child was calculated as follows: One-fifth of his total income and a further sum of £240 were allowed free of tax. The remainder of the income was classed as taxable income: tax was charged on the first £50 of it at 15p in the pound, on the next £200 at 30p in the pound, and on the rest at the standard rate of 45p in the pound. If the man's total income was £1 260 calculate the total tax he paid on it, and find to the nearest penny the average rate in the pound it represented on the total income.    (*W*)*

## XXV

**1** (*a*) The sine of an acute angle A is $\frac{15}{17}$. *Without using tables*, calculate tan A and cos $(180° - A)$.

(*b*) ABC is a triangle with an obtuse angle at C. $\overline{AD}$ is the perpendicular from A to $\overline{BC}$ produced. If sin $A\widehat{C}D = \frac{3}{5}$, and sin $A\widehat{B}D = \frac{5}{13}$, and BC is 640 m, calculate AD *without using tables*. (*N*)*

**2** The diagonal $\overline{AC}$ of the convex quadrilateral ABCD divides it into two triangles ABC and ADC of equal area. Prove that $\overline{AC}$ bisects $\overline{BD}$

If, in addition, $\overline{AB}$ is parallel to $\overline{DC}$, prove that $\overline{BD}$ divides the quadrilateral into two triangles of equal area. (*N*)

**3** (i) Factorise: (*a*) $6x^2 + 5x - 6$, (*b*) $x^3 + 8y^3$.

(ii) Express as a single fraction in its simplest form

$$\frac{1}{x - 2} + \frac{2x - 1}{2x^2 - 3x - 2} - \frac{2}{2x + 1}.$$ (*L*)

**4** A man bought a house and, in addition, spent a sum equal to 15 per cent of the purchase price on improvements. A year later he sold the house for £5 796, making a profit of 12 per cent on his total outlay. Find the price he paid for the house. (*OC*)

**5** Prove that the area of a triangle is $\frac{1}{2}bc$ sin A.

A circle has radius 4 cm; a chord of length 6 cm divides it into two segments. Calculate the area of the minor segment. (*W*)

**6** Prove that angles in the same segment of a circle are equal.

Perpendiculars $\overline{AD}$ and $\overline{BE}$ are drawn from the vertices A and B of a triangle ABC, inscribed in a circle, to meet the opposite sides $\overline{BC}$ and $\overline{CA}$ in D and E. If P is the point of intersection of $\overline{AD}$ and $\overline{BE}$, and if $\overline{AD}$ is produced to meet the circumference of the circle in Q, prove that D is the mid-point of $\overline{PQ}$. (*L*)

**7** (i) Solve the equation $2x^2 - 5x = 4$, giving each root correct to two decimal places.

(ii) Solve the simultaneous equations

$$8x^2 - 6xy + 1 = 0, \quad 2x + 3y = 4. \qquad (W)$$

**8** A playing-field has an area of 3·8 hectares. Calculate the amount of rain falling on the field during a fall of 13·5 mm. Give your answer in tonnes to the nearest tonne. $(O)^*$

**9** The fee per person at a certain school consists of two parts, the first proportional to the number of lessons given and the second inversely proportional to the number in the class. If the fee for 3 lessons with a class of 4 is £2·40, while that for 8 lessons with a class of 6 is £5·20, what will be the fee for 5 lessons with a class of 8? $(C)^*$

**10** (i) In the figure the equation of the curve is $y^2 = 4x$ and the equation of the line is $x + y = 8$. Draw a rough sketch of the figure and shade the area for which

$$y \geqslant 0, \quad x + y \leqslant 8, \quad y^2 \leqslant 4x.$$

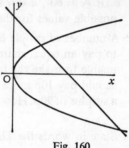

Fig. 160

(ii) A factory employs both men and women, more than one-third of the workers being women. The men are each paid £30 per week and the women £24. The average output of a man and of a woman are in the ratio 7 : 5. If the total weekly wage bill is not to exceed £480, find the numbers of men and women to be employed to achieve a maximum output. $(MEI)^*$

## XXVI

**1** (i) Find the remainder when $3x^3 + x^2 + 24$ is divided by $x + 2$.

(ii) When the expression $x^3 + 3x^2 + px + q$ is divided by $x - 3$, the remainder is 42; when the expression is divided by $x + 1$, the remainder is $-2$. Find $p$ and $q$. $(C)$

**2** $\overline{\text{TX}}$ is a tangent to a circle at X, and $\overline{\text{TYZ}}$ is another line cutting the circle at Y, Z; prove that
  (i) the triangles TXZ, TYX are similar
  (ii) $XY^2 : XZ^2 = TY : TZ$. (*OC*)

**3** The vertical section of a haystack perpendicular to its length is a rectangle of width 5 m and height 4 m, surmounted by an isosceles triangle; the greatest height of the stack is 6 m and its length is 10 m. The sloping parts are thatched. Calculate
  (i) the mass of hay in the stack, correct to the nearest tonne, if the mass of 1 m³ of hay is 120 kg.
  (ii) the area thatched, correct to the nearest square metre.(*N*)*

**4** Prove the formula $a^2 = b^2 + c^2 - 2bc \cos A$ for the cases in which A is an acute angle.
  If $A = 60°$, $a = 7$ cm, $b = 8$ cm, show that there are two possible values for the side $c$ and find them. (*W*)*

**5** A number of people hired a coach for an outing, each person to pay an equal share of the cost of £18. Three people were unable to make the trip, and the remainder agreed that each should pay 10p more than the original share. This resulted in a surplus of 90p. How many people actually made the journey?
  (*W*)*

**6** State in words the Theorem of Pythagoras for a right-angled triangle.
  The diagonals $\overline{\text{AC}}$ and $\overline{\text{BD}}$ of a quadrilateral are at right angles to each other. Prove that $AB^2 + CD^2 = AD^2 + BC^2$.
  Prove the converse: that if PQRS is a quadrilateral in which $PQ^2 + RS^2 = QR^2 + SP^2$, then $\overline{\text{PR}}$ and $\overline{\text{QS}}$ intersect at right angles. (A suggested method is to let $\overline{\text{PM}}$ and $\overline{\text{RN}}$ be the perpendiculars from P and R to $\overline{\text{QS}}$ and to prove that $SN = SM$.)
  (*S*)

**7** The following list defines a number of transformations:
  R is a rotation of 90° anticlockwise about the origin.
  H is a rotation of 180° about the origin.
  $M_x$ is a reflection in the $x$ axis.
  $M_y$ is a reflection in the $y$ axis.

$T_x$ is a translation of 2 units parallel to the $x$ axis.

$T_y$ is a translation of 2 units parallel to the $y$ axis.

The ends A and B of a line segment have co-ordinates (2, 0) and (2, 4) respectively. Show, by clear diagrams, that the effect of the transformation

$$T_x M_y T_y R$$

is to move $\overline{AB}$ to a position $\overline{BC}$. State the co-ordinates of C.

Show also that $RT_y M_y T_x$ produces a different result but that $KRT_y M_y T_x$ will transform $\overline{AB}$ to $\overline{BC}$ if K is one of the transformations in the list above. Which transformation is K?

(*O*)

8 A rectangular plate of sides 6 cm and 4 cm is placed in a hemispherical bowl of radius 5 cm so that each corner is in contact with the bowl. Find, **either** by drawing and measurement **or** by calculation, (i) the radius of the circular section containing the plate, (ii) the distance of the centre of this section from the centre of the hemisphere. (*OC*)*

9 (i) Show, with proof, how to construct the two tangents from an external point to a circle, and prove that the tangents are equal.

(ii) $\overline{AB}$ is a straight line 5 cm long and $\overline{BC}$ is drawn such that $\widehat{ABC} = 40°$. Draw as accurately as you can the circle passing through A and B and touching $\overline{BC}$ at B. State briefly your construction and measure the radius of the circle. (*L*)*

10 Draw the graph of $y = x^2 + 3x - 3$ for values of $x$ between $-4$ and $+1$, taking 2 cm as unit for $x$ and for $y$.

Find from your graph (i) the value of $x$ for which $y$ is least, and (ii) the approximate values of $x$ which satisfy the equation $x^2 + 3x - 3 = 0$. (*L*)*

## XXVII

1 Construct a pentagon ABCDE for which AB = 6 cm, $\widehat{ABC} = 90°$, BC = 4 cm, EA = 3 cm, EC = 6 cm, and CD = ED = 4 cm. Construct a triangle equal in area to the pentagon,

showing your construction lines. Measure the base and height of the triangle and so calculate its area. $(S)^*$

2 (i) If $x + 2$ is a factor of the expression $4x^3 + px^2 - 11x - 6$, find the value of $p$, and the remaining factors.

(ii) Solve the equation $4x^2 - 5x = 2$, giving each root correct to two decimal places. $(W)$

3 The cross-section of a piece of elastic is a circle of diameter 5 mm. The elastic is stretched uniformly to twice its natural length, the volume remaining unaltered. What is now the diameter of the circular cross-section? Give your answer to the nearest tenth of a millimetre. $(OC)^*$

4 A vertical pole 3 m high is 2 m south of a wall which runs directly east and west. The sun is south-west at an elevation of 35°. Find to the nearest centimetre the height of the shadow of the pole on the wall. $(W)^*$

5 Express $\dfrac{2a}{x - a} + \dfrac{3a}{x + a} - \dfrac{6a^2}{a^2 - x^2}$ as a single fraction in its

lowest terms. What is the value of the above expression when $x = 6a$? $(N)$

6 Prove that equiangular triangles have their corresponding sides in the same proportion.

ABC is an isosceles triangle having AB = AC and $\overline{AD}$ as altitude. E is a point on $\overline{AB}$ such that BD = DE. Prove that AB × BE = 2BD². $(L)$

7 A man inherits £4 000. He puts half of it into a Building Society, which pays $4\frac{1}{2}\%$ interest free of Income Tax. The other half he invests so as to get $7\frac{1}{2}\%$ interest on which Income Tax at 45p in the pound is deducted before payment. How much does he receive from each investment? Calculate the man's average net percentage income on the £4 000, giving your answer to two places of decimals. $(OC)^*$

8 B lies 39 km north-east of A, C lies 27° east of north from A, and C is due north of B. Calculate BC and CA. $(O)^*$

9 Prove that the opposite angles of a cyclic quadrilateral are supplementary.

ABCD is a cyclic quadrilateral in which $\overline{AD}$ is produced to E. The bisector of the angle CDE meets the circumference of the circle in F. Prove that $\overline{BF}$ bisects the angle ABC.     (L)

10 A number formed by two digits exceeds the number formed by reversing the digits by 18, and three times the product of the digits exceeds five times their sum by 5. Find the number. (C)

## XXVIII

1 (i) Solve the equations $3x^2 + 2y^2 = 5$, $3x + 2y = 1$.

(ii) If $\dfrac{1}{a}(2x - b) + \dfrac{1}{b}(3x + b) = 1$, find $x$ in terms of $a$ and $b$.

(W)

2 (i) Construct geometrically a right-angled triangle, given that the hypotenuse is 7·5 cm and one side is 5 cm. Measure the third side and verify your result by calculation.

(ii) Construct a triangle ABC whose sides are: AB = 6 cm, BC = 9 cm and CA = 7 cm. Construct the circumcircle of the triangle and measure its radius.     (L)*

3 From a circular piece of paper of radius 35 cm is cut away a sector with an angle of 72° at the centre. The portion left has its cut edges joined so as to form a cone. Find (a) the radius of its circular base, (b) the height of the vertex above this base, (c) the area of the curved surface of the cone. Take $\pi$ as $\frac{22}{7}$.

(N)*

4 (i) The tangent of an acute angle A is $\frac{21}{20}$. Without using tables calculate cos (180° − A) and tan (90° + A).

(ii) A balloon is floating at a height of 1 000 m, vertically above a line AB 550 m long. Its elevation from A is 70°. Calculate its elevation from B.     (N)*

5 A tug steamed for a distance of 24 km at a uniform speed of V km h$^{-1}$; the speed on the return journey was 2 km h$^{-1}$ greater and the time required was 36 minutes less than on the outward journey. Find the value of V.     (L)*

**6** Two chords $\overline{PQ}$, $\overline{RS}$ of a circle intersect at a point O outside the circle, and $\overline{OT}$ is a tangent from O.

Prove that $OP \times OQ = OR \times OS = OT^2$.

$\overline{AB}$ is a diameter of a circle, X is a point inside the circle and C is the foot of the perpendicular from X to $\overline{AB}$. $\overline{AX}$ produced meets the circle again at Y. Prove that $AX \times AY = AC \times AB$.

$(OC)$

**7** A man buys 120 shares at £3·90 each and holds them for a year. At the end of the year he receives a dividend of 36p per share, and he is also given, free, one extra share for every ten he holds, but he receives no dividend for the year on these extra shares. He then sells all his shares at £3·40 each. Find, to three significant figures, his profit per cent on his original outlay.

$(O)*$

**8** A vertical pole is erected on a piece of level ground. A man whose eye is 160 cm above the ground is standing 15 m from the foot of the pole. He observes that the pole subtends an angle of 50° at his eye. Calculate with the help of your tables the height of the top of the pole above ground level. Give your answer to the nearest tenth of a metre.

$(OC)*$

**9** X is on the surface of the earth in latitude 71° N, longitude 30° W and Y is in latitude 71°N, longitude 150° E. Find, to the nearest 10 kilometres, the difference between the distances from X to Y measured (i) along the meridian (through the north pole) and (ii) along the circle of latitude eastwards from X to Y.

An aeroplane followed the north pole route from X to Y flying at an average speed of 800 km h$^{-1}$. Find the time taken for the journey, correct to the nearest minute.

[Take $2\pi R = 4 \times 10^4$ km.]

$(O)*$

**10** Taking 2 cm as the unit on each axis, draw the graph of $y = \frac{1}{2}(6 + x - 2x^2)$ for values of $x$ from $-2$ to 3.

Use your graph to find each of the roots of the equation $6 + x - 2x^2 = 2$, correct to one place of decimals.

$(C)$

## XXIX

**1** ABCD is a parallelogram whose sides are $2a$ and $2b$ units in length. The mid-point of $\overline{AB}$ is L, and the mid-point of $\overline{AD}$ is M. By using the cosine formula, or otherwise, prove that $CL^2 + CM^2 - CA^2 = a^2 + b^2$. *(OC)*

**2** Vancouver and Kharkov are both on latitude 50° N. The longitude of Vancouver is 123° W and the longitude of Kharkov is 36° E. If an aircraft flies from Vancouver due north to the North Pole and then due south to Kharkov, what is the total distance to the nearest ten km?

What is the distance (travelling eastwards) from Vancouver to Kharkov along latitude 50° N? (Assume that the circumference of the earth is $4 \times 10^4$ km.) *(S)\**

**3** A closed box is made of wood 2 cm thick; its outside dimensions are 86 cm, 54 cm and 54 cm. Calculate the total surface area of the inside in square metres. *(N)*

**4** Prove that the opposite angles of a cyclic quadrilateral are supplementary. State the converse of this theorem.

A, B, C, D, E, F are six points in order on the circumference of a circle such that $\overline{AB}$ is parallel to $\overline{ED}$, and $\overline{BC}$ is parallel to $\overline{FE}$. Prove that $\overline{CD}$ is parallel to $\overline{AF}$. *(W)*

**5** A pyramid has as its base an equilateral triangle of side 6 cm. The other edges of the pyramid are each 5 cm long. Determine (i) the height of the pyramid, (ii) the angle between a sloping face and the base, (iii) the angle between a sloping edge and the base. *(O)\**

**6** (a) Simplify $\left(x - \dfrac{27}{x^2}\right) \div \left(x - \dfrac{9}{x}\right)$.

(b) Simplify $\dfrac{3a}{x^2 + ax - 2a^2} - \dfrac{a}{x^2 + 3ax + 2a^2} + \dfrac{2x}{x^2 - a^2}$

giving your answer as a single fraction in its lowest terms. *(N)*

**7** (i) A man sold a house for £3 000 and said that he had made 25 per cent profit. Calculate how much he paid for the house assuming that his profit was (*a*) 25 per cent of the selling price, (*b*) 25 per cent of the cost price.

(ii) If the length of a box is increased by 50 per cent, its width increased by 20 per cent, and its depth decreased by 25 per cent, by how much per cent is its volume increased or decreased? (*W*)

**8** Prove that equal chords of a circle are equidistant from its centre.

$\overline{\text{KAB}}$ and $\overline{\text{KCD}}$ are secants of a circle such that AB = CD. If O is the centre of the circle and E and F are the mid-points of $\overline{\text{AB}}$ and $\overline{\text{CD}}$ respectively, prove that $\text{O}\hat{\text{E}}\text{F} = \frac{1}{2}\hat{\text{K}}$. (*L*)

**9** (i) Prove that $(a^2 - b^2)^2 + (2ab)^2 = (a^2 + b^2)^2$.

(ii) Given that $x + y = p$ and $x - y = q$, prove that $p^2 + 3pq + q^2 = 5x^2 - y^2$. (*OC*)

**10** Draw the graph of $y = \sin x°$, where $x$ is between 0 and 180.

On the same axes and with the same scales, draw the graph of $y = 0\cdot3 + 0\cdot003x$ between the same limits.

Show that the equation $\sin x° - 0\cdot003x = 0\cdot3$ has two solutions between 0° and 180°, and find the smaller solution as accurately as you can. (*O*)

## XXX

**1** The three following expressions have a common factor; find it, and give the other factor in each case:

(i) $(a - b)^2 - a + b$    (ii) $a^2 - b^2 - a - b$

(iii) $ab - a - b^2 + 1$. (*C*)

**2** A vertical cylindrical tank is 1·6 m high and 1·05 m in diameter. Calculate its capacity in litres.

If water flows in at the rate of 84 litres per minute, at what rate, in centimetres per minute, correct to the nearest whole number, does the level of the water rise? (Take $\pi$ as $\frac{22}{7}$.)

(*N*)*

**3** Two circles intersect at A and B. Two points P and Q are taken on one of the circles. $\overline{\text{PA}}$ meets the other circle again at L, $\overline{\text{QB}}$ meets it again at M. Prove that $\overline{\text{LM}}$ is parallel to $\overline{\text{PQ}}$.

(*OC*)

4 Two lighthouses, X and Y, are 8 km apart and X is due east of Y. From a ship, in position P, the bearing of X is 20° E of N and the bearing of Y is 30° W of N. Twenty-one minutes later the ship is in position Q from which Y is due north and X is 50° E of N. Find by drawing the positions P and Q (scale 1 cm = 1 km). Find by measurement the distance of Q from Y. Also measure PQ and so calculate the speed of the ship (2 sig. fig.). (*S*)*

5 (i) Use logarithms to calculate the value of $\sqrt{\dfrac{mg \tan \theta}{7 \cdot 27}}$ when

$m = 0 \cdot 325\ 6$, $g = 32 \cdot 2$ and $\theta = 15°$.

(ii) Solve the equation $2x^2 - 11x + 4 = 0$, giving the roots correct to 2 places of decimals. (*L*)

6 A rectangular lawn 20 m long and 12 m wide is surrounded by a gravel path of uniform width. The width of the path is doubled and it is found that the area of the path is increased by 123 m². Find the original width of the path. (*W*)*

7 Two partners A and B start a business of which A acts as manager; A provides £4 000 of the necessary capital and B provides £8 000. Of the total profit at the end of a year A draws £450 as manager, A and B each receive 5% on their capital, and the remainder of the profit is divided between A and B in proportion to the amount of capital contributed. If B receives a total of 8% on his capital, find the total profit. (*L*)

8 Construct the quadrilateral ABCD in which AB = 6 cm, the angles ACB and ADB are each 35° and the sides AD and BC are each 5 cm. Measure AC. Give a brief description of your construction. (*OC*)*

9 Two points A, B, 40 m apart, are on horizontal ground through the foot F of a tower. FA = FB and the angle AFB = 152°. The elevation of the top of the tower from A is 66°. Calculate (i) the height of the tower, correct to 3 sig. fig., (ii) the elevation from the middle point of $\overline{AB}$ of a point on the tower whose distance from the foot is one-quarter of the height of the tower. (*N*)*

**10** Sketch on the same diagram the graphs $y = 2 - x$ and

$$y = \frac{x^3 - 1}{2}.$$

Show that there is only one real solution to the equation $x^3 + 2x = 5$.

By drawing large-scale graphs for values of $x$ near the solution, determine it to three significant figures. *(O)*

# Chapter 22

# *Gradients*

## Gradient of a straight line

In Fig. 161 the triangles ABC, PQR, UVW are clearly similar, so that $\dfrac{BC}{AB} = \dfrac{QR}{PQ} = \dfrac{VW}{UV}$. Each of these fractions measures the gradient (slope) of the straight line $\overline{HK}$.

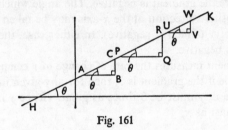

Fig. 161

Hence the gradient of the straight line is the same at any point on it.

Also $\tan \theta = \dfrac{BC}{AB}$ or $\dfrac{QR}{PQ}$ or $\dfrac{VW}{UV}$, so that the gradient is also measured by $\tan \theta$.

In Fig. 162 (i) the point A has co-ordinates $(x, y)$. In going from A to B the *increase* in $x$ is AM, and the corresponding *increase* in $y$ is MB.

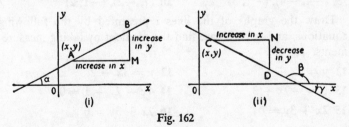

Fig. 162

Gradient $= \dfrac{MB}{AM} = \dfrac{\text{increase in } y}{\text{increase in } x}$, and since MB and AM are

both positive the gradient is positive. The angle which $\overline{AB}$ makes with the positive direction of the $x$-axis is the acute angle $\alpha$, and $\tan \alpha$ is positive.

In Fig. 162 (ii) the point C has co-ordinates $(x, y)$. In going from C to D the *increase* in $x$ is CN, and the corresponding *decrease (or negative increase)* in $y$ is ND.

Gradient $= \dfrac{ND}{CN} = \dfrac{\text{decrease in } y}{\text{increase in } x}$, and since CN is positive and

ND negative the gradient is negative. The angle which $\overline{CD}$ makes with the positive direction of the $x$-axis may be taken as $\beta$ (which is obtuse) or $\gamma$ (which is negative). In either case, the tangent of the angle is negative.

The gradient measures the **rate of change of $y$ compared with $x$.** For example if the gradient is 3, then for any given increase in $x$, the increase in $y$ must be 3 times as great. Hence $y$ is increasing 3 times as fast as $x$.

### Exercise 22a

Find the gradients of the lines joining the following pairs of points.

1 $(9, 7), (2, 5)$       2 $(2, 5), (4, 8)$

3 $(5, 3), (0, 0)$       4 $(6, 1), (1, 5)$

5 $(0, 4), (3, 0)$       6 $(-3, 2), (4, 4)$

7 $(2, 3), (6, -5)$       8 $(-4, 3), (8, -6)$

9 $(-4, -4), (-1, 5)$       10 $(7, -2), (-1, 2)$

Draw the graphs of the lines represented by the following equations, and in each case find the gradient by taking measurements.

11 $y = 3x + 1$       12 $y = 3x - 2$

13 $y = -2x + 3$       14 $4x - 2y + 1 = 0$

15 $2x + 3y = 0$       16 $2x + 3y = 6$

**17** $4x - 3y = 5$          **18** $2x - 5y = 6$

**19** $5x - 2y = 5$          **20** $7x + 4y - 8 = 0$

Through the point

**21** $(2, 1)$      draw the line with gradient 3.

**22** $(5, 0)$    „    „    „    „       „    $-2$.

**23** $(1, -3)$    „    „    „    „       „    $-3$.

**24** $(-4, -2)$    „    „    „    „       „    $\frac{2}{3}$.

**25** $(5, -2)$    „    „    „    „       „    $-\frac{4}{3}$.

From the experience gained in working through Ex. 22a it will be seen that the gradient of a line depends only on the coefficients of $x$ and $y$ in its equation, and is not affected by the absolute term. The gradient may also be calculated, without drawing the graph.

Consider the line whose equation is $y = 4x - 5$. Take any two convenient points on it, such as those where $x = 2$ and $x = 3$.

$$\text{If} \quad x = 2, \ y = 4 \times 2 - 5 = 3.$$
$$\text{If} \quad x = 3, \ y = 4 \times 3 - 5 = 7.$$

$$\text{Gradient} = \frac{\text{increase in } y}{\text{increase in } x} = \frac{7 - 3}{3 - 2} = \frac{4}{1} = 4.$$

Again, consider the line whose equation is $2x + 3y = 11$.

$$\text{If} \quad x = 1, \ 3y = 11 - 2 \times 1 = 9 \quad \therefore \ y = 3.$$
$$\text{If} \quad x = 2, \ 3y = 11 - 2 \times 2 = 7 \quad \therefore \ y = 2\tfrac{1}{3}.$$

$$\text{Gradient} = \frac{\text{increase in } y}{\text{increase in } x} = \frac{2\frac{1}{3} - 3}{2 - 1} = \frac{-\frac{2}{3}}{1} = -\frac{2}{3}.$$

Notice that the given equation can be rearranged thus:

$$2x + 3y = 11$$
$$\therefore \ 3y = -2x + 11$$
$$\therefore \ y = -\tfrac{2}{3}x + 3\tfrac{2}{3}.$$

With the equation written in this form, the coefficient of $x$ gives the gradient. Hence an equation of the form $y = mx + c$ is that of a straight line with gradient $m$.

If, in addition to the gradient, one point on the line is known, the graph may be roughly sketched. The simplest point is usually one of the intersections with the axes.

In this example,

$$\text{if } x = 0,$$
$$3y = 11, \quad \text{i.e. } y = 3\tfrac{2}{3}.$$

Hence the line cuts the $y$-axis at the point $(0, 3\tfrac{2}{3})$.

The line may now be sketched, and is as in Fig. 163.

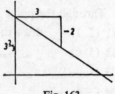

Fig. 163

## Exercise 22b

In each of the following write down the gradient of the line represented by the given equation, and sketch the graph.

**1** $y = 2x + 3$     **2** $y = 2x - 2$     **3** $y = \tfrac{1}{3}x$

**4** $y = \tfrac{1}{3}x + 1$     **5** $y = \tfrac{5}{4}x - 2$     **6** $3x - 5y = 4$

**7** $3x + 7y = 5$     **8** $4x + 3y = 2$     **9** $4x - 7y = 7$

**10** $8x + 5y = 4$

## Gradient of a curve

The gradient of a curve, unlike that of a straight line, varies from point to point. The gradient at any particular point on a curve is defined as being the gradient of the tangent to the curve at that point.

Consider the curve $y = \tfrac{1}{4}x^2$, as in Fig. 164.

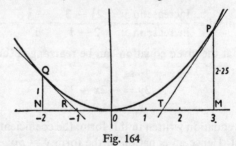

Fig. 164

If $x = 3$, $y = \tfrac{1}{4} \times 3^2 = 2\tfrac{1}{4}$, so that the curve passes through the point P with co-ordinates $(3, 2\cdot25)$.

232

If the gradient at this point is required, a ruler is placed carefully against the curve, and the tangent $\overline{PT}$ is drawn, cutting the $x$-axis in T.

The length of $\overline{TM}$ appears to be 1·5, so that the gradient required is

$$\frac{MP}{TM} = \frac{2 \cdot 25}{1 \cdot 5} = \frac{2\frac{1}{4}}{1\frac{1}{2}} = \frac{9}{6} = \frac{3}{2}.$$

Hence at the point P, $y$ is increasing $1\frac{1}{2}$ times as fast as $x$.

Q is the point on the curve at which $x = -2$, $y = 1$. A tangent drawn at this point cuts the $x$-axis at R, and NR = 1.

Hence since the gradient is clearly negative, and NR and NQ are numerically equal, the gradient at Q is $-1$.

Hence, at the point Q, $y$ is *decreasing* at the same rate as $x$ is *increasing*.

*N.B.* The method of drawing a tangent by placing a ruler against the curve may clearly lead to considerable inaccuracy. The results obtained must therefore be taken to be only approximate.

### Exercise 22c

1 Draw the graph of $y = \frac{1}{5}x^2$ for values of $x$ from 4 to $-4$, and find the gradient at the point where $x$ has the value (i) 3, (ii) 1·5, (iii) $-2$.

In nos. 2–10 follow the instructions given for no. 1.

| | | |
|---|---|---|
| 2 $y = x^2 - 4x$ | 5 to $-1$ | 4, 2, 0 |
| 3 $y = x^2 - 3x + 2$ | 4 to $-1$ | $2\frac{1}{2}$, $1\frac{1}{2}$, 0, $-\frac{1}{2}$ |
| 4 $y = x^2 - x - 1$ | 3 to $-2$ | $2\frac{1}{2}$, $1\frac{1}{2}$, $\frac{1}{2}$, $-1$ |
| 5 $y = x^2 + 2x - 3$ | 2 to $-4$ | 0, $-1$, $-1\frac{1}{2}$, $-2\frac{1}{2}$ |
| 6 $y = 2x^2 - 5x$ | 4 to $-1$ | 0, 1, 3 |
| 7 $y = x^3 - 6x$ | 3 to $-3$ | 2, 0, $-1$ |
| 8 $y^2 = x + 2$ | 7 to $-2$ | 2, $-1$, $-2$ |
| 9 $y = \sin x$ | 0 to $180°$ | 0, $60°$, $90°$, $120°$ |
| 10 $y = 3x^2 - 5x - 4$ | 3 to $-2$ | 2, 1, 0, $-1$ |

# Chapter 23

# *Area under a curve*

It is often necessary to estimate the area enclosed between a curve
and the axes (or other lines), and this can be done in several ways.
The simplest method is that of **counting squares,** as in the example
which follows.

**Example 1** *Estimate the area enclosed between the curve*
$y = 20 + x - x^2$ *and the axes (positive quadrant).*

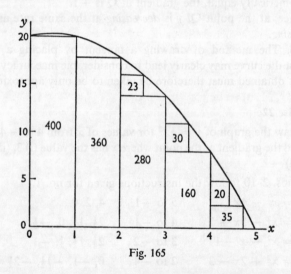

Fig. 165

Using graph paper which has 2-cm squares divided into 2-mm
squares, draw the curve and divide the required area into a
number of convenient rectangles, based on the squares of the
graph paper.

In each rectangle write the number of 'small' squares which it
contains (in this case the small squares have 2-mm sides).

Then consider the remaining areas. In estimating, ignore any-

234

thing less than half a small square, and count as one anything more than a half.

The total area is 1 414 small squares.

In the direction of the $x$-axis, 2 mm represents $\frac{1}{10}$ of a unit of length.

In the direction of the $y$-axis, 2 mm represents $\frac{1}{2}$ of a unit of length.

$\therefore$ one small square represents $\frac{1}{10} \times \frac{1}{2}$ of a unit of area
$$= \frac{1}{20} \text{ of a unit of area.}$$

$\therefore$ 1 414 small squares represent $\frac{1\,414}{20}$ units of area.

$\therefore$ the area under the graph $\simeq 70 \cdot 7$ units of area.

Notice particularly the importance of the relationship between 'squares' and units of area.

Example 2, which follows, illustrates the use of area to represent distance gone. If, for instance, a car travels at 15 m s⁻¹ for 3 seconds the distance gone is 45 m, since distance = velocity × time.

Also area of rectangle=length × breadth, so that if length and breadth represent velocity and time respectively, then the area represents the distance gone.

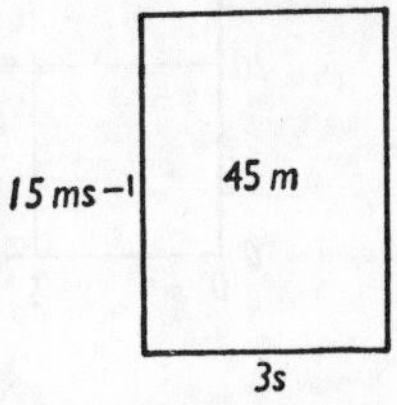

Example 2 also shows the use of the gradient of a velocity–time graph to give the acceleration. In Chapter 22, page 230, it was shown that, in a graph connecting $x$ and $y$, the gradient measures the rate of change of $y$ compared with $x$.

Fig. 166

Hence if the graph connects velocity and time, the gradient measures the rate of change of velocity compared with time, which is by definition the acceleration.

**Example 2** *The speed of a car in a built-up area is noted at half-minute intervals, and the results are as follows:*

| Time (minutes) | 0 | $\frac{1}{2}$ | 1 | $1\frac{1}{2}$ | 2 | $2\frac{1}{2}$ | 3 |
|---|---|---|---|---|---|---|---|
| Velocity (km h⁻¹) | 20 | $36\frac{1}{2}$ | 42 | 37 | 20 | 20 | $26\frac{1}{2}$ |

*Estimate the distance travelled during these three minutes to the nearest 10 metres.*

*Estimate also the acceleration (in m s⁻²) at ½ min and 2 min from the start.*

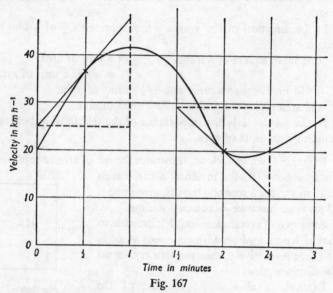

Fig. 167

The squares in Fig. 167 are 2-cm squares.

The graph is drawn to a suitable scale and the area estimated by counting small squares (= 1 796 squares).

1 small square represents $1 \text{ km h}^{-1} \times \frac{1}{20} \text{ min}$

$$= \frac{1\,000}{60 \times 60} \text{ m s}^{-1} \times 3 \text{ s}$$

$$= \frac{5}{6} \text{ m}$$

$\therefore$ distance travelled $= 1\,796 \times \frac{5}{6} \text{ m}$

$$= 1\,496\frac{2}{3} \text{ m}$$

$$\simeq 1\,500 \text{ m}.$$

Draw the tangent to the curve at the point $(\frac{1}{2}, 36\frac{1}{2})$.

The gradient shows an increase of velocity of 23 km h⁻¹ in 1 min.

But acceleration is defined as the rate of increase of velocity compared with time.

Here rate of increase of velocity = 23 km h$^{-1}$ in 1 min

$$= \frac{23\ 000}{60 \times 60}\ \text{m s}^{-1}\ \text{in 60 s,}$$

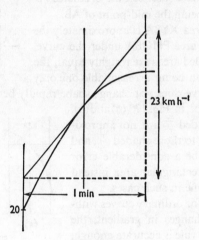

23 km h$^{-1}$

1 min

20

Fig. 168

$$\therefore\ \text{acceleration} = \frac{23\ 000}{60 \times 60 \times 60}\ \text{m s}^{-1}\ \text{per second}$$

$$\simeq 0.106\ \text{m s}^{-2}.$$

Similarly at the point (2, 20), the rate of change of velocity = −18 km h$^{-1}$ in 1 min,

$$\therefore\ \text{deceleration} = \frac{18\ 000}{60 \times 60 \times 60}\ \text{m s}^{-2}$$

$$\simeq 0.083\ \text{m s}^{-2}.$$

It should be noticed that, just as the gradient on a velocity–time graph gives the acceleration, so on a distance–time graph the gradient gives the velocity, since velocity is defined as the rate of change of distance compared with time.

*New General Mathematics*

## Mid-ordinate rule

Instead of counting squares the **mid-ordinate rule** may be used, which is sometimes quicker but generally less accurate.

Consider Fig. 169, in which CM is called the mid-ordinate (between the ordinates AP and BQ), C being the mid-point of $\overline{AB}$.

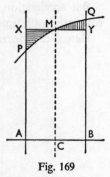

Fig. 169

Here the area XYBA is approximately the same as the area PMQBA under the curve, since the shaded areas are roughly equal, the approximation being a reasonable one only when the curve does not change shape rapidly between P and Q.

For instance, in Fig. 170 (*a*) and (*b*), the areas shaded ≣ are not approximately equal to those shaded ‖‖, and there would be a considerable error in using the rectangular area instead of the true one in such cases.

However, for ordinary curves without rapid changes in gradient, the mid-ordinate rule is accurate enough, especially if small intervals are taken.

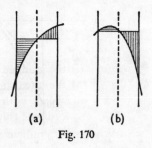

(a)      (b)

Fig. 170

The application of the rule to worked Example 1 would be as follows (Fig. 171):

the mid-ordinates, at $x = \frac{1}{2}, 1\frac{1}{2}, 2\frac{1}{2}, 3\frac{1}{2}, 4\frac{1}{2}$, are successively $20\frac{1}{4}$, $19\frac{1}{4}, 16\frac{1}{4}, 11\frac{1}{4}, 4\frac{1}{4}$.

∴ the areas of the vertical rectangles, each 1 unit wide, are successively $20\frac{1}{4} \times 1, 19\frac{1}{4} \times 1, 16\frac{1}{4} \times 1, 11\frac{1}{4} \times 1, 4\frac{1}{4} \times 1$ sq. units.

∴ the total area $= (20\frac{1}{4} + 19\frac{1}{4} + 16\frac{1}{4} + 11\frac{1}{4} + 4\frac{1}{4}) \times 1$ sq. units
$= 71\frac{1}{4}$ sq. units.

## Exercise 23

1 Use the mid-ordinate rule to estimate the distance gone in worked Example 2, taking six mid-ordinates.

2 Draw the curve $y = 6x - x^2$ for values of $x$ from 0 to 6, taking 2 cm for each $x$-unit and 1 cm for each $y$-unit.

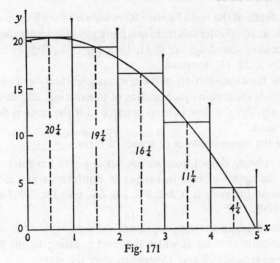

Fig. 171

Find (i) the gradient when $x = 1$, $x = 2$, $x = 4$;

     (ii) the area included between the curve and the $x$-axis, both by counting squares and by the mid-ordinate rule.

What is the gradient when $x = 3$?

3 Draw the curve $y = 2x(3 - x)$ for values of $x$ from 0 to 3, taking 4 cm for each $x$-unit and 2 cm for each $y$-unit.

Find (i) the gradient when $x = \frac{1}{2}$, 1, $2\frac{1}{2}$;

     (ii) the area included between the curve and the $x$-axis.

For what value of $x$ is the gradient zero?

4 The velocity of a car accelerating from rest is taken at 10-second intervals, and the results are shown below:

| $t$ (seconds) | 0 | 10 | 20 | 30 | 40 | 50 | 60 | 70 |
|---|---|---|---|---|---|---|---|---|
| $v$ (m s$^{-1}$) | 0 | 14·3 | 20·6 | 24·4 | 26·9 | 28·4 | 29·4 | 30 |

Draw a $v$–$t$ graph. Estimate the accelerations 10 seconds and 45 seconds from the start, and also the total distance covered in the 70 seconds.

5 The depth of the bed of a river 60 m wide is taken by soundings made at equal intervals from one bank straight across the river. Successive soundings are 0, 11, 16·5, 18, 19·5, 22·5, 24·5, 25·5, 26, 24·5, 20, 11, 0 metres.

Draw the cross-section of the river as accurately as possible.

Estimate the area in square metres of this section, and calculate to 2 sig. fig. the flow in litres per second if the river is flowing at 4 km h$^{-1}$.

Give the second answer in standard form.

6 Beer is being drawn from a cask into a jug of irregular shape, and the depth of beer in the jug in centimetres at successive 5-second intervals is 0, 2·2, 3·8, 5·0, 6·0, 6·8, 7·4, 7·9, 8·4, 8·9, 9·5, 10·6, 15·2.

Plot a graph showing depth against time.

Estimate the rate at which the level is rising in the jug (in cm per second) 20 and 35 seconds after the start.

Deduce from the graph the probable shape of the jug.

7 A particle moves along a straight line so that its distance ($s$ m) from a fixed point O in the line after $t$ seconds is given by the formula $s = 5t - t^2$.

Plot $s$ against $t$ for values of $t$ from 0 to 5, taking a 2-cm scale on both axes.

Estimate the gradients when $t = 1, 3$.

What does the gradient represent? What happens when the gradient is zero?

Explain how the particle moves on the line.

8 A particle moves on a straight line so that its velocity ($v$ cm s$^{-1}$) at time $t$ seconds from the start is given by $v = \frac{1}{10}t^3$. Plot $v$ against $t$ for values of $t$ from 0 to 4.

Estimate the accelerations when $t = 2, 3·5$, and also the distance covered in the 4 seconds.

9 The speed of a car in km h$^{-1}$ is taken at one-minute intervals (there being no sudden bursts of speed or hard braking during the time of the observations) over six minutes of continuous running, and the successive speeds noted are 80, 65·4, 54·8, 47, 44·8, 52, 70 km h$^{-1}$.

Estimate in m s⁻² the acceleration 5 minutes after the first observation, the deceleration after 2 minutes, and also the total distance covered to the nearest 100 m.

**10** The speed of a heavy vehicle accelerating from rest is shown in the table:

| Time(s) | 0 | 10 | 20 | 30 | 40 | 50 | 60 |
|---|---|---|---|---|---|---|---|
| Speed (km h⁻¹) | 0 | 24·0 | 36·0 | 42·5 | 45·0 | 44·2 | 39·0 |

Estimate the distance covered in metres (nearest 10 m) during this time, and also the acceleration 5 seconds after the start and the deceleration 55 seconds after the start (in m s⁻²).

What is the highest speed reached, and when?

**11** Draw the graph of $y = 5 - \dfrac{4}{x}$ for values of $x$ from $\frac{1}{2}$ to 6,

taking 2 cm as unit on both axes.

Draw the tangent to the curve at the point where $x = 2$ and estimate its gradient.

Draw also the straight line whose intersection with the graph will enable you to find one root of the equation

$5 - \dfrac{4}{x} = 4 - x$, and state the approximate value of this root.

(*L*)

**12** Draw on the same diagram the graphs of

$$(4 - x)(x - 1) \quad \text{and} \quad \frac{1}{x^2} - 1$$

for values of $x$ from $\frac{1}{2}$ to 5, taking 2 cm as unit on both axes.

Find the gradients of the graphs at the point on O$x$ where they intersect. Find the co-ordinates of the other point of intersection of the graphs. (*S*)

241

**13** A car travels along a straight road and its speed, $v$ m s$^{-1}$, $t$ seconds after passing a certain telegraph pole is given in the table:

| $t$ | 0 | 5 | 10 | 15 | 20 | 25 | 30 | 35 | 40 | 45 | 50 |
|---|---|---|---|---|---|---|---|---|---|---|---|
| $v$ | 19·7 | 23 | 25·7 | 27·7 | 29 | 29·7 | 29·6 | 29 | 28·2 | 27·2 | 25·8 |

Find  (i) the maximum speed of the car in m s$^{-1}$ and the time when it occurs

     (ii) the acceleration when $t = 13$

     (iii) the total distance travelled (nearest 10 m).

**14** If $y = x - 5 + \dfrac{8}{x}$, copy and complete the table below:

| $x$ | 1 | 1·5 | 2 | 3 | 4 | 5 | 6 |
|---|---|---|---|---|---|---|---|
| $y$ | 4 | | | 0·67 | 1 | | 2·33 |

Taking 2 cm to represent 1 unit on the $x$-axis and 4 cm to represent 1 unit on the $y$-axis, draw the graph of $y = x - 5 + \dfrac{8}{x}$ between $x = 1$ and $x = 6$.

(i) Find the gradient of the graph at the point where $x = 4$.

(ii) Use the graph to solve the equation $x - 5 + \dfrac{8}{x} = 2$.  (*C*)

**15** A beaker is filled with liquid and heated slowly. The temperature is taken at intervals, the readings being:

| Time (min) | 0 | 1 | 2 | 3 | 4 | 4·5 |
|---|---|---|---|---|---|---|
| Temp. (°C) | 20·5 | 21·5 | 23 | 25 | 28 | 30 |

| Time (min) | 5 | 5·5 | 6 | 7 | 8 | 9 |
|------------|---|-----|---|---|---|---|
| Temp. (°C) | 33 | 35·5 | 37·5 | 40 | 42 | 43·5 |

Draw the graph of these readings on a scale of 2 cm to 2 min horizontally and 2 cm to 5° C vertically.

(i) Calculate the average rate of heating in °C per minute during the first $3\frac{1}{2}$ minutes of the experiment.

(ii) From the graph determine the greatest rate of heating in °C per minute and the time at which this occurs.    (*C*)

# Chapter 24

## *Differentiation*

### Ratio of small quantities

Let $u$ and $v$ be two quantities which vary in such a way that $v$ is always equal to $3u$.

$$v = 3u$$

$$\therefore \frac{v}{u} = 3.$$

If $u = 0{\cdot}1$, $\quad v = 0{\cdot}3$, $\quad$ so that $\dfrac{v}{u} = \dfrac{0{\cdot}3}{0{\cdot}1} = 3$

,, $u = 0{\cdot}01$, $\quad v = 0{\cdot}03$, $\quad$ ,, ,, $\dfrac{v}{u} = \dfrac{0{\cdot}03}{0{\cdot}01} = 3$

,, $u = 0{\cdot}001$, $\quad v = 0{\cdot}003$, $\quad$ ,, ,, $\dfrac{v}{u} = \dfrac{0{\cdot}003}{0{\cdot}001} = 3$

and so on.

As $u$ and $v$ are made smaller and smaller, the ratio $\dfrac{v}{u}$ remains equal to 3.

For example, if $u = \dfrac{1}{1\,000\,000\,000} = 0{\cdot}000\,000\,001$,

$$v = \frac{3}{1\,000\,000\,000} = 0{\cdot}000\,000\,003,$$

and $\qquad \dfrac{v}{u} = \dfrac{0{\cdot}000\,000\,003}{0{\cdot}000\,000\,001} = 3.$

Hence although $u$ and $v$ may be so small *separately* as to be negligible, the ratio $\dfrac{v}{u}$ remains equal to 3.

It is important to notice that $v$ and $u$, although extremely small,

244

are not actually zero, as in this case the fraction $\dfrac{v}{u}$ would be equal to $\dfrac{0}{0}$, which is meaningless.

## Average velocity

Suppose a man is walking along a path, and his distance from a fixed post on the path is observed at intervals of one second. If after 3 seconds and 4 seconds he is respectively 23 metres and $25\frac{1}{4}$ metres from the post, then in the fourth second he has gone $2\frac{1}{4}$ metres. This means that while the time has increased by 1 second, the distance has increased by $2\frac{1}{4}$ metres. Hence the distance gone in metres has increased $2\frac{1}{4}$ times as fast as the time in seconds.

The man's **average velocity** during the fourth second is said to be $2\frac{1}{4}$ metres per second, and measures the average rate of change of distance compared with time during that second.

If in the sixth, seventh, eighth and ninth seconds the man goes a total distance of 7 metres, then while the time has increased by 4 seconds the distance has increased by 7 metres. Hence the distance in metres has increased $\frac{7}{4}$ times as fast as the time in seconds, i.e. $1\frac{3}{4}$ times as fast. The average velocity is $1\frac{3}{4}$ metres per second during the interval of 4 seconds, and is obtained by dividing the total distance gone by the total time taken.

## Comparison of rates of change

Suppose an object is moving along a straight line, and $t$ seconds after the beginning of the motion its distance $s$ metres from a fixed point in the line is given by the formula $s = t^2 + 4t + 2$.

If $t = 0$,   $s = 0 + 0 + 2 \qquad\quad = 2$
,, $t = 1$,   $s = 1^2 + 4 \times 1 + 2 = 7$
,, $t = 2$,   $s = 2^2 + 4 \times 2 + 2 = 4 + 8 + 2 = 14$
,, $t = 3$,   $s = 3^2 + 4 \times 3 + 2 = 9 + 12 + 2 = 23$
,, $t = 4$,   $s = 4^2 + 4 \times 4 + 2 = 16 + 16 + 2 = 34.$

The object is clearly not moving with constant velocity, since the distances gone in successive seconds are becoming progressively greater.

During the third second,
the distance gone $= (23 - 14)$ metres $= 9$ metres
and the average velocity $= 9$ m s$^{-1}$.
During the fourth second,
the distance gone $= (34 - 23)$ metres $= 11$ metres
and the average velocity $= 11$ m s$^{-1}$.

Hence if the **actual velocity after 3 seconds** is required, it will evidently be somewhere between $9$ m s$^{-1}$ and $11$ m s$^{-1}$, but a closer approximation will be obtained by considering smaller intervals of time before and after 3 seconds.

If $t = 2 \cdot 9$,  $s = 2 \cdot 9^2 + 4 \times 2 \cdot 9 + 2 = 22 \cdot 01$
„ $t = 3$     $s = 3^2 + 4 \times 3 + 2$     $= 23$
„ $t = 3 \cdot 1$,  $s = 3 \cdot 1^2 + 4 \times 3 \cdot 1 + 2 = 24 \cdot 01$.

During the tenth of a second before 3 seconds
the distance gone $= (23 - 22 \cdot 01)$ metres $= 0 \cdot 99$ metres
and the average velocity $= \dfrac{0 \cdot 99}{0 \cdot 1}$ m s$^{-1}$ $= 9 \cdot 9$ m s$^{-1}$.

During the tenth of a second after 3 seconds
the distance gone $= (24 \cdot 01 - 23)$ metres $= 1 \cdot 01$ metres
and the average velocity $= \dfrac{1 \cdot 01}{0 \cdot 1}$ m s$^{-1}$ $= 10 \cdot 1$ m s$^{-1}$.

It is now evident that the actual velocity after 3 seconds is somewhere between $9 \cdot 9$ m s$^{-1}$ and $10 \cdot 1$ m s$^{-1}$.

A still closer approximation may be obtained by taking the hundredth of a second before and after 3 seconds, and by similar working to that already used, it will be found that the distances are respectively $(23 - 22 \cdot 900\ 1)$ metres and $(23 \cdot 100\ 1 - 23)$ metres, i.e. $0 \cdot 099\ 9$ metres and $0 \cdot 100\ 1$ metres.

Hence the average velocity during the hundredth of a second before 3 seconds $= \dfrac{0 \cdot 099\ 9}{0 \cdot 01}$ m s$^{-1}$ $= 9 \cdot 99$ m s$^{-1}$, and during the hundredth of a second after 3 seconds it is $\dfrac{0 \cdot 100\ 1}{0 \cdot 01}$ m s$^{-1}$, i.e. $10 \cdot 01$ m s$^{-1}$.

It should now be clear that as the interval of time before or after 3 seconds is made progressively smaller and smaller, the average velocity during that small interval of time is becoming more and more nearly equal to 10 m s$^{-1}$.

It may therefore be assumed that if the change in time is made so small as to be almost negligible, the change in distance will also be so small as to be almost negligible, but the numerical value of the ratio $\dfrac{\text{change in distance}}{\text{change in time}}$ will be very nearly equal to 10.

In other words, although the changes in distance and time are themselves *separately* negligible, the numerical value of the ratio of one to the other is 10.

This may be expressed by saying that as the changes in distance and time each **approach the limit 0,** the ratio $\dfrac{\text{change in } s}{\text{change in } t}$ approaches the limit 10.

Hence $s$ is increasing 10 times as fast as $t$, and the actual velocity after 3 seconds is therefore 10 m s$^{-1}$.

The calculation may be considerably reduced by working in general terms, instead of using a particular numerical value for the change in $t$.

Consider the distance gone when the time is $(3 + h)$ seconds, where $h$ is small and may be positive or negative.

If $t = 3$, $\qquad s = 3^2 + 4 \times 3 + 2 = 23$.

If $t = 3 + h$, $\quad s = (3 + h)^2 + 4(3 + h) + 2$
$$= 9 + 6h + h^2 + 12 + 4h + 2$$
$$= 23 + 10h + h^2.$$

$\therefore$ the distance gone in the interval $h$ seconds
$$= (23 + 10h + h^2) \text{ metres} - 23 \text{ metres}$$
$$= (10h + h^2) \text{ metres}.$$

This is the change in $s$ which corresponds to the change $h$ in $t$.

$\therefore$ average velocity during the interval $h$ seconds
$$= \frac{\text{change in } s}{\text{change in } t}$$
$$= \frac{10h + h^2}{h} \text{ m s}^{-1}$$
$$= (10 + h) \text{ m s}^{-1}.$$

As *h* becomes smaller and smaller, the average velocity becomes more and more nearly equal to 10 m s⁻¹,

i.e. as *h* approaches the limit 0, the velocity in metres per second approaches the limit 10.

This is usually expressed thus: $\lim_{h \to 0} (10 + h) = 10$

where $h \to 0$ means '*h* approaches 0'.

Hence the actual velocity after 3 seconds is 10 m s⁻¹.

### Graphical representation

The working of the preceding example may be represented graphically. Corresponding numerical values for *s* and *t* are found from the equation $s = t^2 + 4t + 2$, and when these are plotted the graph may be drawn.

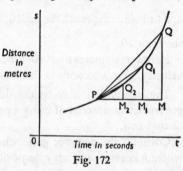

Fig. 172

Fig. 172 represents a portion of the graph, enlarged for the sake of clarity. P is the point where $t = 3$ and $s = 23$. If PM represents the small change *h* in *t*, then MQ represents the corresponding change in *s*,

i.e.   PM = *h*   and   MQ = $10h + h^2$ as calculated above.

The ratio $\dfrac{\text{change in } s}{\text{change in } t} = \dfrac{MQ}{PM}$, and this gives the gradient of the chord $\overline{PQ}$. Hence the gradient of the chord $\overline{PQ}$ shows graphically the average rate of change of *s* compared with *t*, i.e. the average velocity during the short interval *h* seconds.

As *h* is made smaller and smaller, PM becomes smaller and smaller, and Q takes up successively positions such as $Q_1$ and $Q_2$, moving along the curve nearer and nearer to P. The chord $\overline{PQ}$ correspondingly takes up positions such as $\overline{PQ_1}$ and $\overline{PQ_2}$, for which its gradient has values such as $\dfrac{M_1Q_1}{PM_1}$ and $\dfrac{M_2Q_2}{PM_2}$.

In the limit, as $h \to 0$,

(i) PM $\to$ 0 and MQ $\to$ 0,

(ii) Q approaches indefinitely close to P,

(iii) the chord $\overline{PQ}$ occupies more and more nearly the position of the tangent to the curve at P.

Hence the rate of change of $s$ compared with $t$ after 3 seconds, i.e. the numerical value of the actual velocity after 3 seconds, is given by the **gradient of the tangent** to the curve at P.

Since the tangent at P is the limiting position of the chord $\overline{PQ}$ as PM approaches zero, the gradient of the tangent is the limit of $\dfrac{MQ}{PM}$ as PM $\to$ 0

$$= \lim_{h \to 0} \frac{10h + h^2}{h}$$
$$= \lim_{h \to 0} (10 + h)$$
$$= 10.$$

Hence the velocity after 3 seconds is $10 \text{ m s}^{-1}$.

When two variables $s$ and $t$ are connected by an equation such as $s = t^2 + 4t + 2$, $s$ is said to be a **function** of $t$, since its value depends on the value of $t$ (see Chapter 12).

$t$ is called the **independent variable,** and $s$ is the **dependent variable.**

### Exercise 24a

1 A particle is moving along a straight line, and travels $s$ metres in $t$ seconds where $s = t^2 + t - 3$. Find its average velocity during the interval of time in which $t$ varies from

(i)  2 to 2·1     (ii) 2 to 2·01     (iii) 1·9 to 2
(iv) 1·99 to 2    (v) 2 to 2 + $h$

Hence find the velocity of the particle after 2 seconds.

Work nos. 2 and 3 as in no. 1.

2 $s = t^2 - 2t + 1$

(i)  4 to 4·1     (ii) 4 to 4·01     (iii) 3·9 to 4
(iv) 3·99 to 4    (v) 4 to 4 + $h$

Velocity after 4 seconds.

**3** $s = t^2 + 5t$

   (i)   3 to 3·1      (ii)  3 to 3·01      (iii)  2·9 to 3

   (iv)  2·99 to 3     (v)  3 to $3 + h$

   Velocity after 3 seconds.

### Differential coefficient

Consider two variables $x$ and $y$ which are connected by the equation $y = x^2$.

As $x$ varies, $y$ varies in such a way that $y$ is always equal to the square of $x$. For any value
of $x$ the corresponding value
of $y$ may be calculated, and
when such pairs of values are
plotted on a graph a curve
is obtained as in Fig. 173.

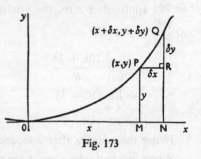

From earlier work with
graphs it will be known
that the curve is said to be
the graph of the equation
$y = x^2$, and $y = x^2$ is the

Fig. 173

equation of the curve. This means that if any point is taken at random on the curve, its co-ordinates satisfy the equation $y = x^2$.

Let P be any general point on the curve, and let its co-ordinates be $(x, y)$.

Let Q be another point on the curve; and let Q lie very close to P, so that its co-ordinates differ from those of P by very small amounts, called **increments.** Let a small increment in $x$ be denoted by the symbol $\delta x$, which must be regarded as a single quantity and not as the product of $\delta$ and $x$; and let the corresponding increment in $y$ be $\delta y$. (Notice that as $\delta x$ is a single quantity, its square may be written as $\delta x^2$ instead of $(\delta x)^2$. Similarly $(\delta y)^2$ may be written as $\delta y^2$.)

Then in Fig. 173,   $PR = \delta x$,   $RQ = \delta y$,   $ON = x + \delta x$, $NQ = y + \delta y$. Hence the co-ordinates of Q are $(x + \delta x, y + \delta y)$.

The gradient of the chord $\overline{PQ}$ is $\dfrac{RQ}{PR}$, i.e. $\dfrac{\delta y}{\delta x}$, and this measures the average rate of change of $y$ compared with $x$ between P and Q.

Since P and Q both lie on the curve, their pairs of co-ordinates satisfy the equation of the curve.

$$\therefore \quad y = x^2 \qquad \text{at P}$$
$$\text{and} \quad y + \delta y = (x + \delta x)^2 \qquad \text{at Q.}$$

Subtracting,
$$\delta y = (x + \delta x)^2 - x^2$$
$$= x^2 + 2x \times \delta x + \delta x^2 - x^2$$
$$= 2x \times \delta x + \delta x^2$$

$$\therefore \quad \frac{\delta y}{\delta x} = 2x + \delta x.$$

This is the gradient of the chord $\overline{\text{PQ}}$.

In the limit, as $\delta x \to 0$, $\delta y$ also $\to 0$, Q approaches and becomes indefinitely close to P, and the chord $\overline{\text{PQ}}$ more and more nearly coincides with the tangent at P.

$\therefore$ the gradient of the tangent at P is given by $\lim\limits_{\delta x \to 0} \dfrac{\delta y}{\delta x}$,

i.e. by $\lim\limits_{\delta x \to 0} (2x + \delta x)$,

i.e. by $2x$.

Hence, at P, $y$ is increasing $2x$ times as fast as $x$, since $2x$ is the gradient of the tangent (and of the curve) at P.

The expression $\lim\limits_{\delta x \to 0} \dfrac{\delta y}{\delta x}$ is usually abbreviated to $\dfrac{dy}{dx}$,

so that if $\qquad \dfrac{\delta y}{\delta x} = 2x + \delta x$

then $\qquad \lim\limits_{\delta x \to 0} \dfrac{\delta y}{\delta x} = 2x,$

i.e. $\qquad \dfrac{dy}{dx} = 2x.$

$\dfrac{dy}{dx}$ is called the **differential coefficient of $y$ with respect to $x$,** and measures the rate of change of $y$ compared with $x$.

For example when $x = 4$, $y = 16$ (since $y = x^2$) and $y$ is increasing 8 times as fast as $x$ (since $2x = 8$).

Hence at the point (4, 16) the gradient of the tangent is 8.

Similarly „ „ „ (−3, 9)„ „ „ „ „ is −6.

Notice that when the gradient is negative, as at the point $(-3, 9)$ just considered, an *increase* in $x$ corresponds to a *decrease* in $y$, i.e. if $\delta x$ is $+$ve then $\delta y$ is $-$ve (Fig. 174 (i)). Alternatively, a *decrease* in $x$ corresponds to an *increase* in $y$, i.e. if $\delta x$ is $-$ve then $\delta y$ is $+$ve (Fig. 174 (ii)). Hence when the gradient is negative, i.e. when $\dfrac{dy}{dx}$ is negative, $y$ decreases as $x$ increases, and vice versa.

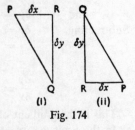

Fig. 174

In general, when $x$ is said to increase by the increment $\delta x$, it must be remembered that $\delta x$ may be $+$ve or $-$ve, so that if $x$ increases by a negative increment, then $x$ actually decreases.

The process of finding the differential coefficient of a function is called **differentiation,** and the function so obtained is called the **derived function.**

If $y = x^2$, then $\dfrac{dy}{dx} = 2x$; so that the derived function of $x^2$ is $2x$. The *process* of differentiation is denoted by $\dfrac{d}{dx}$,

$$\text{so that} \quad \frac{d}{dx}(x^2) = 2x,$$

$$\text{or} \quad \frac{d(x^2)}{dx} = 2x.$$

**Example 1** *If $y = x^3$, find the value of $\dfrac{dy}{dx}$.*

Let $x$ increase to $x + \delta x$, and let $y$ correspondingly increase to $y + \delta y$, where $\delta x$ and $\delta y$ are small.

Then $\qquad y = x^3$

and $\qquad y + \delta y = (x + \delta x)^3$

$\therefore$ subtracting,

$$\delta y = (x + \delta x)^3 - x^3$$
$$= x^3 + 3x^2 \times \delta x + 3x \times \delta x^2 + \delta x^3 - x^3$$

$$= 3x^2 \times \delta x + 3x \times \delta x^2 + \delta x^3$$

$$\therefore \frac{\delta y}{\delta x} = 3x^2 + 3x \times \delta x + \delta x^2$$

$$\therefore \lim_{\delta x \to 0} \frac{\delta y}{\delta x} = 3x^2 \text{ since } 3x \times \delta x \to 0 \text{ and } \delta x^2 \to 0,$$

i.e. $\dfrac{dy}{dx} = 3x^2.$

Alternatively this may be written as $\dfrac{d}{dx}(x^3) = 3x^2.$

**Example 2** *Find the differential coefficient, with respect to x, of the function $5x^2 - 3x + 2$.*

Let $y = 5x^2 - 3x + 2$.

Let $x$ increase by the small increment $\delta x$, and let $y$ correspondingly increase by the small increment $\delta y$.

Then

$$y + \delta y = 5(x + \delta x)^2 - 3(x + \delta x) + 2$$

$\therefore$ subtracting,

$$\begin{aligned} \delta y &= 5(x + \delta x)^2 - 3(x + \delta x) + 2 - (5x^2 - 3x + 2) \\ &= 5x^2 + 10x \times \delta x + 5\delta x^2 - 3x - 3\delta x + 2 - 5x^2 + 3x - 2 \\ &= 10x \times \delta x + 5\delta x^2 - 3\delta x \end{aligned}$$

$$\therefore \frac{\delta y}{\delta x} = 10x + 5\delta x - 3.$$

$\therefore$ taking limits as $\delta x \to 0$,

$$\frac{dy}{dx} = 10x - 3.$$

Hence the derived function of $5x^2 - 3x + 2$ is $10x - 3$,

i.e. $\dfrac{d}{dx}(5x^2 - 3x + 2) = 10x - 3.$

The graphical significance of this result is that if the graph of $y = 5x^2 - 3x + 2$ is drawn, the gradient at any point is given by the value of $10x - 3$ at that point.

**Exercise 24b**

Find the differential coefficients, with respect to $x$, of the following functions.

**1** $7x^2$      **2** $5x^3$      **3** $ax$      **4** $bx^2$      **5** $cx^3$

**6** $x^2 + 4x - 1$      **7** $3x^2 - 5x$      **8** $x^3 + x^2$

**9** $x^4$      **10** $6x^4$      **11** $2x^3 - 3x^2$      **12** $x^5$

**13** $3x^2 - 7x - 4$      **14** $4 + 6x - 7x^2$      **15** $x^3 - 5x^2 + 3x - 2$

Find the rate of change of $s$ compared with $t$ if

**16** $s = 4t - 5$      **17** $s = t^2 - 3t$      **18** $s = 7 - t^2$

**19** $s = 2t - 3t^2$      **20** $s = 5t^2 - 4t + 3$

**Differentiation by rule**

From the examples just worked in Ex. 24b, it should be clear that the results may be written down by rule, without going through the process of finding $\dfrac{\delta y}{\delta x}$ and taking limits. From the results:

$$\frac{d}{dx}(x^2) = 2x \qquad \frac{d}{dx}(x^3) = 3x^2$$

$$\frac{d}{dx}(x^4) = 4x^3 \qquad \frac{d}{dx}(x^5) = 5x^4$$

it seems probable that in general

$$\text{if} \quad y = x^n, \quad \text{then} \frac{dy}{dx} = nx^{n-1},$$

so that    $\dfrac{d}{dx}(x^6) = 6x^5, \qquad \dfrac{d}{dx}(x^7) = 7x^6,$

and so on.

This is, in fact, true, but the proof is beyond the scope of the present chapter.

Also a constant multiplier remains a constant multiplier without affecting the differentiation,

i.e. if    $y = Ax^n, \quad \text{then} \dfrac{dy}{dx} = Anx^{n-1},$

so that $\quad \dfrac{d}{dx}(3x^6) = 3 \times 6x^5 = 18x^5,$

$$\dfrac{d}{dx}(2x^7) = 2 \times 7x^6 = 14x^6,$$

and so on. Notice that $x$ is $x^1$, so that

if $\quad y = x$

$\quad\quad = x^1$

then $\quad \dfrac{dy}{dx} = 1 \times x^0$

$\quad\quad\quad = 1 \quad$ since $\quad x^0 = 1.$

Hence if, for example,

$$y = 5x$$

then $\quad \dfrac{dy}{dx} = 5 \times 1$

$\quad\quad\quad = 5,$

or alternatively, $\quad \dfrac{d}{dx}(5x) = 5.$

Therefore if the graph of $y = mx$ is drawn, a straight line with gradient $m$ is obtained, since $\dfrac{dy}{dx} = m.$

Notice also that the differential coefficient of a constant is 0, since, being constant, its rate of change is zero. Connect this with the graph of $y = k$ (where $k$ is a constant), which is a straight line parallel to the $x$-axis and at a distance $k$ from it. The gradient of the line is 0, and if $y = k$, then $\dfrac{dy}{dx} = 0.$

From the results obtained in working through Ex. 24b it should also be clear that if a function consists of the sum of a number of terms, the differential coefficient of the function is the sum of the differential coefficients of the separate terms,

e.g. if $\quad y = 5x^3 - 3x^2 + 4x - 6$

then $\dfrac{dy}{dx} = 5 \times 3x^2 - 3 \times 2x^1 + 4 \times 1x^0 - 0$

$= 15x^2 - 6x + 4.$

If $y = \dfrac{1}{x}$,

then working from first principles,

$$y + \delta y = \frac{1}{x + \delta x}$$

$$\therefore \ \delta y = \frac{1}{x + \delta x} - \frac{1}{x}$$

$$= \frac{x - x - \delta x}{x(x + \delta x)}$$

$$= -\frac{\delta x}{x(x + \delta x)}$$

$$\therefore \ \frac{\delta y}{\delta x} = -\frac{1}{x(x + \delta x)}.$$

$\therefore$ taking limits as $\delta x \to 0$,

$$\frac{dy}{dx} = -\frac{1}{x^2}.$$

If $y = \dfrac{1}{x^2}$

then $y + \delta y = \dfrac{1}{(x + \delta x)^2}$

$$\therefore \ \delta y = \frac{1}{(x + \delta x)^2} - \frac{1}{x^2}$$

$$= \frac{x^2 - (x + \delta x)^2}{x^2(x + \delta x)^2}$$

$$= \frac{x^2 - x^2 - 2x \times \delta x - \delta x^2}{x^2(x + \delta x)^2}$$

$$= -\frac{2x \times \delta x + \delta x^2}{x^2(x + \delta x)^2}$$

$$\therefore \frac{\delta y}{\delta x} = -\frac{2x + \delta x}{x^2(x + \delta x)^2}$$

$\therefore$ taking limits as $\delta x \to 0$,

$$\frac{dy}{dx} = -\frac{2x}{x^4}$$

$$= -\frac{2}{x^3}.$$

Hence the rule on page 254 for differentiating a power of $x$ appears to hold also for a negative index.

For if $\quad y = \dfrac{1}{x}$

$$= x^{-1}$$

then by rule, $\quad \dfrac{dy}{dx} = -1 \times x^{-2}$

$$= -\frac{1}{x^2},$$

which agrees with the result obtained above.

If $\quad y = \dfrac{1}{x^2}$

$$= x^{-2}$$

then by rule, $\quad \dfrac{dy}{dx} = -2 \times x^{-3}$

$$= -\frac{2}{x^3},$$

which also agrees with the result obtained above.

Hence if $\quad y = \dfrac{1}{x^3} = x^{-3}$

then $\quad \dfrac{dy}{dx} = -3x^{-4} = -\dfrac{3}{x^4}$

and if $\quad y = \dfrac{7}{x^5} = 7x^{-5}$

then $\quad \dfrac{dy}{dx} = 7 \times (-5x^{-6}) = -\dfrac{35}{x^6}.$

**Exercise 24c**

Write down the differential coefficients with respect to $x$ of the following functions.

| | | | |
|---|---|---|---|
| **1** $x^5$ | **2** $x^6$ | **3** $4x^2$ | **4** $7x^3$ |
| **5** $3x^5$ | **6** $\dfrac{1}{x^4}$ | **7** $\dfrac{5}{x}$ | **8** $-\dfrac{3}{x^2}$ |
| **9** $x^2 + 3x$ | **10** $x^3 - 6$ | **11** $2x^4 - 5x^2$ | **12** $4x + 5$ |
| **13** $6x - 2$ | **14** $x + \dfrac{1}{x}$ | **15** $\dfrac{3}{x} - \dfrac{2}{x^2}$ | **16** $5x^2 - 3x$ |

**17** $x^2 - 7x + 2$     **18** $3x^2 + 5x - 3$     **19** $5x + 1 + \dfrac{2}{x}$

**20** $8x^5 - 2$         **21** $7x^2 - 3x - 3$     **22** $3x^2 - \dfrac{2}{x^3}$

**23** $x^3 - 2x^2 + x$            **24** $4x^3 - 3x + 8$

**25** $x^3 + 7x^2 - 4x - 5$      **26** $x^3 - x^2 - x + 1$

**27** $2x^3 - 4x^2 + 3x - 2$     **28** $3x^3 - 7x^2 - 9x + 4$

**29** $\dfrac{1}{3x^3} + \dfrac{1}{2x^2} + \dfrac{1}{x}$       **30** $\dfrac{5}{x^3} - \dfrac{3}{x^2} + \dfrac{2}{x}$

## Gradients

**Example 3** *Find the gradient of the curve* $y = x^2 + 3x - 1$ *at the point on it where* (*i*) $x = 3$, (*ii*) $x = -2$, (*iii*) $x = 0$.

$$y = x^2 + 3x - 1$$

$$\therefore \frac{dy}{dx} = 2x + 3, \quad \text{which gives the gradient.}$$

(i)   If $x = 3$,     gradient $= 2 \times 3 + 3 = 9$

(ii)   ,, $x = -2$,     ,,    $= 2 \times (-2) + 3 = -1$

(iii)   ,, $x = 0$,       ,,    $= 2 \times 0 + 3 = 3$.

**Example 4** *Find the points on the curve* $y = x^3 + 3x^2 - 9x + 3$ *at which the gradient is* (*i*) 0, (*ii*) 15.

$$y = x^3 + 3x^2 - 9x + 3$$

$$\therefore \frac{dy}{dx} = 3x^2 + 6x - 9$$

(i) If the gradient is 0,

$$\text{then} \quad 3x^2 + 6x - 9 = 0$$
$$\therefore \quad x^2 + 2x - 3 = 0$$
$$\therefore \quad (x - 1)(x + 3) = 0$$
$$\therefore \quad x = 1 \quad \text{or} \quad -3.$$

$\therefore$ the gradient is 0 at the points on the curve at which $x = 1$ or $-3$.

If $x = 1$, then

$$y = 1^3 + 3 \times 1^2 - 9 \times 1 + 3 = 1 + 3 - 9 + 3 = -2.$$

If $x = -3$, then

$$y = (-3)^3 + 3 \times (-3)^2 - 9 \times (-3) + 3$$
$$= -27 + 27 + 27 + 3 = 30.$$

$\therefore$ the co-ordinates of the points at which the gradient is zero are $(1, -2)$ and $(-3, 30)$.

(ii) If the gradient is 15,

$$\text{then} \quad 3x^2 + 6x - 9 = 15$$
$$\therefore \quad 3x^2 + 6x - 24 = 0$$
$$\therefore \quad x^2 + 2x - 8 = 0$$
$$\therefore \quad (x - 2)(x + 4) = 0$$
$$\therefore \quad x = 2 \quad \text{or} \quad -4.$$

$\therefore$ the gradient is 15 at the points on the curve at which $x = 2$ or $-4$.

If $x = 2$, then

$$y = 2^3 + 3 \times 2^2 - 9 \times 2 + 3 = 8 + 12 - 18 + 3 = 5.$$

If $x = -4$, then

$$y = (-4)^3 + 3 \times (-4)^2 - 9 \times (-4) + 3$$
$$= -64 + 48 + 36 + 3 = 23.$$

$\therefore$ the co-ordinates of the points at which the gradient is 15 are $(2, 5)$ and $(-4, 23)$.

## Exercise 24d

**1** Verify that the curve $y = x^2 - 3x - 5$ passes through the points $(5, 5)$, $(4, -1)$, $(2, -7)$, $(0, -5)$, $(-2, 5)$. Calculate the gradient of the curve at each of these points, and sketch the graph.

2 Calculate the gradient of the curve $y = x^3 - 5x + 3$ at each of the points (3, 15), (1, −1), (0, 3), (−2, 5), (−3, −9) which lie on it. Sketch the graph.

3 Calculate the gradient of the curve $y = 2x^2 - 3x - 7$ at the points where $x = 4, 2, 0, -2, -3$. Sketch the graph.

4 Calculate the gradient of the curve $y = \dfrac{4}{x}$ at the points where $x = 4, 2, \frac{4}{3}, \frac{1}{4}, -1, -3, -\frac{1}{2}$. Sketch the graph.

5 Sketch the curve $y = 6 - 3x - x^2$, and calculate the gradient at the points where $x = 3, 1, -1, -3, -5$.

6 Find the co-ordinates of the point on the graph of $y = x^2 + 2x - 10$ at which the gradient is equal to 8.

7 If $y = 2x^2 - 7x + 3$, find the co-ordinates of the point on the graph at which the gradient is equal to 5.

8 If $y = x^2 - 3x + 5$, find the co-ordinates of the point on the graph at which the tangent makes an angle of 45° with the positive direction of the $x$-axis.

9 Find the co-ordinates of the point on the graph of $y = 5x^2 + 8x - 1$ at which the gradient is equal to −2.

10 Find the co-ordinates of the point on the graph of $y = 3x^2 - x + 1$ at which the gradient is equal to −7.

11 Find the co-ordinates of the points on the graph of $y = \dfrac{8}{x}$ at which the gradient is equal to −2.

Calculate the gradients of the following curves at the points where $x$ has the given values.

12 $y = 5 - 3x^2$; $1\frac{1}{2}, \frac{1}{2}, -\frac{1}{2}, -1$.

13 $y = x + \dfrac{1}{x}$; $1, \frac{2}{3}, -\frac{1}{2}, -2$.

14 $y = x^3 - 4x + 1$; $2, 0, -1, -3$.

15 $y = x^3 - 5x^2 + 6x - 3$; $3, 1, -1, -2$.

**16** $y = 3 - \dfrac{1}{2x^2}$; 2, $\frac{1}{2}$, $-\frac{2}{3}$, $-1$.

**17** $y = x^4 - 5x^2 + 1$; 2, 0, $-1$, $-2$.

**18** $y = 2x^3 - 4x^2 - 7x + 2$; 2, 1, 0, $-1$.

**19** If $y = (x - 1)(x^2 - 4)$, find the gradient of the curve at each of the points at which it cuts the $x$-axis. Hence sketch the curve.

**20** Find the co-ordinates of the points on the graph of $y = 2x^3 - 9x^2 + 12x - 4$ at which the gradient is zero.

**21** Find the co-ordinates of the points on the graph of $y = 2x^3 + 3x^2 - 36x - 20$ at which the gradient is zero.

**22** If $y = 2x^3 - 6x^2 - 15x + 19$, find the co-ordinates of the points on the graph at which the gradient is equal to 3.

**23** Find the co-ordinates of the points on the graph of $y = 3x^3 + 18x^2 + 24x + 5$ at which the gradient is equal to $-3$.

**24** If $y = x^3 + 4x^2 - 3x + 2$, find the co-ordinates of the points on the graph at which the gradient is zero.

**25** If $y = x^3 - 2x^2 + x - 3$, find the co-ordinates of the points on the graph at which the gradient is equal to 5.

## Velocity and acceleration

Suppose a particle is moving along a straight line, and that after $t$ seconds its distance $s$ metres from a fixed point O in the line is given by $s = 4t + 3$.

The **velocity** of the particle is measured by the rate of change of $s$ compared with $t$ (see page 245), i.e. by $\dfrac{ds}{dt}$.

$$\therefore \text{ since } s = 4t + 3,$$

$$\frac{ds}{dt} = 4.$$

Hence the velocity of the particle is constant and equal to $4 \text{ m s}^{-1}$.

The distance–time graph, shown in Fig. 175, is a straight line, and its gradient is constant and equal to 4, which is the numerical value of the velocity. For any increase in $t$ the corresponding increase in $s$ is 4 times as great.

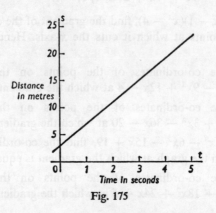

Fig. 175

When $t = 0$, i.e. at the beginning of the motion,

$$s = 4 \times 0 + 3 = 3.$$

Hence the particle was originally 3 m from O, and this is shown in the figure where the graph intersects the vertical axis.

If the distance $s$ metres after $t$ seconds is given by

$$s = t^2 + 3t + 5$$

then $$\frac{ds}{dt} = 2t + 3.$$

Hence the velocity after $t$ seconds is given by $2t + 3$.

To draw the distance–time graph a table of values is made as follows:

| $t$ | 0 | 1 | 2 | 3 | 4 | 5 |
|---|---|---|---|---|---|---|
| $s$ | 5 | 9 | 15 | 23 | 33 | 45 |

The graph is shown in Fig. 176, and the numerical value of the velocity at any point is given by $\dfrac{ds}{dt}$,

i.e. by the gradient of the curve at that point,
i.e. by the gradient of the tangent to the curve at that point.

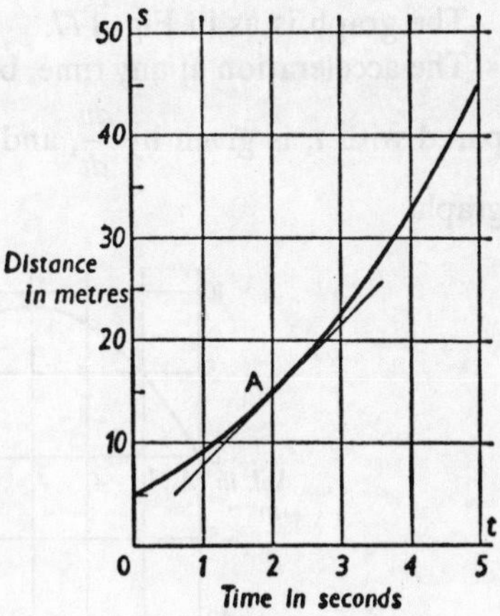

Fig. 176

If $t = 0, \dfrac{ds}{dt} = 2 \times 0 + 3 = 3$.

Hence the initial velocity is $3 \,\mathrm{m\,s^{-1}}$.

If $t = 2, \quad \dfrac{ds}{dt} = 2 \times 2 + 3 = 7$.

Hence the velocity after 2 seconds is $7 \,\mathrm{m\,s^{-1}}$, and the gradient of the tangent at A can be seen to be 7.

The **acceleration** is the rate of change of velocity compared with time. Hence if the velocity is $v \,\mathrm{m\,s^{-1}}$ after $t$ seconds, then the acceleration is given by $\dfrac{dv}{dt}$.

When distance is measured in metres and time in seconds, velocity is expressed in metres per second ($\mathrm{m\,s^{-1}}$) and acceleration in metres per second per second ($\mathrm{m\,s^{-2}}$).

Suppose a particle is moving in such a way that its velocity in terms of $t$ is given by $v = 6t - t^2$.

To draw the velocity–time graph a table of values is made as follows:

| $t$ | 0 | 1 | 2 | 3 | 4 | 5 | 6 | 7 | 8 |
|---|---|---|---|---|---|---|---|---|---|
| $v$ | 0 | 5 | 8 | 9 | 8 | 5 | 0 | $-7$ | $-16$ |

263

The graph is as in Fig. 177.

The acceleration at any time, being the rate of change of $v$ compared with $t$, is given by $\dfrac{dv}{dt}$, and $\dfrac{dv}{dt}$ measures the gradient of the graph.

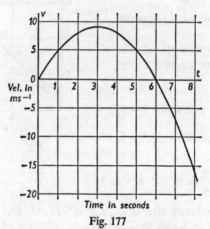

Fig. 177

Hence the acceleration is given by the gradient of the velocity–time graph, just as the velocity is given by the gradient of the distance–time graph.

In Fig. 177 it will be seen that when $t = 3$, the gradient of the curve is zero.

Hence after 3 seconds the acceleration is zero, and this may be checked by differentiation:

$$v = 6t - t^2$$

$$\therefore \frac{dv}{dt} = 6 - 2t$$

$$\therefore \text{ when } t = 3, \qquad \frac{dv}{dt} = 6 - 2 \times 3 = 0.$$

For values of $t$ from 0 to 3 the gradient is positive,

i.e. the acceleration is positive,
i.e. the velocity is increasing.

When $t = 3$, $v$ reaches a maximum of 9, and the acceleration is momentarily zero.

The velocity then begins to decrease, since the gradient, i.e. the acceleration, is negative.

When $t = 6$ the curve cuts the horizontal axis, i.e. after 6 seconds the velocity is zero. For higher values of $t$ the velocity is negative, which means that the particle is returning to its starting point.

**Example 5** *After $t$ seconds a particle has travelled a distance $s$ metres, where $s = -27t + 15t^2 - t^3$. When is the velocity zero? When is the acceleration zero? Find the velocity and the acceleration after (i) 2 seconds, (ii) 6 seconds, (iii) 10 seconds.*

$$s = -27t + 15t^2 - t^3$$

$$\therefore \frac{ds}{dt} = -27 + 30t - 3t^2,$$

i.e. velocity $= v = -27 + 30t - 3t^2$

$$\therefore \frac{dv}{dt} = 30 - 6t,$$

i.e. acceleration $= 30 - 6t.$

If the velocity is zero,

$$\text{then} \quad -27 + 30t - 3t^2 = 0$$
$$\therefore \quad -3(t^2 - 10t + 9) = 0$$
$$\therefore \quad (t - 1)(t - 9) = 0$$
$$\therefore \quad t = 1 \quad \text{or} \quad 9.$$

$\therefore$ the velocity is zero after 1 second and after 9 seconds.

If the acceleration is zero,

$$\text{then} \quad 30 - 6t = 0$$
$$\therefore \quad t = 5$$

$\therefore$ the acceleration is zero after 5 seconds.

(i) When $t = 2$,

$$\text{velocity in m s}^{-1} = -27 + 30 \times 2 - 3 \times 2^2$$
$$= -27 + 60 - 12$$
$$= 21$$

and acceleration in m s$^{-2}$ $= 30 - 6 \times 2$
$$= 18.$$

(ii)  When $t = 6$,

$$\text{velocity in m s}^{-1} = -27 + 30 \times 6 - 3 \times 6^2$$
$$= -27 + 180 - 108$$
$$= 45$$

and acceleration in m s$^{-2}$ = $30 - 6 \times 6$
$$= -6.$$

(iii)  When $t = 10$,

$$\text{velocity in m s}^{-1} = -27 + 30 \times 10 - 3 \times 10^2$$
$$= -27 + 300 - 300$$
$$= -27$$

and acceleration in m s$^{-2}$ = $30 - 6 \times 10$
$$= -30.$$

∴  after   2 s, vel. is   21 m s$^{-1}$ and accel. is   18 m s$^{-2}$
     ,,   6 s, ,,   ,,   45 m s$^{-1}$ ,,   ,,   ,,   $-6$ m s$^{-2}$
and  ,,   10 s, ,,   ,,   $-27$ m s$^{-1}$ ,,   ,,   ,,   $-30$ m s$^{-2}$.

## Exercise 24e

**1**  A particle moves along a straight line in such a way that after $t$ seconds it has gone $s$ metres, where $s = t^2 + t$. Draw the distance–time graph for values of $t$ from 0 to 4, and by measuring the gradient find the velocity of the particle (i) after 1 second, (ii) after 3 seconds. Check the results by differentiation.

**2**  A particle moves along a straight line in such a way that after $t$ seconds its velocity is $v$ m s$^{-1}$, where $v = t^2 - t + 2$. Draw the velocity–time graph for values of $t$ from 0 to 4, and by measuring the gradient find the acceleration of the particle (i) after 2 seconds, (ii) after 3 seconds, (iii) after $\frac{1}{2}$ second. Check the results by differentiation.

**3**  After $t$ seconds the velocity of a moving particle is $v$ m s$^{-1}$, where $v = 2t + 1$. By drawing the velocity–time graph, show that the acceleration is constant, and find its value. Check by differentiation.

**4**  After $t$ seconds the distance which a particle has moved is $s$ metres, where $s = 3t - 2$. By drawing the distance–time graph, show that the velocity is constant, and find its value. Check by differentiation.

5 The distance moved by a particle in $t$ seconds is $s$ metres, where $s = 10t - 2t^2$. Draw the distance–time graph for values of $t$ from 0 to 5, and by measuring the gradient find the velocity of the particle after (i) 1 second, (ii) $2\frac{1}{2}$ seconds, (iii) 3 seconds. Check by differentiation.

6 The velocity of a moving particle after $t$ seconds is $v \, \text{m s}^{-1}$, where $v = 30 - t^2$. Draw the velocity–time graph for values of $t$ from 0 to 5, and by measuring the gradient find the acceleration of the particle after (i) 1 second, (ii) 3 seconds. Check by differentiation.

7 After $t$ seconds a moving body has gone $s$ metres, where $s = 4t^2 - 4t + 1$. Calculate the velocity after 2 seconds and after 3 seconds. When is the body momentarily at rest?

8 After $t$ seconds a moving body has a velocity of $v \, \text{m s}^{-1}$, where $v = 5t^2 - 12t + 7$. Calculate the acceleration after 2 seconds and after 3 seconds.

9 A moving body goes $s$ metres in $t$ seconds, where $s = 4t^2 - 3t + 5$. Find its velocity after 4 seconds. Show that the acceleration is constant, and find its value.

10 A particle travels $s$ metres in $t$ seconds, where $s = t^2 - 2t + 5$. Show by differentiation that the acceleration is constant, and find its value. Calculate the velocity after 1 second, 3 seconds and 4 seconds, and check by drawing the distance–time graph for values of $t$ from 0 to 5.

11 A stone is thrown vertically into the air, and its height is $s$ metres after $t$ seconds where $s = 29.4t - 4.9t^2$.

  (i) After how many seconds does it reach its greatest height?
  (ii) What is its greatest height?
  (iii) What is its initial velocity?

12 A marble is projected up a sloping groove, and after $t$ seconds its distance from the starting point is $s$ cm, where $s = 24t - 3t^2$.

  (i) What is its initial velocity?
  (ii) After how many seconds does it reach its furthest point?

(iii) What is its velocity after 8 seconds?

(iv) What is the value of $s$ when $t = 8$?

(v) What is its acceleration?

**13** After $t$ seconds a particle has gone $s$ metres, where $s = t^3 - 6t^2 + 9t + 5$. After how many seconds is its velocity zero? When is its acceleration zero? Find its velocity and acceleration (i) initially, (ii) after 4 seconds.

**14** A particle moves in such a way that after $t$ seconds it has gone $s$ metres, where $s = 5t + 15t^2 - t^3$. Find its velocity and acceleration after (i) 3 seconds, (ii) 6 seconds. When is the acceleration zero?

**15** The distance $s$ metres that a particle has gone in $t$ seconds is given by $s = 20t + 12t^2 - 2t^3$. After how many seconds is its acceleration zero? Find its velocity and acceleration after (i) 1 second, (ii) 4 seconds.

# Chapter 25

# *Maxima and minima*

It is convenient to use the symbol $f(x)$ to mean 'a function of $x$' (see Chapter 12). In this way, $y = f(x)$ is a short way of writing an equation such as $y = x^2 - 3x + 5$, or $y = 2x^3 - x^2 - 1$, or $y = \dfrac{x+3}{x^2-2}$, and so on.

Suppose the graph of the equation $y = f(x)$ is drawn, and that it is as in Fig. 178. At the points A, B and C the gradient of the curve is zero, and these are called **turning points**. A and C are said to be **maximum points**, and B is a **minimum point**.

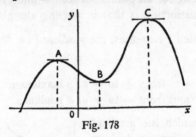

Fig. 178

The fact that A is a maximum point does not necessarily mean that at A the value of $y$ (i.e. of $f(x)$) is greater than at any other point on the curve, since from the figure this is clearly not so. What is meant is that at A the value of $f(x)$ is greater than at any *neighbouring* point on *either side* of A. Similarly there are points on the curve at which the value of $f(x)$ is less than at B, but the value of $f(x)$ is less at B than at any other point in the immediate vicinity.

**To distinguish between a maximum and a minimum point,** the gradient on each side of it is considered.

In Fig. 179 there is a maximum at P. At all points on the curve between C and P the gradient $\left(\text{given by } \dfrac{dy}{dx}\right)$ is positive, but in passing from C to P the gradient steadily decreases until at P it becomes zero. The gradient then continues to decrease, so that between P and D it is negative.

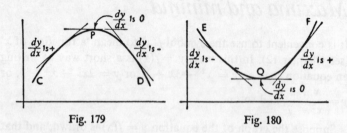

Fig. 179                              Fig. 180

Similarly for the minimum point Q in Fig. 180. Between E and Q the gradient is negative but increasing to zero at Q, then becoming positive for all points between Q and F.

Hence the distinction is that in passing along a curve in the direction in which $x$ increases, the gradient $\left(\text{i.e. the value of } \dfrac{dy}{dx}\right)$ changes

> from + to − at a **maximum**,
> and from − to + at a **minimum**.

A point at which the gradient is zero need not necessarily be a maximum or a minimum. In Fig. 181 the gradient is zero at both H and K; but on each side of H the gradient is positive, and there is no change in its sign. Similarly the gradient is negative on both sides of K. A point such as H or K is called a **point of inflexion.**

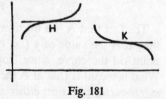

Fig. 181

## Application to curve-tracing

When the graph of a curve is to be drawn, the co-ordinates of a number of points may be calculated from the equation, and the points plotted. In this way an accurate drawing is made of a *limited part* of the curve, but some characteristic feature of the curve may be missed because it occurs at a point beyond the range of those plotted.

When a *sketch* of a curve is to be drawn, the requirement is for a drawing that will show all the characteristic features of the curve, and accurate plotting of points is less important. Information concerning the turning points, if any, will clearly be of major importance.

**Example 1** *Find the maximum and minimum values of the function* $2x^3 - 3x^2 - 12x + 8$. *Hence sketch the curve whose equation is* $y = 2x^3 - 3x^2 - 12x + 8$.

$$\text{If} \quad y = 2x^3 - 3x^2 - 12x + 8$$

$$\text{then} \quad \frac{dy}{dx} = 6x^2 - 6x - 12.$$

$$\text{At a turning point} \quad \frac{dy}{dx} = 0$$

$$\therefore \ 6(x^2 - x - 2) = 0$$
$$\therefore \ 6(x - 2)(x + 1) = 0$$
$$\therefore \ x = 2 \quad \text{or} \quad -1.$$

Hence the turning points occur where $x = 2$ or $-1$, and it remains to distinguish between them.

(i) If $x$ is a little less than 2,

$$x - 2 \text{ is negative and } x + 1 \text{ is positive}$$
$$\therefore \ 6(x - 2)(x + 1) \text{ is negative.}$$

If $x$ is a little greater than 2,

$$x - 2 \text{ is positive and } x + 1 \text{ is positive}$$
$$\therefore \ 6(x - 2)(x + 1) \text{ is positive.}$$

$\therefore$ as $x$ passes through the value 2, $\dfrac{dy}{dx}$ passes from negative to positive.

$\therefore$ a minimum occurs when $x = 2$, and this minimum value of $2x^3 - 3x^2 - 12x + 8$ is $2 \times 2^3 - 3 \times 2^2 - 12 \times 2 + 8$

$$= 16 - 12 - 24 + 8$$
$$= -12.$$

(ii) If $x$ is a little less than $-1$ (e.g. $-1 \cdot 1$)

$x - 2$ is negative and $x + 1$ is negative
$\therefore\ 6(x - 2)(x + 1)$ is positive.

If $x$ is a little greater than $-1$ (e.g. $-0 \cdot 9$)

$x - 2$ is negative and $x + 1$ is positive
$\therefore\ 6(x - 2)(x + 1)$ is negative.

$\therefore$ as $x$ passes through the value $-1$, $\dfrac{dy}{dx}$ passes from positive to negative.

$\therefore$ a maximum occurs when $x = -1$, and this maximum value of $2x^3 - 3x^2 - 12x + 8$ is $2 \times (-1)^3 - 3 \times (-1)^2 - 12 \times (-1) + 8$

$= -2 - 3 + 12 + 8$
$= 15.$

The characteristic features of the curve are now known, but as an additional aid it may be as well to find the point at which the curve cuts the $y$-axis.

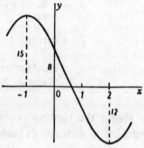

If $x = 0$,
$y = 2 \times 0^3 - 3 \times 0^2 - 12 \times 0 + 8$
$= 8.$

The curve may now be sketched, and is as in Fig. 182.

Fig. 182

Notice that graph paper is not needed for this sketch.

**Example 2** *Investigate the turning points, if any, of* $x^3 - 3x^2 + 3x + 2$, *and sketch the graph of the function.*

Let $\quad y = x^3 - 3x^2 + 3x + 2$

then $\quad \dfrac{dy}{dx} = 3x^2 - 6x + 3.$

At a turning point $\quad \dfrac{dy}{dx} = 0$

$\therefore\ 3(x^2 - 2x + 1) = 0$

$\therefore\ 3(x - 1)^2 = 0$

$\therefore\ x = 1$ (twice)

∴ the gradient is zero only at the point where $x = 1$.

If $x$ is a little less than 1, $3(x - 1)^2$ is positive.

„ „ „ „ „ greater „ 1, $3(x - 1)^2$ „ „

∴ the gradient is *positive* on *both* sides of the point at which it is zero.

Hence there is a point of inflexion where $x = 1$, and there is no maximum or minimum.

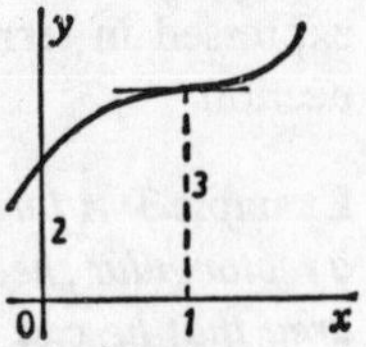

If $x = 1$, $\quad y = 1^3 - 3 \times 1^2 + 3 \times 1 + 2$
$\quad\quad\quad = 3$.

∴ the point of inflexion is at (1, 3).

If $x = 0$, $\quad y = 0^3 - 3 \times 0^2 + 3 \times 0 + 2$
$\quad\quad\quad = 2$.

Fig. 183

∴ the curve cuts the $y$-axis at (0, 2).

The curve may now be sketched, and is as in Fig. 183.

## Exercise 25a

For the following functions find the values of $x$ at which turning points occur, and distinguish between them. Find the value of the function at each turning point, and sketch the graph.

**1** $x^2 - 6x + 3$ $\quad\quad$ **2** $7 - 4x - x^2$ $\quad\quad$ **3** $6x - x^2$

**4** $x^2 + 3x$ $\quad\quad\quad$ **5** $2x^2 - x^3$ $\quad\quad\quad$ **6** $x^3 - 3x - 1$

**7** $3x^2 + 2x - 5$ $\quad\quad$ **8** $4 - 12x - 3x^2$ $\quad\quad$ **9** $x(5 - 2x)$

**10** $x^3 - 12x + 2$ $\quad\quad\quad\quad$ **11** $2x^3 - 9x^2 + 12x - 4$

**12** $1 + 9x + 3x^2 - x^3$ $\quad\quad\quad$ **13** $1 - 3x - 3x^2 - x^3$

**14** $x^3 - 6x^2 + 12x - 11$ $\quad\quad$ **15** $x + \dfrac{1}{x} + 2$

**16** $2x^3 - 3x^2 - 36x + 6$ $\quad\quad$ **17** $6 + 12x - 3x^2 - 2x^3$

**18** $3 - x^3$ $\quad$ **19** $2x^3 + 3x^2 - 36x - 6$ $\quad$ **20** $x^3 + 2$

**21** $x^2 + \dfrac{2}{x}$ $\quad$ **22** $2x + \dfrac{8}{x} + 3$ $\quad$ **23** $x^3 - 5x^2 + 7x - 3$

**24** $29 - 27x + 9x^2 - x^3$ $\quad\quad$ **25** $x^2 - \dfrac{16}{x}$

**Problems**

The examples which have just been done involved finding the turning points of a function which was given. In the problems which follow, a variable is chosen and the function of this variable has to be constructed.

Notice that the constructed function must be in terms of *only one* variable, so that if two letters are originally used, one must be expressed in terms of the other by means of a geometrical connection.

**Example 3** *A farmer has 120 metres of fencing with which to enclose a rectangular sheep-pen, using a wall for one side. Find the maximum area that he can enclose.*

Let the side parallel to the wall be of length $y$ metres, and the other two sides $x$ metres each.

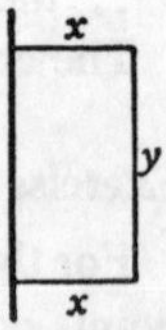

Then        $2x + y = 120$

$\therefore y = 120 - 2x.$

If the area of the pen is A square metres,

$A = xy$

$= x(120 - 2x)$

$= 120x - 2x^2$   (*N.B.*, a single variable $x$)

$\therefore \dfrac{dA}{dx} = 120 - 4x$

Fig. 184

$\therefore$ for a maximum or minimum

$120 - 4x = 0$

$\therefore x = 30.$

If $x$ is slightly $< 30$, $120 - 4x$ is positive.

„ $x$ „    „    $> 30$, $120 - 4x$ is negative.

$\therefore$ in passing through the value 0, $\dfrac{dA}{dx}$ changes from $+$ to $-$.

$\therefore x = 30$ gives a maximum.

Also    $y = 120 - 2x = 120 - 60 = 60.$

$\therefore$ the pen of maximum area measures 30 m by 60 m,

i.e. its area is 1 800 square metres.

**Example 4** *A stained glass window is in the shape of a rectangle surmounted by a semicircle, the diameter of the semicircle being equal to the width of the rectangle. Find the radius of the semicircle if the window is to admit as much light as possible, the perimeter being 20 metres.*

Let $r$ m and $h$ m be as in the figure, and let the area of the window be A $m^2$.

Then $\pi r + 2r + 2h = 20$     (*perimeter*)

$$\therefore 2h = 20 - \pi r - 2r$$
$$\therefore A = \tfrac{1}{2}\pi r^2 + 2rh$$
$$= \tfrac{1}{2}\pi r^2 + r[20 - \pi r - 2r]$$
$$= 20r - \tfrac{1}{2}\pi r^2 - 2r^2$$
$$\therefore \frac{dA}{dr} = 20 - \pi r - 4r$$

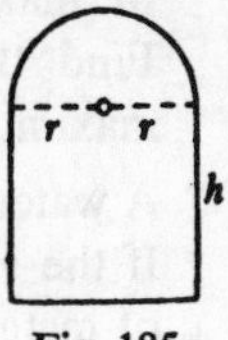

$\therefore$ for a max. or min.

$$20 - r(\pi + 4) = 0$$
$$\text{i.e.} \quad r = \frac{20}{\pi + 4}.$$

Fig. 185

If $r$ is slightly $< \dfrac{20}{\pi + 4}$,    $20 - r(\pi + 4)$ is +ve.

  ,, $r$ ,,    ,, $> \dfrac{20}{\pi + 4}$,     ,,    is −ve.

$\therefore$ in passing through the value 0, $\dfrac{dA}{dr}$ changes from $+$ to $-$.

$$\therefore r = \frac{20}{\pi + 4} \text{ gives a maximum.}$$

$\therefore$ the area of the window is a maximum when the radius of the semicircle is $\dfrac{20}{\pi + 4}$ metres.

### Exercise 25b

**1** A rectangular sheet of metal measures 8 cm by 3 cm. From each corner a square of side $x$ cm is removed, and the flaps so formed are bent up to make a small open box. Show that the volume of the box is $(4x^3 - 22x^2 + 24x)$ cm³, and find its maximum value.

**2** In no. 1, if the width of the metal sheet had been 5 cm instead of 3 cm, what would have been the maximum volume of the box?

**3** If A $= xy$ where $3x + y = 18$, find the maximum value of A.

**4** If P $= 9x + 8y$ where $xy = 2$, find the minimum value of P, taking $x$ and $y$ to be both positive.

**5** Find the maximum area of a rectangle whose perimeter is 32 metres.

**6** A piece of wire 36 cm long is cut and bent to make the shape shown in Fig. 186. Find the dimensions that will give the maximum volume outlined by the wire.

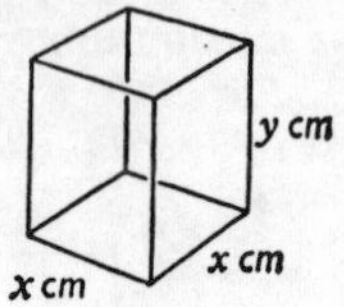

Fig. 186

**7** A water-tank is to be made, open at the top, on a square base. If the volume of the tank is to be 32 m³, find the least area of metal sheet that can be used.

**8** When an object is projected into the air its height, $s$ metres, after $t$ seconds is given by the formula $s = 98t - 4{\cdot}9t^2$. Find the greatest height to which it rises.

**9** A rectangular sheet of metal measures 20 cm by 15 cm. Equal squares of side $x$ cm are cut from two adjacent corners, and the flaps so formed are bent up to form the tray of a shovel, as in Fig. 187. Find the value of $x$ if the volume of the shovel is a maximum.

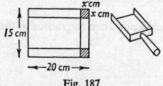

Fig. 187

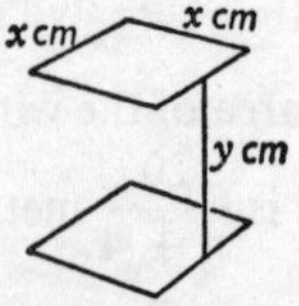

Fig. 188

**10** Fig. 188 shows the shape to which some wire is bent to reinforce a package. If the volume of the package is to be a maximum, and the total length of the wire is 60 cm, find the length marked *y* cm.

**11** A sheet of metal is 24 cm square. From each corner equal squares are removed, and the flaps so formed are bent up to make an open box. Find its maximum volume.

**12** A farmer uses some 2-m hurdles to enclose a rectangular pen of area 200 m². If one side of the pen is a river bank and needs no fencing, find the least number of hurdles needed.

**13** A swimming-bath is of the shape shown in Fig. 189. Find the maximum area of the bath if the perimeter is 132 m.

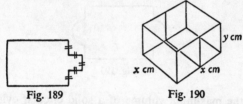

Fig. 189                    Fig. 190

**14** A total length of 54 cm of wire is used to make the shape shown in Fig. 190. Find the maximum volume outlined by the wire.

**15** The Post Office will not accept a parcel if the sum of its length and girth exceeds 2 metres. Find the volume of the largest parcel with square ends that can be sent by post.

**16** In no. 15, if the parcel is cylindrical and has circular ends, what is the maximum volume that can be sent? (3 sig. fig.).

**17** An open trough is made as in Fig. 191. The ends are right-angled isosceles triangles, and are perpendicular to the sides. If the total area of wood used is 1 728 cm², find the values of *x* and *y* that will give the maximum volume for the trough.

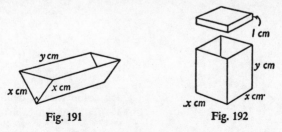

Fig. 191                    Fig. 192

277

**18** A tin box with a lid is to be made as in Fig. 192, the lid being 1 cm deep. If the total area of metal is 960 cm², find the dimensions that will give the maximum volume.

**19** Sheet metal is used for making a closed rectangular box with square ends. If the total area of the metal is 216 cm², find the dimensions that will give the greatest volume.

**20** A swimming-pool is of the shape shown in Fig. 193, the radius of each semicircular part being $\frac{1}{4}$ of the width. If the perimeter of the bath is 200 m, find the width when the area is a maximum. (Leave $\pi$ in the answer.)

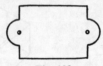

Fig. 193

**21** Find the maximum volume of a solid circular cylinder if its total surface area is $6\pi$ cm². (Leave $\pi$ in the answer.)

**22** Find the minimum surface area of a solid circular cylinder if its volume is $16\pi$ cm³. (Leave $\pi$ in the answer.)

**23** A piece of wire of given length is bent to form the perimeter of a sector of a circle. If the area of the sector is a maximum, find the angle between the bounding radii. (Leave $\pi$ in the answer.)

# Chapter 26

# *Integration*

Integration is the process which is the reverse of differentiation. The main object of Chapter 24 was to show how to find the differential coefficient (or derived function) of a given function. In the present chapter the derived function is given, and the original function has to be found. This process is called **integration.**

When a power of $x$ is differentiated, the power of the derived function is 1 degree less,

e.g.   if $y = x^6$, then $\dfrac{dy}{dx} = 6x^{6-1} = 6x^5$.

Hence when the derived function is given as a power of $x$, the power of the original function which has to be found will be 1 degree higher.

For example, if   $\dfrac{dy}{dx} = x^3$, $y$ will involve $x^4$.

But         $\dfrac{d}{dx}(x^4) = 4x^3$

$\therefore \dfrac{d}{dx}\left(\dfrac{x^4}{4}\right) = \dfrac{4x^3}{4} = x^3$.

Hence if         $\dfrac{dy}{dx} = x^3$

then         $y = \dfrac{x^4}{4} + c.$

The constant $c$ is added because a general answer is wanted. It is quite true that

$$\dfrac{d}{dx}\left(\dfrac{x^4}{4}\right) = x^3$$

but also   $\dfrac{d}{dx}\left(\dfrac{x^4}{4} + 2\right) = x^3$

$$\frac{d}{dx}\left(\frac{x^4}{4} - 5\right) = x^3$$

$$\frac{d}{dx}\left(\frac{x^4}{4} + 5\right) = x^3, \text{ and so on.}$$

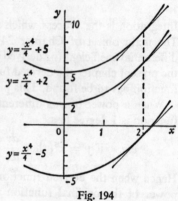

In fact, any constant may be added, since it disappears in the process of differentiation.

The graphical significance of this is shown in Fig. 194.

The three curves $y = \frac{x^4}{4} + 5$,

$y = \frac{x^4}{4} + 2, y = \frac{x^4}{4} - 5$ have

the same shape, and for any given value of $x$ their gradients are the same.

Fig. 194

For example, since $\frac{dy}{dx} = x^3$ for each, then if $x = 2$ the gradient is 8 for each curve.

If $\frac{dy}{dx} = x^3$, then $y = \frac{x^4}{4} + c$ is called the **general solution,** and $c$ is called the **arbitrary constant.**

### Exercise 26a

Find the functions of which the following are the derived functions.

| | | | | |
|---|---|---|---|---|
| **1** $x^2$ | **2** $3x^2$ | **3** $5x^2$ | **4** $x^4$ | **5** $5x^4$ |
| **6** $3x^4$ | **7** $x$ | **8** $2x$ | **9** $3x$ | **10** $5$ |
| **11** $\dfrac{x}{2}$ | **12** $\dfrac{x^2}{2}$ | **13** $-\dfrac{x^3}{4}$ | **14** $\dfrac{1}{x^2}$ | **15** $-\dfrac{2}{x^3}$ |

### Integration by rule

In working through Ex. 26a it will have been found that

$$\text{if } \frac{dy}{dx} = x, \quad \text{then } y = \frac{x^2}{2} + c$$

280

if $\dfrac{dy}{dx} = x^2$, then $y = \dfrac{x^3}{3} + c$

„ $\dfrac{dy}{dx} = x^3$, „ $y = \dfrac{x^4}{4} + c$, and so on.

Hence it appears that in general the rule is that

if $\dfrac{dy}{dx} = x^n$, then $y = \dfrac{x^{n+1}}{n+1} + c$.

Also if $\dfrac{dy}{dx} = kx^n$, where $k$ is a constant,

then $y = \dfrac{kx^{n+1}}{n+1} + c$.

In each of these cases $n$ is a positive integer. If $n$ is zero,

i.e. if $\dfrac{dy}{dx} = k$ $(since\ kx^0 = k \times 1)$

then $y = kx + c$,

so that the rule still holds when $n = 0$.

Now consider a case in which $n$ is negative,

e.g. when $\dfrac{dy}{dx} = \dfrac{1}{x^3} = x^{-3}$.

$$\dfrac{d}{dx}\left(\dfrac{1}{x^2}\right) = \dfrac{d}{dx}(x^{-2}) = -2x^{-2-1} = -2x^{-3}$$

$$\therefore \text{ if } \dfrac{dy}{dx} = x^{-3} \quad \left(= \dfrac{1}{x^3}\right)$$

$$y = \dfrac{x^{-2}}{-2} + c \quad \left(= -\dfrac{1}{2x^2} + c\right)$$

which shows that the rule still holds when $n$ is negative.

There is an exception when $n = -1$,

i.e. when $\dfrac{dy}{dx} = \dfrac{1}{x}$.

*New General Mathematics*

In this case $n + 1 = 0$, and the general rule does not apply. Special treatment is needed which is beyond the scope of the present volume.

**Example 1** *Integrate the expression $x^3 - 4x^2 - 6x + 3$.*

$$\text{If } \frac{dy}{dx} = x^3 - 4x^2 - 6x + 3$$

$$\text{then } y = \frac{x^4}{4} - 4 \times \frac{x^3}{3} - 6 \times \frac{x^2}{2} + 3x + c$$

$$= \frac{x^4}{4} - \frac{4x^3}{3} - 3x^2 + 3x + c.$$

**Exercise 26b**

Integrate the following expressions.

| | | | | |
|---|---|---|---|---|
| **1** $3x^3$ | **2** $\dfrac{x^3}{3}$ | **3** $\dfrac{3}{x^3}$ | **4** $-\dfrac{3}{x^4}$ | **5** $-\dfrac{2}{x^5}$ |
| **6** $0$ | **7** $4x - 3$ | **8** $x + 1$ | **9** $6x^2 - 2x + 1$ | |

**10** $2 - 6x$     **11** $3x - x^2$     **12** $9x^2 + 8$     **13** $x^2 - \dfrac{1}{x^2}$

**14** $x^3 + \dfrac{1}{x^3}$               **15** $x^3 + x^2 + x + 1$

**16** $\dfrac{x^3}{2} + \dfrac{x^2}{3} + \dfrac{x}{4} + \dfrac{1}{5}$        **17** $6x^5 - 4x^3 - 2x + 3$

**18** $\tfrac{1}{2}x^3 - \tfrac{1}{3}x^2$     **19** $\dfrac{2}{x^2} - \dfrac{5}{x^3}$      **20** $\dfrac{5}{x^2} - \dfrac{6}{x^3} + \dfrac{6}{x^4}$

In any particular case the value of the arbitrary constant can be calculated from the information given in the question, as in Examples 2, 3, 4 and 5 which follow.

**Example 2** *A curve passes through the point $(-3, 7)$, and its gradient at any point is given by $6x^2 + 10x - 7$. Find the equation of the curve.*

The gradient is given by $\dfrac{dy}{dx}$.

$$\therefore \ \frac{dy}{dx} = 6x^2 + 10x - 7$$

$$\therefore \quad y = 2x^3 + 5x^2 - 7x + c.$$

But this equation is satisfied by the co-ordinates of the point $(-3, 7)$.

$$\therefore \ 7 = 2 \times (-3)^3 + 5 \times (-3)^2 - 7 \times (-3) + c$$
$$= -54 + 45 + 21 + c$$
$$= 12 + c \qquad \therefore \ c = -5.$$

$\therefore$ the equation of the curve is $y = 2x^3 + 5x^2 - 7x - 5$.

**Example 3** *A particle moves in a straight line, and its velocity after $t$ seconds is $(t^2 - 3t - 2)\ m\,s^{-1}$. The distance of the particle from a fixed point on the line is $s$ m after $t$ seconds, and $s = 10$ when $t = 6$. Find the formula for $s$ in terms of $t$.*

The velocity is given by $\dfrac{ds}{dt}$.

$$\therefore \ \frac{ds}{dt} = t^2 - 3t - 2$$

$$\therefore \ s = \frac{t^3}{3} - 3 \times \frac{t^2}{2} - 2t + c.$$

But $s = 10$ when $t = 6$,

$$\therefore \ 10 = \frac{6^3}{3} - 3 \times \frac{6^2}{2} - 2 \times 6 + c$$

$$= 72 - 54 - 12 + c$$

$$= 6 + c \qquad \therefore \ c = 4$$

$$\therefore \ s = \frac{t^3}{3} - \frac{3t^2}{2} - 2t + 4.$$

*New General Mathematics*

**Example 4** *A particle moves in a straight line with a constant acceleration of* 3 *cm* $s^{-2}$. *If its velocity after t seconds is v cm* $s^{-1}$, *find v in terms of t, given that the velocity after 2 seconds is* 13 *cm* $s^{-1}$.

The acceleration is given by $\dfrac{dv}{dt}$.

$$\therefore \; \frac{dv}{dt} = 3$$

$$\therefore \; v = 3t + c.$$

But $\quad v = 13$ when $t = 2$,
$$\therefore \; 13 = 3 \times 2 + c.$$
$$= 6 + c$$
$$\therefore \; c = 7$$
$$\therefore \; v = 3t + 7.$$

**Example 5** *A particle moves in a straight line in such a way that its velocity after t seconds is* $(2t + 5)$ *m* $s^{-1}$. *Find the distance travelled in the first* 4 *seconds*.

Let the distance after $t$ seconds be $s$ metres. Then velocity $= \dfrac{ds}{dt}$.

$$\therefore \; \frac{ds}{dt} = 2t + 5$$

$$\therefore \; s = t^2 + 5t + c.$$

When $\quad t = 0, \; s = 0 + 0 + c = c$
„  $\quad t = 4, \; s = 16 + 20 + c = 36 + c.$

$\therefore$ by subtraction, the distance travelled in the first 4 seconds is 36 metres.

*Alternatively*, when the formula $s = t^2 + 5t + c$ has been found, it could be said that $s = 0$ when $t = 0$, since the distance gone initially is zero.

Hence $\quad 0 = 0 + 0 + c,$
i.e. $\quad c = 0$
$$\therefore \; s = t^2 + 5t.$$

$\therefore$ distance gone after 4 seconds $= (4^2 + 5 \times 4)$ metres
$$= 36 \text{ metres}.$$

284

**Exercise 26c**

1 If $u$ and $v$ are two variables such that $\frac{du}{dv} = 4v - 3$, and $u = 5$ when $v = 2$, find $u$ in terms of $v$.

2 Find the equation of the curve whose gradient is given by $2x + 3$, and which passes through the point $(2, 3)$.

3 Find the equation of the line with gradient 3 which passes through the point $(-1, 4)$.

4 A particle moves in a straight line, and its velocity after $t$ seconds is given by $36 - 4t$. The distance of the particle from a fixed point on the line after $t$ seconds is $s$ metres, and $s = 40$ when $t = 1$. Find $s$ in terms of $t$.

5 Two variables $w$ and $u$ are such that $\frac{dw}{du} = 9u^2 + 6u - 3$. If $w = -16$ when $u = -3$, find $w$ in terms of $u$.

6 A line passes through the point $(5, -2)$, and its gradient is $-3$. Find the equation of the line.

7 A curve passes through the point $(4, -3)$, and its gradient is given by $2 - x$. Find the equation of the curve.

8 A particle is projected along a straight line from a point A in the line, and its velocity after $t$ seconds is $(48 - 3t)\,\text{cm s}^{-1}$. If its distance from A after $t$ seconds is $s$ cm, find $s$ in terms of $t$. Hence find the time that elapses before the particle is back again at A.

9 A particle moves along a straight line in such a way that its acceleration after $t$ seconds is $(2t + 1)\,\text{cm s}^{-2}$. If its velocity after $t$ seconds is $v\,\text{cm s}^{-1}$, find $v$ in terms of $t$, given that $v = 11$ when $t = 2$.

10 The point $(2, 8)$ lies on a curve whose gradient at any point is given by $3x + 6$. Find the co-ordinates of the point on the curve at which the gradient is zero.

11 The gradient of a curve at any point is given by $x^2 - 2$. Find the equation of the curve, given that the point $(-1, 3)$ lies on it.

12 A curve passes through the point (1, 3), and its gradient at any point on it is given by $2x - \dfrac{1}{x^2}$. Find the equation of the curve.

13 A particle is moving in a straight line in such a way that its velocity after $t$ seconds is $(2t^2 - t)$ m s$^{-1}$. Find the distance gone in the first 3 seconds.

14 A body is projected vertically into the air, and its upward velocity after $t$ seconds is $(147 - 9 \cdot 8t)$ m s$^{-1}$. If its height after $t$ seconds is $h$ metres, find the formula giving $h$ in terms of $t$. Find also the greatest height reached.

15 The gradient of a curve at any point is $5 - 6x$. Find the equation of the curve if it passes through the point (1, 2).

16 A curve passes through the point (3, $-5$), and its gradient at any point is $2x - 2$. Find the values of $x$ at the points where the curve cuts the $x$-axis.

17 Find the equation of the curve which passes through the point (2, $-8$), and whose gradient at any point is given by $3x^2 - 6x - 2$.

18 If a curve passes through the point ($-1$, 4), and its gradient at any point is $2x - 1$, find the co-ordinates of the point on the curve at which the gradient is $-7$.

19 A body is moving along a straight line, and its acceleration after $t$ seconds is $(9 - 4t)$ cm s$^{-2}$. Its velocity after $t$ seconds is $v$ cm s$^{-1}$, and its initial velocity is 3 cm s$^{-1}$. Find $v$ in terms of $t$.

20 A curve passes through the point (2, 7), and its gradient is given by $3 + 8x - 6x^2$. Find the equation of the curve.

21 A curve passes through the point ($-4$, $-6$), and its gradient at any point is $2x + 3$. Find the points where the curve crosses the axis of $x$.

22 A particle moves along a straight line $\overline{AB}$, starting from A, and its velocity after $t$ seconds is $(12 - \frac{1}{3}t^2)$ m s$^{-1}$. If $s$ metres is the distance it has gone after $t$ seconds, find $s$ in terms of $t$. Find also the time that elapses before the particle comes to rest, and its distance from A at that instant.

**23** The gradient of a curve is given by $3x^2 - 4x + \dfrac{2}{x^2}$. Find the equation of the curve if the point $(2, -4)$ lies on it.

**24** A particle moves along a straight line in such a way that its velocity after $t$ seconds is $(3t^2 - 4t + 1)$ m s$^{-1}$. The distance of the particle from a fixed point A in the line is $s$ metres after $t$ seconds, and $s = 5$ when $t = 2$. Find the distance of the particle from A (i) initially, (ii) after 1 second, (iii) after 4 seconds.

**25** A body is projected vertically into the air with an initial velocity of $58 \cdot 8$ m s$^{-1}$, and the constant deceleration due to gravity is $9 \cdot 8$ m s$^{-2}$. If the velocity after $t$ seconds is $v$ m s$^{-1}$, find $v$ in terms of $t$. Find also $h$ in terms of $t$, where $h$ m is the height after $t$ seconds. Hence find the height after (i) 5 seconds, (ii) 7 seconds. What do these last two results imply?

## Areas

Fig. 195 shows part of the graph of the equation $y = f(x)$. The point P on the curve has co-ordinates $(x, y)$, and Q with co-ordinates $(x + \delta x, y + \delta y)$ is a neighbouring point on the curve.

Let A be the area bounded by $\overline{\text{OR}}$, $\overline{\text{OM}}$, $\overline{\text{MP}}$ and the curve RP.

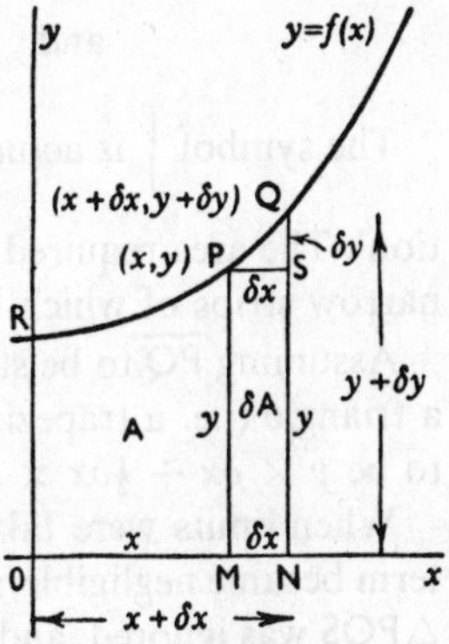

In going from P to Q,

$$x \text{ increases to } x + \delta x,$$
$$y \text{ ,, ,, } y + \delta y,$$
$$\text{and} \quad A \text{ ,, ,, } A + \delta A.$$

Fig. 195

Hence the area RPMO $= A$,

,, ,, RQNO $= A + \delta A$,

and ,, ,, PQNM $= \delta A$.

But if Q is very close to P, the curve between P and Q may be taken to be a straight line.

Hence $\delta A = \text{rect. PSNM} + \triangle \text{PQS}$

$$= y \times \delta x + \tfrac{1}{2}\delta x \times \delta y.$$

287

$$\therefore \quad \frac{\delta A}{\delta x} = y + \tfrac{1}{2}\delta y.$$

In the limit, as $\delta x \to 0$, $\dfrac{\delta A}{\delta x}$ becomes $\dfrac{dA}{dx}$, and $\delta y$ becomes negligible compared with $y$.

$$\text{Hence} \quad \frac{dA}{dx} = y,$$

$$\text{i.e.} \quad \frac{dA}{dx} = f(x).$$

Hence A is the function of which $f(x)$ is the derived function, i.e. A is found by integrating $f(x)$.

The symbol used for integration is $\displaystyle\int$,

$$\text{so that} \quad \frac{dA}{dx} = f(x)$$

$$\text{and} \quad A = \int f(x)\, dx.$$

The symbol $\displaystyle\int$ is actually an elongated S, standing for 'summation'. The area required is the sum of a very large number of very narrow strips of which PQNM is typical (see Fig. 196).

Assuming $\overline{PQ}$ to be straight, the area PQNM is a rectangle plus a triangle (i.e. a trapezium) and its area has already been shown to be $y \times \delta x + \tfrac{1}{2}\delta x \times \delta y$.

When limits were taken, the second term became negligible, so that in effect $\triangle PQS$ was ignored, and the trapezium PQNM taken to be approximately equal to the rectangle PSNM. It should be clear from Fig. 196 that if the elementary strips are made indefinitely narrow, the areas of the triangles will be negligible, and the area required will be the sum of the areas of the rectangles.

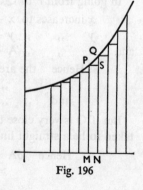
Fig. 196

**Example 6** *Find the area bounded by the curve* $y = 3x^2 - 4x + 2$, *the x-axis, and the lines* $x = 2$ *and* $x = 5$.

The curve is as in Fig. 197, cutting the $y$-axis at F. B and D are the points on the curve where $x = 2$ and $x = 5$, and $\overline{BC}$ and $\overline{DE}$ are perpendicular to the $x$-axis. ($\overline{BC}$ is called the **ordinate** $x = 2$; $\overline{DE}$ is the ordinate $x = 5$.) The area required is BDEC.

Let the required area be divided into a very large number of very narrow strips parallel to the $y$-axis, and let a typical strip be PQNM.

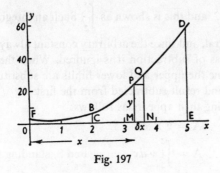

Fig. 197

Let the area FPMO be A; the area PQNM is $\delta$A.

Then, as before, $\qquad \dfrac{dA}{dx} = y$, approximately,

i.e. $\qquad \dfrac{dA}{dx} = 3x^2 - 4x + 2$

$\qquad \therefore \; A = x^3 - 2x^2 + 2x + c.$

Hence, putting $x = 5$,

$$\text{area FDEO} = 5^3 - 2 \times 5^2 + 2 \times 5 + c$$
$$= 125 - 50 + 10 + c$$
$$= 85 + c,$$

and putting $x = 2$,

$$\text{area FBCO} = 2^3 - 2 \times 2^2 + 2 \times 2 + c$$
$$= 4 + c.$$

*New General Mathematics*

∴ by subtraction,

$$\text{area BDEC} = (85 + c) - (4 + c)$$
$$= 81.$$

∴ the required area is 81 units of area.

Notice that the arbitrary constant disappears.

In practice, the working is arranged more concisely, and the symbol $\int$ is used. The process is called **integrating between the limits** 5 and 2, and this is shown as $\int_2^5$. Such an integral is called a **definite integral,** and since the arbitrary constant always disappears in the process of subtraction it is ignored. When the integration has been done the upper and lower limits are substituted in turn, and the second result subtracted from the first.

The working then appears as follows:

$$\delta A = y \times \delta x$$

$$\therefore A = \int_2^5 y\, dx$$

$$= \int_2^5 (3x^2 - 4x + 2)\, dx$$

$$= \left[ x^3 - 2x^2 + 2x \right]_2^5$$

$$= [125 - 50 + 10] - [8 - 8 + 4]$$
$$= 85 - 4$$
$$= 81.$$

∴ the required area is 81 units of area.

It will probably have been noticed in this working that $\dfrac{dA}{dx}$ has been treated as a fraction. The validity of this has not yet been justified, and to do so is beyond the scope of this chapter.

An **indefinite integral** is the kind which was discussed earlier in this chapter, in which there are no limits of integration, and in which the arbitrary constant appears.

**Example 7** *Find the area lying between the curve $y = 18 + 3x - x^2$ and the x-axis.*

The curve cuts the x-axis where $y = 0$,

i.e. where $18 + 3x - x^2 = 0$,

i.e. where $x = 6$ or $-3$.

These values are therefore the limits of integration.

There is a maximum of $20\frac{1}{4}$ when $x = 1\frac{1}{2}$.

∴ the curve is as in Fig. 198.

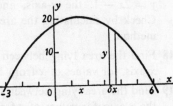

Fig. 198

$$A = \int_{-3}^{6} y \, dx$$

$$= \int_{-3}^{6} (18 + 3x - x^2) dx$$

$$= \left[ 18x + \frac{3x^2}{2} - \frac{x^3}{3} \right]_{-3}^{6}$$

$$= [108 + 54 - 72] - [-54 + 13\frac{1}{2} + 9]$$

$$= 90 - [-31\frac{1}{2}]$$

$$= 121\frac{1}{2}$$

∴ the required area is $121\frac{1}{2}$ units of area.

## Exercise 26d

Evaluate the following definite integrals.

**1** $\int_{1}^{2} x^2 \, dx$ **2** $\int_{2}^{4} x^3 \, dx$ **3** $\int_{3}^{5} 2x \, dx$ **4** $\int_{4}^{3} 3x^2 \, dx$

**5** $\int_{6}^{4} 5x \, dx$ **6** $\int_{3}^{8} 3 \, dx$ **7** $\int_{0}^{5} 9x^2 \, dx$ **8** $\int_{0}^{3} 8x^3 \, dx$

**9** $\int_{1}^{2} \frac{5}{x^2} \, dx$ **10** $\int_{4}^{2} \frac{4}{x^2} \, dx$ **11** $\int_{1}^{6} (6x + 2) \, dx$

**12** $\int_{0}^{3} (6x^2 - 4x + 1) \, dx$ **13** $\int_{3}^{6} \left( x + \frac{1}{x^2} \right) dx$

**14** $\int_{4}^{1} (3x^2 - 6x - 4) \, dx$ **15** $\int_{2}^{3} (5x^2 - 3x + 2) \, dx$

**16** Find the area enclosed between the curve $y = x^2$, the $x$-axis, and the ordinates $x = 1$ and $x = 3$.

**17** Find *by integration* the area bounded by the straight line $y = 2x - 1$, the $x$-axis, and the lines $x = 3$ and $x = 6$. Check by calculating the area of the trapezium by the usual method.

**18** Find the area lying between the curve $y = 3x^2 - 2$ and the $x$-axis, for values of $x$ from 1 to 3.

**19** Find the area lying between the curve $y = 2x^2 - 5x + 6$ and the $x$-axis, for values of $x$ from 1 to 3.

**20** Find the area lying between the curve $y = x^2 - 2x + 1$, the $x$-axis, and the line $x = 5$.

**21** Find the area enclosed by the curve $y = -x^2 + 7x - 10$ and the $x$-axis.

**22** Find the area enclosed by the curve $y = 10 + 3x - x^2$ and the $x$-axis.

**23** Find the area lying between the curve $y = \frac{1}{2}x^2 + 5$ and the $x$-axis, for values of $x$ from 3 to 4.

**24** Find the area bounded by the curve $y = 3x^2 - 12x + 16$, the $x$-axis, the $y$-axis, and the ordinate $x = 5$.

**25** Find the area bounded by the curve $y = 2x + \dfrac{1}{x^2}$, the $x$-axis, and the ordinates $x = 2$ and $x = 5$.

**26** Find the area lying between the curve $y = -x^2 + 8x - 7$ and the $x$-axis.

**27** Find the area enclosed by the two axes, the line $x = 6$, and the curve $y = x^2 + 4x + 1$.

**28** Find the area bounded by the curve $y = 6 + 5x - x^2$ and the $x$-axis.

**29** Find the area lying between the curve $y = x^2$ and the straight line $y = 4x$. (*Difference of two areas.*)

**30** Find the area lying between the curves $y = x^2$ and $y = \frac{1}{2}x^2$ from the origin as far as $x = 6$.

## Volumes of revolution

**Example 8** *The curve $y^2 = 6x$ is revolved about the x-axis. Find the volume generated by that part of the curve which lies between $x = 1$ and $x = 4$.*

Consider the volume as made up of a very large number of very thin circular slices, with the $x$-axis passing through the centre of each, and perpendicular to each.

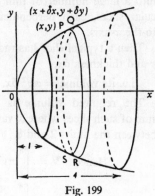

In Fig. 199, PQRS is a typical slice, where P has co-ordinates $(x, y)$, and Q is $(x + \delta x, y + \delta y)$.

Let the volume as far as $\overline{PS}$ be denoted by V.

In passing from P to Q, $x$ increases to $x + \delta x$, $y$ increases to $y + \delta y$, and the volume V increases to $V + \delta V$.

Hence the volume as far as $\overline{QR}$ is $V + \delta V$, and the volume of the slice PQRS is $\delta V$.

Fig. 199

The thickness of the slice is $\delta x$, and the radius is $y$ approximately.

Hence $\delta V = \pi y^2 \, \delta x$ approximately.

Since the required volume is the sum of a large number of slices of which this is a typical one, the result is obtained by integrating $\pi y^2 \, dx$.

The limits of integration are 1 and 4.

$$\text{Hence} \quad V = \int_1^4 \pi y^2 \, dx$$

$$= \int_1^4 \pi 6x \, dx$$

$$= \left[ \pi 3x^2 \right]_1^4$$

$$= \pi \times 3 \times 4^2 - \pi \times 3 \times 1^2$$

$$= 3\pi(16 - 1)$$

$$= 45\pi.$$

$\therefore$ the required result is $45\pi$ units of volume.

The curve $y^2 = 6x$ is a parabola, and the volume obtained by revolving it about its axis is called a **paraboloid of revolution.**

**Example 9** *Find the volume generated by revolving about the x-axis that part of the curve $xy = 2$ which lies between $x = 2$ and $x = 8$.*

Divide the required volume into a large number of thin circular slices, each perpendicular to the $x$-axis.

Then a typical slice has radius $y$ and thickness $\delta x$,

i.e. its volume $= \pi y^2\, \delta x$.

The required volume is the sum of such slices where $x$ varies between the limits 2 and 8.

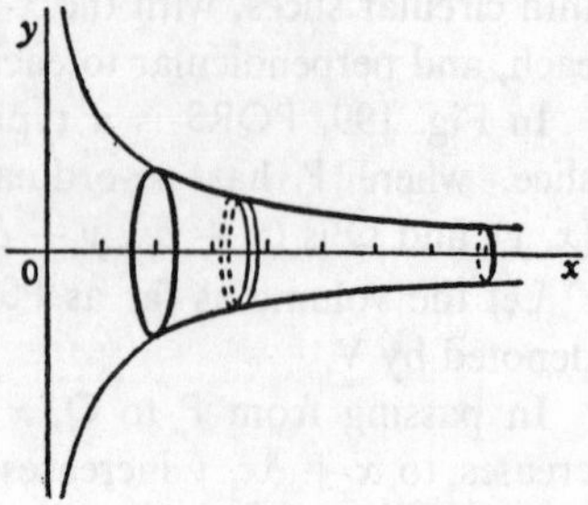

Fig. 200

Hence
$$V = \int_2^8 \pi y^2\, dx$$
$$= \int_2^8 \pi \frac{4}{x^2}\, dx \quad \text{since } y = \frac{2}{x}$$
$$= 4\pi \left[ -\frac{1}{x} \right]_2^8$$
$$= 4\pi [(-\tfrac{1}{8}) - (-\tfrac{1}{2})]$$
$$= 4\pi [-\tfrac{1}{8} + \tfrac{1}{2}]$$
$$= 4\pi \times \tfrac{3}{8}$$
$$= \frac{3\pi}{2}.$$

$\therefore$ the required result is $\dfrac{3\pi}{2}$ units of volume.

**Exercise 26e**

*In calculating these answers, do not substitute for $\pi$.*

1 The curve $y^2 = 5x + 2$ is revolved about the $x$-axis. Find the volume generated by that part of the curve which lies between $x = 2$ and $x = 4$.

**2** Find the volume generated by revolving about the $x$-axis that part of the curve $y = \frac{1}{3}x^2$ which lies between the origin and $x = 3$.

**3** Find, *by integration*, the volume of the cone formed by rotating about the $x$-axis the line $y = 2x$ for values of $x$ from 0 to 5. Check by calculating the volume of the cone in the usual way.

**4** The curve $y = \dfrac{6}{x}$ is revolved about the $x$-axis. Find the volume generated for values of $x$ from 2 to 9.

**5** The equation $x^2 + y^2 = 9$ represents a circle of radius 3 units, with its centre at the origin. By integrating between the limits $-3$ and $+3$, find the volume of a sphere of radius 3 units.

**6** Find, by integrating, the volume of the frustum of a cone formed by rotating about the $x$-axis the line $y = \frac{1}{2}x$ for values of $x$ from 3 to 6.

**7** Find the volume generated by revolving about the $x$-axis that part of the curve $y = x^2 - x$ which lies between its intersections with the $x$-axis.

**8** The curve $x^2 - y^2 = 4$ is revolved about the $x$-axis. Find the volume generated by the part of the curve from $x = 3$ to $x = 4$.

**9** The equation $x^2 + y^2 = 16$ represents a circle of radius 4 units, with its centre at the origin. Find the volume of the zone of a sphere of radius 4 units, cut off by parallel planes at distances of 1 unit and 3 units from the centre.

**10** Sketch the curve $y = x^2 - x - 2$. The part of the curve lying between the points where it cuts the $x$-axis is rotated about that axis. Find the volume so generated.

# Quick revision tests

## I

1 How many squares are there (Fig. 201)?

2 Write down the next two terms in the series:

  (i) $\frac{1}{2}, \frac{3}{4}, \frac{5}{6}, \frac{7}{8}, \ldots$

  (ii) $1, 2, 4, 7, 11, \ldots$

  (iii) $1, -2a, 3a^2, -4a^3, \ldots$

  (iv) $18, 12, 8, 5\frac{1}{3}, \ldots$

  (v) $2, 5, 10, 17, \ldots$

3 Write down the angles of the triangle (Fig. 202).

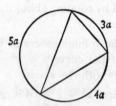

Fig. 201                Fig. 202

4 Without actually working them out, estimate likely answers to the following (i.e. make a rough check):

$$\frac{9 \cdot 83 \times 2 \cdot 84}{6 \cdot 91^2}, \quad \sqrt[3]{0 \cdot 025}, \quad \frac{0 \cdot 031\,6}{0 \cdot 000\,527}, \quad \left(\frac{17 \cdot 96}{6 \cdot 05}\right)^3.$$

5 Write in order of size, smallest first:

  (i) $\frac{13}{40}, \frac{1}{3}, 0 \cdot 3$             (ii) $2a^2, (2a)^2, (1\frac{1}{2}a)^2$

6 If the suffix denotes the base of the number, find $x$ and $y$ when
(i) $312_4 = x_3$, (ii) $101\,101_2 = y_5$.

## II

1 Write down $\begin{cases} \text{as fractions } 20\%, 15\%, 36\%, 12\frac{1}{2}\%, 18\frac{3}{4}\%. \\ \text{as percentages } \frac{3}{10}, \frac{3}{8}, \frac{5}{12}, \frac{1}{15}, \frac{4}{25}. \end{cases}$

**2** Solve the equations:

   (i) $x^2 - 4x = 5$         (ii) $x^2 - 4x = -4$

   (iii) $x^2 - 4x = 0$       (iv) $x^2 - 4 = 0$

**3** Find $a$, $b$, $c$, $d$ (Fig. 203)

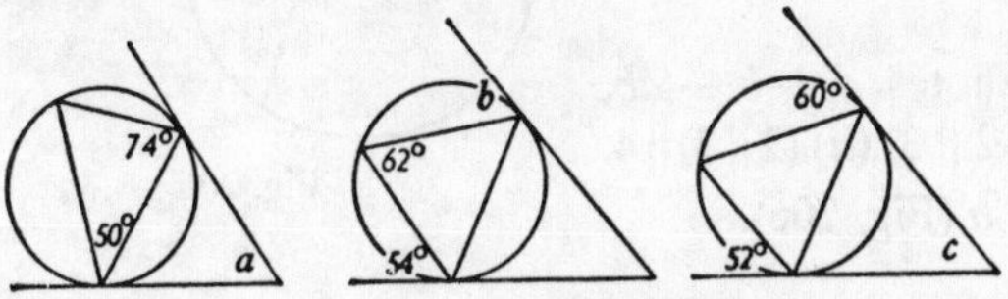

Fig. 203

**4** Fig. 204 shows the dimensions of a room.

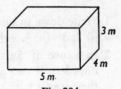

   (i) A wall-to-wall carpet 80 cm wide is laid lengthways. How many metres are needed?

   (ii) Find the cost of painting the ceiling at 18p per square metre.

Fig. 204

   (iii) Find the cost of painting the walls at 30p per square metre.

**5** How many things costing 21p each can be bought for £4, and how much is left over?

**6** Simplify

   (i) $\dfrac{2}{ab} - \dfrac{3}{bc}$     (ii) $\dfrac{5a - b}{4} - \dfrac{3a + 2b}{6}$

   (iii) $\dfrac{2a + b}{a} + \dfrac{a + 3b}{b}$     (iv) $\dfrac{4}{m + n} - \dfrac{3}{m - n}.$

## III

**1** Write down the bearings of A, B, C from the central point, each in two ways (Fig. 205).

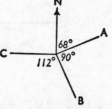

**2** Factorise:

   (i) $x^2 - ax + bx - ab$

   (ii) $x^2 - a^2 - bx + ab$

   (iii) $x^2 + a^2 - 2ax - b^2$

Fig. 205

**3** $\sin \theta = \frac{3}{5}$ and $\theta$ is acute. Write down the values of $\tan \theta$ and $\sec \theta$ (no tables).

**4** Simplify $(2a)^2$, $2a^{-2}$, $(2a)^{-2}$, $\sqrt{1\frac{9}{16}}$.

**5** If $a \parallel b$ denotes $a + b - ab$, evaluate (i) $2 \parallel 3$, (ii) $(2 \parallel 3) \parallel 4$.

**6** Find $a$ and $b$ (Fig. 206).

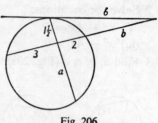

Fig. 206

## IV

**1** Write down in simplified form the equations whose roots are:
(i) 2, 3   (ii) $\frac{1}{2}$, $-\frac{3}{4}$   (iii) 0, $-1$, 2

**2** In a tube of 'Smarties' there are 4 red, 4 green and 4 yellow ones left. If two are shaken out, what is the probability that they are (i) both red, (ii) both the same colour, (iii) different colours?

**3** Simplify, leaving in 'bar' form:
$\bar{1}\cdot4 + \bar{2}\cdot9$,   $\bar{1}\cdot4 - \bar{2}\cdot9$,   $\bar{2}\cdot34 \times 4$,   $\bar{2}\cdot23 \div 3$

**4** A box, with a bottom but no lid, is made to the size shown in Fig. 207 out of wood half a centimetre thick. How many cm³ of wood are there in the box?

**5** What is the tax on £110·50 at 46p in the £?

**6** Find $x$ in degrees (Fig. 208).

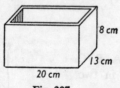

Fig. 207

Fig. 208

## V

**1** $\begin{pmatrix} 2 & 6 \\ 7 & -3 \end{pmatrix} \begin{pmatrix} p & q \\ r & s \end{pmatrix} = \begin{pmatrix} 0 & 28 \\ 24 & 2 \end{pmatrix}$. Find $p, q, r, s$.

**2** Write down the L.C.M. of:

  (i) $25a^3b$, $30a^2b^2$, $12ab^3$

  (ii) $14xyz$, $21x^2y$, $6y^3$

  (iii) $2a - 2b$, $3a + 3b$, $4a^2 + 4ab$

  (iv) $4a - 2b$, $4a^2 - b^2$, $6a + 3b$

  (v) $4a - 2b$, $6a + 3b$, $4a^2 + 4ab + b^2$

**3** A large number of cards, each bearing one of the digits 1 to 9, are available: two cards are drawn at random and placed side by side to form a two-digit number. What is the probability of drawing (i) two cards bearing the same digit, (ii) two consecutive digits (e.g. 45 or 54)?

**4** Find $x$ if $\quad a - x = b, \quad ax = b, \quad \dfrac{a}{x} = b, \quad \dfrac{a}{x} = \dfrac{b}{x} - c.$

**5** The volumes of the sphere and the cone in Fig. 209 are equal. Find $r$.

Fig. 209

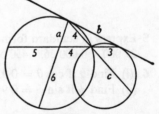

Fig. 210

**6** Find $a$, $b$ and $c$ in Fig. 210.

## VI

**1** Simplify as far as possible:

$$\frac{a^2 - b^2}{a^2 - ab}, \quad \frac{(a - b)^2}{a^2 - ab}, \quad \frac{a^2 + b^2}{a^2 + ab}, \quad \frac{(a + b)^2}{a^2 + ab}, \quad \frac{a^2 - b^2}{a^2 + ab}.$$

**2** Find *a*, *b*, *c*, *d* in Fig. 211.

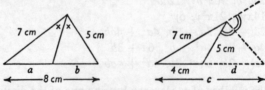

Fig. 211

**3** If $4^{x-1} = 8$, what is *x*?

**4** Find the volumes and total surface areas of each of the solids illustrated in Fig. 212. All lengths given are in cm. Leave $\pi$ in the answer if it occurs.

Fig. 212

**5** Express in standard form (e.g. $4.3 \times 10^{-8}$):
27 000,  0.000 36,  $450 \times 10^{-8}$,  $0.067 \times 10^{15}$.

**6** (i) Find $\theta$ if $\cos \theta = 0.913\ 3$ and $\theta$ is an angle of a triangle.
   (ii) Find $\phi$ if $\sin \phi = 0.913\ 3$ and $\phi$ is an angle of a triangle.

## VII

**1** Express to 3 significant figures:
50.837, 0.063 07, 76 843, 0.300 7, 6.666 6.

**2** Find *x* in Fig. 213.

**3** Solve as far as possible without evaluating square roots:

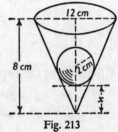

   (i) $3x^2 - 5x = 0$
   (ii) $3x^2 - 5x = 12$
   (iii) $3x^2 - 5x = 1$.

Fig. 213

**4** Find *a*, *b*, *c*, *d*, in Fig. 214.

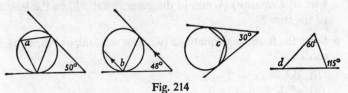

Fig. 214

**5** Evaluate (+ve value only):

$\sqrt{9}$, $\sqrt{0.9}$, $\sqrt{90}$, $\sqrt{900}$, $\sqrt{0.09}$, $\sqrt{\frac{1}{9}}$.

**6** Factorise

$4a^2 + 37a + 9$, $\quad 4b^2 + 20b + 9$,
$4c^2 + 15c + 9$, $\quad 4d^2 + 13d + 9$.

## VIII

**1** Write down the values of $\dfrac{dy}{dx}$ and $\displaystyle\int y\,dx$ when:

(i) $y = x^5$ (ii) $y = x^{\frac{1}{2}}$ (iii) $y = \dfrac{x^2 + 1}{x^2}$ (iv) $y = 3x^2 - 4x^{-\frac{1}{2}}$.

**2** Express as powers of 3:
$\frac{1}{9}$, $\quad 3\sqrt{3}$, $\quad 9^x$, $\quad 27^{-1\frac{1}{3}}$, $\quad 1$.

**3** In Fig. 215 AB = 9 cm, BC = 5 cm, CA = 8 cm. Find the radii of the circles.

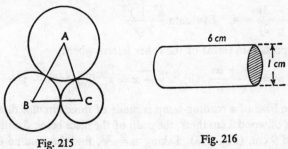

Fig. 215

Fig. 216

**4** A is $(-2, 3)$, B is $(4, 7)$ and C is $(-1, 8)$. Prove that $\overline{AC}$ is perpendicular to $\overline{BC}$.

**5** If the cylinder of metal shown in Fig. 216 is pulled out into a wire (i) 1 mm, (ii) $\frac{1}{10}$ mm in diameter, what will be the length of the wire?

**6** Solve the following equations (without working out the square roots):

(i) $3x^2 - 2x - 2 = 0$
(ii) $x^2 + 3x + 1 = 0$
(iii) $5x^2 + 8x - 3 = 0$.

# IX

**1** A sold an object to B at a profit of 20% and B later sold it to C at a loss of 20% on what it cost him. How did the final price compare with the original one?

**2** In Fig. 217 find $a$, $b$ and the ratio of the areas X : Y.

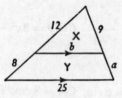

Fig. 217

Fig. 218

**3** $\dfrac{2x - 3y}{3x - 2y} = 4$. Evaluate $\dfrac{x^2 + y^2}{2xy}$.

**4** Express $x$ in terms of the other letters when:

(i) $m = \dfrac{ax + bn}{x + n}$   (ii) $\sqrt{y - x} = z$   (iii) $\sqrt{x^2 - y^2} = z$.

**5** The base of a reading-lamp is made of three circular discs cut out of wood 2 cm thick, the radii of the discs being 3 cm, 6 cm and 9 cm. (Fig. 218). Taking $\pi = \frac{22}{7}$, find the volume of the base in cm³.

**6** Evaluate $\log_2 8$,   $\log_3 \frac{1}{9}$,   $\log_4 32$,   $\log_5 5\sqrt{5}$,   $\log_7 1$.

## X

1 Divide 174 into two parts, one of which is 45% of the other.

2 By writing down two different expressions for the value of sin $\theta$ in the triangle shown in Fig. 219, find $x$ in terms of $a$, $b$ and $c$. Similarly find $y$ in terms of $a$, $b$ and $c$.

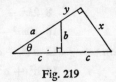

Fig. 219

3 A jar of marmalade has a mass of 3·2 kg when half full and 2·3 kg when one quarter full. What is the mass of the full jar?

4 If $x + \dfrac{1}{x} = 3$, evaluate $x^2 + \dfrac{1}{x^2}$ and $x^3 + \dfrac{1}{x^3}$.

5 Evaluate in standard form (i) $\dfrac{138 \times 10^5}{6 \times 10^{-3}}$ (ii) $\sqrt{14\cdot4 \times 10^9}$.

6 Two geometrically similar cans, made out of the same sheet of tinplate, have masses of 90 g and 810 g when empty. If the smaller holds 250 g of sugar, how much does the larger one hold?

## XI

### Logarithms ('standard form')

Answers to 2 sig. fig., e.g. $2\cdot5 \times 10^{-3}$

1 $(5\cdot7 \times 10^{-3})^3$    2 $\sqrt{8\cdot4 \times 10^{-11}}$    3 $\dfrac{17\cdot4 \times 5\cdot29}{3\cdot87 \times 10^6}$

4 $\pi R^2$, where $R = 6\cdot7 \times 10^5$    5 $\frac{4}{3}\pi R^3$, where $R = 3\cdot5 \times 10^{-4}$

If $a = 3\cdot9 \times 10^{17}$, $b = 4\cdot3 \times 10^8$, $c = 6\cdot5 \times 10^{-9}$, evaluate

6 $ab$    7 $ac$    8 $abc$    9 $bc^2$    10 $\dfrac{a}{b}$    11 $\dfrac{b}{c}$    12 $a^2c^3$

## XII

### Factors

1  $3a^2 + 5a + 2$

2  $3b^2 + 5b - 2$

3  $3c^2 - 5c + 2$

4  $3d^2 - 5d - 2$

5  $t^2 - 15t + 54$

6  $s^2 - 15s - 54$

7  $2h^2 - 15h - 27$

8  $2k^2 - 15k + 27$

9  $10l^2 - 41l - 45$

10  $10m^2 - 43m + 45$

11  $dm - en - dn + em$

12  $ax^2 - axy - bxy + by^2$

13  $a^3 + a^2 + a + 1$

14  $a^3 + a^2 - a - 1$

15  $l(l + m) - n(m + n)$

16  $p(q - r + s) - s(p + q - r)$

17  $x^3 - 8$

18  $8a^3 + 27b^3$

19  $a^2 + 2bc - b^2 - c^2$

20  $x^4 + 20x^2 - 21$

# *Revision examples*

## XXXI

**1** **OA** is the vector **a** and **OB** the
vector **b**. The points D and E are
such that AD = $\frac{1}{3}$AB and OE
= $\frac{1}{3}$OA.

Express, in terms of **a** and **b**,
the vectors **OD** and **BE**.

If OX = kOD and BX = lBE,
express the vector **OX** in two
different ways and hence deduce

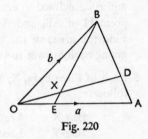

Fig. 220

(i) the values of $k$ and $l$,

(ii) the vector **OX** in terms of **a** and **b** only.          (*C*)

**2** A group of 100 children were given two similar tests with the
following results:

| Mark | 0 | 1 | 2 | 3 | 4 | 5 | 6 | 7 | 8 | 9 | 10 | 11 | 12 | 13 | 14 | 15 |
|---|---|---|---|---|---|---|---|---|---|---|---|---|---|---|---|---|
| Frequency (1) | 0 | 0 | 1 | 4 | 6 | 11 | 8 | 10 | 14 | 7 | 11 | 5 | 8 | 8 | 3 | 4 |
| Frequency (2) | 1 | 1 | 6 | 8 | 2 | 8 | 6 | 13 | 14 | 13 | 4 | 8 | 5 | 7 | 3 | 1 |

On the same graph paper and on the same scales plot the
cumulative frequency curves for Test (1) and Test (2) for
frequencies of children obtaining a certain mark or below that
mark.

Estimate the median mark for each test and comment briefly
on any differences observed between the two curves.          (*L*)

**3** (i) Solve $x + y = 2$, $3x^2 - 2xy + y^2 = 2$.

(ii) The resistance to the motion of a train is R newtons per
tonne, where R is the sum of two terms, the first being a constant (A) and the second varying as the square of the speed
(V km h$^{-1}$). When V = 40, R = 66, and when V = 60,

305

R = 96. Find the relation between R and V, and the resistance for a speed of 50 km h⁻¹.                                                      (*W*)*

**4** A circle of radius 12 cm has a sector cut off by two radii $\overline{AB}$ and $\overline{AC}$, inclined to each other at 50°. C is joined to the mid-point M of $\overline{AB}$, and A is joined to the mid-point P of $\overline{CM}$. Find the areas of the three parts of the sector thus formed, giving each answer to the nearest tenth of a cm².     (*OC*)*

**5** Each of three bags, X, Y and Z, contains 12 balls made up as follows:

| | | | |
|---|---|---|---|
| Bag X | 4 red | 4 white | 4 black |
| Bag Y | 3 red | 6 white | 3 black |
| Bag Z | 6 red | 2 white | 4 black |

A bag is chosen at random; a ball drawn from it and replaced, and then a second ball drawn from it. With the help of a probability tree find the probability that (i) both balls should be red; (ii) the first should be black and the second white.     (*MEI*)

**6** $\overline{AB}$ is a straight line trisected at F and E. $\overline{FD}$ and $\overline{EC}$ are lines perpendicular to $\overline{AB}$ and on opposite sides of it. Prove that
$$AC^2 + AD^2 = BD^2 + BC^2. \quad (L)$$

**7** The flow diagram describes a computer programme to read three numbers A, B and C (which may be assumed to be positive) and to calculate and print a number T.

Calculate the value of T printed when the values of A, B and C read are 3, 4 and 5.

Amend the flow diagram so that after printing a value of T it goes

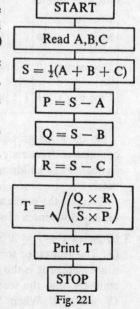

Fig. 221

on to read further sets of values of A, B and C, or to stop when no more are available.

If A = 1, B = 2 and C = 10 the calculation will break down. At what stage in the flow diagram will this happen, and why? *(MEI)*

**8** Find the area between the curve $y = x + 2 + \dfrac{1}{x^2}$, the $x$-axis and the lines $x = 1$ and $x = 2$. *(N)*

**9** If $y = x^3 - 5x^2 - 8x + 12$, find for what values of $x$ maximum or minimum values of $y$ occur, and show carefully whether each is a maximum or a minimum value. *(O)*

**10** A particle moves along the $x$-axis in such a way that its distance $x$ m from the origin after $t$ seconds is given by the formula $x = 7t + 12t^2$. What distance does it travel in the $n$th second? What are its velocity and acceleration at the end of the $n$th second? *(OC)\**

# XXXII

**1** (i) With the help of logarithm tables find, correct to three significant figures, the value of $\dfrac{(85 \cdot 37)^{\frac{1}{3}} - 1 \cdot 06}{3}$.

(ii) Without using tables, find the values of $216^{\frac{2}{3}}$, $0 \cdot 04^{-\frac{3}{2}}$. *(C)*

**2** A, B and C contribute respectively £3 500, £5 000 and £10 000 as capital to an enterprise. It is agreed that out of the total profits A shall receive £400 for services as director; that each shall receive 15% upon the first £2 000 of his capital; and that the remaining profit, if any, shall be divided in proportion to their additional amounts of capital. If A receives in all £1 030, find the total profit, and the amounts which B and C will receive. *(W)*

**3** (i) Construct a triangle ABC in which AB = 5 cm, BC = 6 cm and CA = 7 cm. Construct a triangle ACD equal in area to △ABC with the angle ADC equal to 48°.

(ii) AB = 5 cm. Construct geometrically a line such that the perpendiculars to it from A and B are 3 cm and 7 cm respectively. The line cuts $\overline{BA}$ produced in C: find AC by measurement and calculation. (*L*)*

4 In a triangle ABC perpendiculars $\overline{AL}$, $\overline{BM}$ are drawn to $\overline{BC}$, $\overline{CA}$, meeting them in L, M respectively. If the triangle ALB is equal in area to the triangle ABM, prove that $\triangle$ABC is isosceles. (*N*)

5 Fig. 222 shows a system of paths, all exactly alike, connecting five points A, B, C, D, E. A man starts from A towards the circle. Every time he reaches any of the junctions P, Q, R, S, T he is equally likely to take either of the two possible paths, but having arrived at any of A, B, C, D, E he can not return, and he must stop on reaching either of R, S for the second time. Find the probability that he will finish at (i) A, (ii) B, (iii) C, (iv) R. (*MEI*)

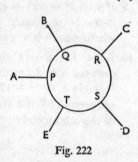

Fig. 222

6 Standing at a point on the 70-m contour I can see a wireless mast which I know to be on the 150-m contour. From where I am the angle of elevation of the foot of the mast is 10° and of the top 12°. Calculate (*a*) the horizontal distance of the mast from me, and (*b*) the height of the mast. (*S*)*

7 Plot the graphs of $y = \dfrac{3x + 2}{x + 2}$ and $y = \dfrac{x(x + 3)}{4}$ between $x = -1$ and $x = +2$, and read off the values of $x$ at the points where the curves intersect. Show that these two values will be roots of the equation $x^3 + 5x^2 = 6x + 8$. (*N*)

8 Differentiate (i) $(2x + 3)^3$, (ii) $x^5(1 + 2x)$.

Find $y$ if $\dfrac{dy}{dx} = 2 + \dfrac{1}{x^2}$, and $y = 3$ when $x = 1$. (*O*)

**9** A point moves in a straight line with velocity $v$ m s$^{-1}$ after $t$ seconds, and $v$ is given by the expression $3t^2 + 2t$. Find the acceleration of the point at the end of 2 seconds, and the distance it travels in the fourth second. (*OC*)*

**10** For the curve $y = x(3 - x)$,

  (i) find the greatest value of $y$,

  (ii) find the area between the $x$-axis and the curve in the first quadrant,

  (iii) show that, if the area in (ii) is revolved about the $x$-axis, the volume thus obtained is $8 \cdot 1\pi$. (*N*)

## XXXIII

**1** Fig. 223 illustrates a shed on a horizontal rectangular base, lengths being given in metres.

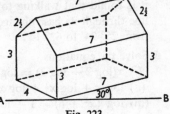

Fig. 223

  (i) Calculate the total area, in m$^2$, of the walls and roof.

  (ii) Calculate the volume, in m$^3$, of the shed.

  (iii) Using a scale of 1 cm to represent 1 m, draw the plan of the shed, and the elevation on the vertical plane through the horizontal line $\overline{AB}$, which is inclined at 30° to the longer sides of the shed. (*W*)*

**2** In a group of 100 language students every student studied at least one language from French, German and Russian.

Ten studied Russian only; 18 studied Russian but not German; 38 studied Russian and French; 59 studied Russian; 60 studied French; 42 studied French and German.

Represent on a Venn diagram the set F of those studying French, the set G of those studying German and the set R of those studying Russian. Determine (i) the number studying only one language, (ii) the number studying two and only two languages.

Describe in words the sets (a) F ∪ G ∪ R, (b) F ∩ G ∩ R, (c) F′ ∩ G′, and evaluate the number of students in each of the sets (a), (b) and (c). *(O)*

3 ABCDE is a pentagon in which $\widehat{A} = \widehat{B} = 90°$, $\widehat{D} = 57°$, AB = 3·58 cm and AE = BC = 6·74 cm. If, in addition, DE = DC, calculate DE and the area of the triangle DAB. *(L)\**

4 Find the values of $a$ and $b$ if the expression $ax^3 + bx^2 - 28x + 15$ is exactly divisible by $(x + 3)$, and leaves a remainder of $-60$ when divided by $(x - 3)$.

When $a$ and $b$ have these values, find all the values of $x$ for which the expression is zero. *(OC)*

5 Find, correct to the nearest metre, the height of a chimney when it is found that walking towards it 50 m along a horizontal line through its base changes the angle of elevation of its top from 25° 24′ to 62° 14′. *(N)\**

6 Solve the equations
  (i) $x(\log 2 + \log 3) = \log 12$,
  (ii) $\log x + \log x^2 + \log x^3 = 1$,
  (iii) $\log (x^2 + 6) = 1 + \log (x - 1)$, the logs being all to base 10. In (i) and (ii) give answers to 3 dec. pl. *(OC)*

7 Two players A and B are frequently opponents at tennis and, on the average, A wins 3 sets out of 5. During a match, to be decided by the first player to win three sets, the score is 2 sets to 0 in favour of B. Calculate the probability that A will win the match.

On another occasion the score is 1 set all. By a probability tree, or otherwise, calculate the probability that B will win this match. *(MEI)*

8 (i) Differentiate w.r. to $x$   (a) $(x^2 - 1)^2$,   (b) $\dfrac{x^3 - x - 2}{x^2}$.

  (ii) Evaluate (a) $\displaystyle\int_1^4 \left(x - \frac{1}{x^2}\right) dx$,

  (b) $\displaystyle\int_{-1}^{+1} (x^3 - x^2 + 1) dx$. *(OC)*

**9** (i) Find the gradient of the curve $y = x + \dfrac{1}{x^2}$ at the point at which $x = 1$. Draw a freehand figure showing the point at which $x = 1$ and the tangent at that point.

(ii) Find the area bounded by the curve $y = x + \dfrac{1}{x^2}$, the ordinates at the points $x = 1$ and $x = 4$, and the $x$-axis.

(*O*)

**10** A particle moves along a straight line $\overline{\text{OX}}$ so that $t$ seconds after passing through O it is $s$ m from O, where $s = 3t^2 - \frac{1}{2}t^3$. Find

  (i) the velocity and acceleration 5 seconds after passing through O, and explain the meanings of the signs;

  (ii) the distance from O of the particle when it is momentarily at rest;

  (iii) the maximum velocity and acceleration in the direction $\overrightarrow{\text{OX}}$.

(*L*)*

## XXXIV

**1** Three men, A, B and C, agreed to share the expenses of a fishing expedition in the ratio $2 : 3 : 4$. A paid 25p for the hire of a boat, B paid 70p for meals, while C paid 49p for travelling expenses. How much must A and C each pay B to settle their agreed shares? (*L*)*

**2** Two dice are loaded so that, in each, the probability of a 6 turning up is $\frac{1}{2}$ and the probabilities of the other numbers (1, 2, 3, 4, 5) are all equal.

If the two dice are thrown simultaneously, find the probability of obtaining a total score of 9 or more. (*MEI*)

**3** Fig. 224 shows a pyramid with vertex V standing on a rectangular base ABCD. AB = 5·4 cm, BC = 7·8 cm, the vertical height of the pyramid is 4·5 cm, and VA = VB = 6·6 cm.

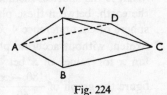

Fig. 224

311

By drawing, obtain the length of the projection of $\overline{VA}$ on the base ABCD. Draw also the plan, and the elevation in a direction perpendicular to $\overline{BC}$, and determine the inclination of the face VCD to the base. (All arcs and lines used in the construction should be left clearly visible: squared paper may be used.)

$(W)^*$

4 Construct a triangle ABC in which the base BC = 8 cm, the sum of the other sides is 9 cm, and the angle A is 120°. Measure AB as accurately as possible.

Explain your construction briefly. $(N)^*$

5 A sports ground (Fig. 225) is to be built with a rectangular playing field $x$ m long and $y$ m wide. The perimeter of this field must be more than 500 m but less than 700 m, and the length must be less than twice the width. Write down three inequalities (other than $x > 0$, $y > 0$ and $x > y$) satisfied by $x$ and $y$.

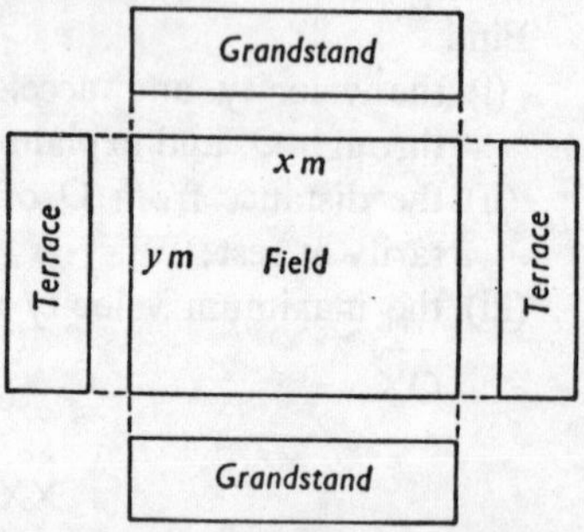

Fig. 225

The grandstand on each of the longer sides will be designed to seat 50 spectators for each metre of its length, while the terrace along each of the shorter sides will be able to hold 20 per metre. If a crowd of 25 000 is to be accommodated determine, using a graphical method, the range of possible values of $x$. $(C)$

6 The latitude and longitude of Cape Town are 33° 40′ S and 18° 30′ E: those of Otranto in Italy are 40° 10′ N and 18° 30′ E. What is the shortest distance, measured along the surface of the earth, between these places? (Consider the earth to be a sphere of circumference $4 \times 10^4$ km.) $(N)^*$

7 Sketch, without accurate plotting, the shape of the graph of tan $x$ for values of $x$ between 0° and 90°, and in the same figure the graph of $\dfrac{180 - x}{60}$.

By accurately plotting these graphs for values of $x$ between 50° and 70°, find a solution of the equation
$$60 \tan x = 180 - x. \qquad (W)$$

8 Find $y$ if $\dfrac{dy}{dx} = 3x^3 + 4x + \dfrac{2}{x^2}$, and $y = 1$ when $x = 1$.

$(O)$

9 An open tank with a square horizontal section is to be constructed to contain 108 m³ of acid. If the side of the square section is $x$ m, find an expression in terms of $x$ for the total surface area of the inside of the tank.

The tank is to be lined with sheet lead at £1·50 per m². Find the dimensions of the tank and the cost of lining it when this cost has its least value. $(L)^*$

10 Draw a rough sketch of the curve $y^2 = 16x$ between $x = 0$ and $x = 4$. Calculate the area contained between the curve and the line $x = 4$, and the volume obtained by completely rotating that area about the axis of $x$. $(OC)$

## XXXV

1 Two factories A and B are both engaged in the manufacture of the same two products P and Q. The respective numbers manufactured per week are as follows:

| Factory | A | | B | |
|---|---|---|---|---|
| Product | P | Q | P | Q |
| Number made per week | $3x$ | $y$ | $2x$ | $2y$ |

The following requirements are to be met:

(i) the total production of *both* products from *both* factories is not to exceed 60;

(ii) the number of *both* products manufactured by A is to exceed that manufactured by B;

(iii) the total production of Q must not be less than 15.

Express each of these requirements in the form of an inequality and illustrate graphically, shading the area in which all the conditions are satisfied.

Find from your graph the (whole number) values of $x$ and $y$ which, while complying with all the given conditions, will make the total production of P and Q as large as possible. *(MEI)*

**2** State the meaning given to $Z^{-1}$.

A formula for intensity of light contains the expression $D = (1 - Zp)(1 - Z^{-1}p)$.

Multiply this out and arrange the result as a quadratic expression in $p$, simplifying the $p^2$ term.

If $Z + Z^{-1} = 2(1 - 2S^2)$, show that $D = (1 - p)^2 + 4pS^2$.

If $C^2 + S^2 = 1$, obtain an expression for D in terms of $p$ and C in a similar form, with two terms only. *(S)*

**3** In a certain year it is found that one nut in every 5 grown in a certain district is bad. Find the probability that, of a given sample of 8 such nuts, 2 will be found to be bad. Express your answer as a decimal correct to 2 places. *(MEI)*

**4** X is a point between P and Q on the common chord $\overline{PQ}$ of two intersecting circles, and a line through X meets the circles at A, C, B, D, in that order. Prove that $AX : CX = DX : BX$. *(W)*

**5** In a triangle ABC, $AB = AC$. From a point X on $\overline{BC}$ produced a perpendicular $\overline{XR}$ is drawn to $\overline{AB}$ and a perpendicular $\overline{XS}$ to $\overline{AC}$ produced. Show that $XR - XS$ is the same, whatever the position of X on $\overline{BC}$ produced.

Calculate AB when $XR - XS = 6$ cm and $BC = 7.5$ cm. *(N)\**

**6** A and B are two points at sea-level, and B is 2 000 m due north of A. C, the top of a hill, bears N 30° E from A and N 70° E from B. The angle of elevation of C from A is 8° 6'. Calculate the height of C above sea-level, and also the angle of elevation of C from B. *(W)\**

**7** A, B, C and D are respectively the matrices

$$\begin{pmatrix} 2 & 0 \\ 0 & 3 \end{pmatrix} \quad \begin{pmatrix} 5 & 0 \\ 0 & 7 \end{pmatrix} \quad \begin{pmatrix} 2 & 1 \\ 1 & 1 \end{pmatrix} \quad \begin{pmatrix} 1 & -1 \\ -1 & 2 \end{pmatrix}.$$

(i) Determine the matrix products AB, BA, BC, CB, CD and DC. Hence state which of the following statements are true and which are false:

    (a) $AB = BA$,  (b) $BC = CB$,  (c) $CD = DC$.

(ii) Solve the equation $\begin{pmatrix} 1 & -1 \\ -1 & 2 \end{pmatrix} \begin{pmatrix} x \\ y \end{pmatrix} = \begin{pmatrix} 11 \\ 8 \end{pmatrix}$

(iii) Determine the column vectors $A\begin{pmatrix} 3 \\ 2 \end{pmatrix}$ and $AB\begin{pmatrix} 3 \\ 2 \end{pmatrix}$.

(iv) Find $p$ and $q$ such that $\begin{pmatrix} 3 \\ 2 \end{pmatrix} + \begin{pmatrix} p \\ q \end{pmatrix} = A\begin{pmatrix} 3 \\ 2 \end{pmatrix}$.     (O)

**8** (i) If $y = 3x^2 + x$, find $\dfrac{dy}{dx}$ when $x = 1$.

(ii) If $pv = 1\,000$, find $\dfrac{dp}{dv}$ in terms of $v$.

(iii) Find the area enclosed by the graph of $y = x(4 - x)$ and the $x$-axis.     (L)

**9** A box on a square base, without a lid, is made of thin sheet metal, and the area of the metal used in making it is 300 cm². If $x$ cm is the length of the base and V cm³ the volume of the box, prove that $V = 75x - \frac{1}{4}x^3$.

What are the dimensions of the box if its volume is the greatest possible for the given area of metal, and what is then its volume?     (O)*

**10** At a certain instant a body is moving in a straight line at 20 cm s⁻¹: its acceleration during the first five seconds of the subsequent motion is $(30-6t)$ cm s⁻², where $t$ is the time in seconds. After five seconds it travels with a constant speed. Find

  (i) its velocity after 2 seconds,
  (ii) the greatest velocity attained,
  (iii) the total distance travelled in 10 seconds.     (OC)*

## XXXVI

**1** Indicate on graph paper the region for which $x \geqslant 1$; $y \geqslant 1$; $2x + 2y \geqslant 15$; $2x + y \geqslant 10$; $2x + 5y \geqslant 25$.

(i) With these restrictions find the least values of the following expressions, (a) $4x + 3y$, (b) $x + 2y$. In each case give the co-ordinates of the points which give these least values.

(ii) Find the least values of the same expressions (a) and (b) with the added restriction that $x$ and $y$ must be integers. (*O*)

**2** A cheese is made in the form of a cylinder of radius 14 cm and height 30 cm. The slice shown (where $AB = 9$ cm and lies along the axis of the cylinder, and where $X\hat{A}Y = 30°$) has a mass of 555 g.

Calculate (i) the mass of the whole cheese in kg, (ii) its density in $g\,cm^{-3}$ (Take $\pi$ to be $\frac{22}{7}$). (*C*)*

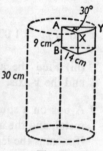

Fig. 226

**3** A force F varies directly as $v^2$ and inversely as $r$: if $v$ is halved and $r$ doubled, find the ratio of the new to the original value of F.

If at another time the force is 8F, and it is known that $r$ has been halved, find the ratio of the new to the original value of $v$. (*N*)

**4** ABC is a triangle in which $BC = 17$ cm, $CA = 9$ cm, $AB = 10$ cm. Without using tables, calculate as fractions in their simplest form (i) cos A, (ii) sin A, (iii) sin C.

Calculate, also without using tables, the area of $\triangle ABC$. (*OC*)

**5** Construct a right-angled isosceles triangle OPQ in which $OQ = QP = 6$ cm. With centre O and radius 4·5 cm describe a circle. Construct a circle touching externally the circle already drawn, and also touching $\overline{PQ}$ at P. Measure its radius as accurately as possible. (*N*)*

**6** In the triangle OAB, X is the point on $\overrightarrow{OA}$ such that $OX = \frac{2}{3}OA$ and Y is the mid-point of $\overrightarrow{AB}$. The point Z on $\overrightarrow{OB}$ produced is such that $OB = BZ$.

Given that $\overrightarrow{OA}$ is the vector **a** and $\overrightarrow{OB}$ the vector **b**, state in terms of **a** and **b** the vectors (i) $\overrightarrow{OX}$, (ii) $\overrightarrow{OY}$, (iii) $\overrightarrow{OZ}$, (iv) $\overrightarrow{XY}$, (v) $\overrightarrow{YZ}$.

Deduce a property of the points X, Y and Z and state the ratio of the lengths of XY and YZ. (*C*)

**7** Draw the graphs of $\dfrac{7x-2}{3x+1}$ and $2 - \dfrac{x}{3}$, using the same axes, from $x = 0$ to $x = 5$, taking 2 cm as unit for both $x$ and $y$.

Find the abscissa of the point of intersection of the two graphs, and show that the value is approximately a root of the equation $3x^2 + 4x - 12 = 0$. (*L*)

**8** The gradient of a curve at any point $(x, y)$ on it is given by $\dfrac{dy}{dx} = kx^{-2}$, where $k$ is a constant. The curve passes through the points $(4, 7)$ and $(6, 8)$.

Find (i) the value of $k$,

(ii) the co-ordinates of the points on the curve where the gradient is 3. (*O*)

**9** The cost of running a ship at a steady speed of S knots is $£\left(8 + \dfrac{S^3}{250}\right)$ per hour. Show that the total cost £C for a voyage of 1 000 nautical miles at a steady speed of S knots is given by $C = 1\,000\left(\dfrac{8}{S} + \dfrac{S^2}{250}\right)$. Find the most economical speed for the voyage and the total cost of the voyage at this speed. (*L*)

**10** A point moves in a straight line in such a way that its velocity ($v$ m s$^{-1}$) and the time ($t$ sec) are connected by the equation $v = at^3 - t + b$, where $a$ and $b$ are certain numbers. When

$t = 0$ the point is at the origin O; when $t = 1$ it is 2 m from O; when $t = 2$ it is 10 m from O. Find $a$ and $b$, and the velocity, acceleration and distance from O of the point when $t = 3$.

$(N)^*$

## XXXVII

**1** A man possesses sufficient $4\frac{1}{2}\%$ stock to give him an income of £216 p.a. He sells out a portion of this stock at $97\frac{1}{2}$ and, on investing the proceeds in a 6% stock at 117, increases his total income by £18. What fraction of the first stock did he sell?

$(C)$

**2** A point B is 1 000 m due east of a point A. A balloon is observed from A in a direction 27° E of N, and at the same instant from B in a direction 18° W of N. From A its elevation is observed to be 33°. Calculate the height of the balloon to 3 sig. fig.

$(OC)^*$

**3** (i) The following are used to signify the transformations given:

$M_x$ reflection in the x-axis

$M_y$ reflection in the y-axis

R a positive (anticlockwise) quarter turn about the origin

H a half turn about the origin

Find a single transformation from the table equivalent to (a) $M_x M_y$, (b) $H M_x$, (c) $R^2$. In each case draw a small diagram showing the first (A′) and the second (A″) transformations of the point A whose co-ordinates are (2, 3).

(ii) The co-ordinates of A and B, the ends of a straight line segment, are (0, 9) and (0, 4) respectively. $\overline{AB}$ is to be transformed to a position $\overline{A'B'}$ where the co-ordinates of A′ and B′ are (8, 7) and (4, 4) respectively. Show that the transformation can be effected by a single rotation. On graph paper draw the two lines $\overline{AB}$ and $\overline{A'B'}$. Calculate or find by drawing the centre of rotation and the angle of rotation.

$(O)$

**4** A horizontal triangular frame is made of three wires each of length 10 cm. A sphere of radius 5 cm rests on it. Draw a plan and an elevation and find, by measurement, the height of the centre of the sphere above the plane of the frame.    (*S*)*

**5** (i) When the expression $x^2(x + 2) + ax - 2$ is divided by $x + 3$ the remainder is $-8$. Find the value of $a$ and, using this value, factorise the expression completely.

(ii) Without using tables, find the value of $x$ if $9^{x-1} = 27$.

(iii) If $\frac{4}{3}\pi r^3 = 2\cdot747$, use logarithms to calculate the value of $r$, giving the answer correct to three significant figures. (Take $\pi = 3\cdot142$.)    (*W*)

**6** The average speed of a goods train over the second half-distance of its run is equal to two-thirds of its average speed over the first half-distance, and its time for the whole run is 2 hours. If its average speeds over the first and second half-distances had been greater by 2 km h$^{-1}$ and 4 km h$^{-1}$ respectively, its time for the whole run would have been $1\frac{3}{4}$ hours. Find its average speed over the first half-distance.

(*O*)*

**7** Mark on squared paper the triangle whose vertices O, A and B are given respectively by the column-vectors

$$\begin{pmatrix} 0 \\ 0 \end{pmatrix}, \begin{pmatrix} 1 \\ -4 \end{pmatrix} \text{ and } \begin{pmatrix} \frac{1}{2} \\ -1 \end{pmatrix}.$$

(a) The triangle is transformed by the matrix $\begin{pmatrix} 1 & 0 \\ 4 & 1 \end{pmatrix}$ into a triangle $OA_1B_1$. Mark this triangle on the same diagram.

(b) The triangle $OA_1B_1$ is now transformed into a triangle $OA_2B_2$ by the matrix $\begin{pmatrix} 1 & -\frac{1}{2} \\ 0 & 1 \end{pmatrix}$.

Mark this triangle also on your diagram. What is the area of the triangle $OA_2B_2$? Deduce the area of the triangle $OAB$, giving reasons.

(c) What single matrix will transform the triangle $OAB$ into the triangle $OA_2B_2$?    (*MEI*)

**8** A rectangular box without a lid is made of cardboard of negligible thickness. The sides of the base are $2x$ cm and $3x$

cm, and the height is $y$ cm. If the total area of the cardboard

is 200 cm², prove that $y = \dfrac{20}{x} - \dfrac{3x}{5}$.

Find the dimensions of the box when its volume is a maximum. *(OC)*

**9** A particle is moving along a straight line and its velocity $v$ is connected with the time $t$ by the equation $v = 3t^2$.

At time $t = 0$ the particle is at the origin. If $a$ is the acceleration and $s$ the distance described in time $t$, show that $2v^2 = 3as$.

How far does the particle go in the third second?

(Units cm and seconds throughout.) *(N)*

**10** (i) Evaluate $\displaystyle\int_0^2 \{1 + 3x(1 + x)^2\}\, dx$.

(ii) Obtain the area between the $x$-axis and the part of the curve $y = x(x - 1)(x - 2)$ between (a) $x = 0$ and $x = 1$, and (b) $x = 1$ and $x = 2$. Explain why one result is positive and the other negative.

(iii) Obtain the volume of revolution formed by rotating about the $x$-axis that part of the curve $y^2 = 4x - 4$ which lies between $x = 1$ and $x = 3$. *(L)*

## XXXVIII

**1** Half a kilogramme of mercury is poured into a straight glass tube of circular section, and fills 18·3 cm length of the tube. Taking the specific gravity of mercury to be 13·6, find the internal diameter of the tube to the nearest mm. (Log $\pi =$ 0·497 1.) How many grammes of mercury, to the nearest whole number, should be withdrawn so as to leave 10 cm of mercury in the tube? *(W)*

**2** A man walks 1 200 m along a path, which coincides with a line of greatest slope of a plane hillside, and finds that he rises 100 m in doing so. He then turns through a certain angle, and walks along a second path in a straight line for a further 1 200 m, thereby rising a further 80 m. Calculate (i) the

angle the plane makes with the horizontal, (ii) the angle the
second path makes with the horizontal, (iii) the angle between
the two paths. *(OC)\**

3 A certain type of radar equipment can detect aircraft within a
range of $x$ nautical miles. Two ships carrying this type of
equipment are on the equator in longitudes 10° W and 30° W.
An aircraft flying along the equator can be detected by both
ships at the same time over a distance of 300 nautical miles.
Show that $x = 750$.

A second aircraft flies along a parallel of latitude so that it
just avoids detection by either ship. Calculate in nautical miles
the distance it flies along this line of latitude from 10° W to
30° W. *(C)*

4 (i) Given that $\log_{10} 2 = 0.301\ 03$ and $\log_{10} 3 = 0.477\ 12$, find
without using tables the values of $\log_{10} 1.5$ and $\log_{10} 1.2$.
(ii) Solve, correct to two places of decimals, $2.3^{2x} = 25$.

*(L)*

5 A machine manufacturing a certain article rejects faulty ones.
The number of rejects during 80 observed periods are given in
the table below:

| Number rejected in a period $(x)$ | 0 | 1 | 2 | 3 | 4 | 5 | 6 | 7 | 8 | 9 | 10 | 11 | 12 | 13 | 14 |
|---|---|---|---|---|---|---|---|---|---|---|---|---|---|---|---|
| Number of periods when this number was rejected $(f)$ | 3 | 2 | 5 | 8 | 11 | 11 | 8 | 6 | 6 | 5 | 5 | 4 | 3 | 2 | 1 |

Construct a cumulative frequency table and the corresponding cumulative frequency curve.

Use your curve to determine the median and upper and lower
quartiles.

Use the median as a trial mean to determine the true mean
of this distribution. *(O)*

**6** ABC is a triangle inscribed in a circle and $B\widehat{A}C$ is 60°. The bisectors of $A\widehat{B}C$ and $A\widehat{C}B$ meet the circumference of the circle in D and E respectively. Prove that $\overline{BE}$ is parallel to $\overline{CD}$. (*L*)

**7** The average weekly earnings of women in 56 principal trades shortly after the second world war were calculated, the distribution being shown in the table below:

| Earnings (£) | 2·50 | 2·75 | 3·00 | 3·25 | 3·50 | 3·75–4·00 |
|---|---|---|---|---|---|---|
| No. of trades | 1 | 4 | 19 | 17 | 13 | 2 |

    (i) Calculate the arithmetic mean of the average earnings in the 56 trades.

    (ii) Construct a cumulative-frequency diagram from the data and use it to find in how many trades the average earnings were higher than the arithmetic mean. (*MEI*)

**8** The curve $y^2 = 3 + 2x - x^2$ represents a circle whose centre is at the point (1, 0) and whose radius is 2. If the part of the circle in the first quadrant is revolved about the $x$-axis, prove that the volume thus obtained is approximately 28 cubic units. (Take $\pi$ as 3·14.)

    Find by calculation the co-ordinates of the points where the line $y = \frac{1}{2}(x + 1)$ meets the circle. (*N*)

**9** A particle is moving in a straight line and its distance ($s$ m) from a fixed point in the line after $t$ seconds is given by the equation $s = 12t - 15t^2 + 4t^3$.

    Find (i) the velocity and acceleration of the particle after 3 seconds,

           (ii) the distance travelled between the two times when the velocity is instantaneously zero. (*OC*)\*

**10** Find the values of $x$ for which the function $(2 + x)^2(3 - x)^2$ has maximum or minimum values: find these values and say which are maximum and which minimum.

    Sketch roughly the graph of the function. (*L*)

## XXXIX

**1** Two men A and B join partnership with capitals of £5 400 and £2 800 respectively in a business which makes a profit at the rate of 16% per annum on the capital invested. At the end of nine months they are joined by C with a capital of £2 500. For the next three months the profit falls to 12% per annum on the total capital invested. Find the amount received by each as his share of the profits at the end of the first year. (*N*)

**2** A man crosses a river flowing at 0·6 m s⁻¹ by means of a rowing-boat which he can propel through still water at 1·5 m s⁻¹. Q is the point on the far bank directly opposite his starting-point P. By accurate drawing or calculation, find (i) at what angle to $\overline{PQ}$ he must head in order to land at Q; (ii) how far downstream from Q he will land if the river is 24 m wide and he heads the boat slightly upstream at 15° to $\overline{PQ}$. (*C*)\*

**3** (i) Taking the circumference of the earth to be $4 \times 10^4$ km, calculate the distance, measured along the parallel of latitude 74° N corresponding to a change of longitude of 1°.

(ii) An aircraft-carrier at noon is at lat. 74° N and long. 1° W, sailing eastwards at 30 km h⁻¹ along the parallel of latitude. An aircraft leaves the carrier at noon and flies south along the 1° W meridian to an air-base at 54° N and 1° W at an average speed of 400 km h⁻¹. Calculate:

(*a*) the time of arrival, to the nearest minute, of the aircraft at the air-base,

(*b*) the position of the ship at this time. (*O*)\*

**4** In a certain income group, 75% of the members read *The Times* and 35% of the members read *The Guardian*. Each of the following statements is either TRUE or FALSE or NOT NECESSARILY TRUE. Say to which category each statement belongs:

(i) All members read either *The Times* or *The Guardian*, but not both.

(ii) Most readers of *The Guardian* read *The Times* also.

323

    (iii) A minority of the readers of *The Times* also read *The Guardian*.

    (iv) If *The Guardian* lost 20% of its readers and *The Times* increased its readership by $6\frac{2}{3}$%, all those who stopped reading *The Guardian* started reading *The Times*.

    Illustrate the two situations by Venn diagrams.   (*L*)

**5** Two circles having centres at E and F intersect at D and B. A point A is taken on one circle, and $\overline{AD}$ is drawn and produced beyond D to meet the other circle in C. Prove that $E\hat{D}F = A\hat{B}C$.   (*L*)

**6** In Fig. 227 PQRS is a square, LMNP is a rectangle and $\overline{MR}$ is parallel to $\overline{LS}$.

By describing three successive shears which transform the square into the rectangle LMNP, or otherwise, show that they have the same area.

Given in addition that SR = 6 cm and MN = 8 cm, calculate (i) LM, (ii) LS, (iii) the distance between the lines $\overline{MR}$ and $\overline{LS}$.   (*C*)

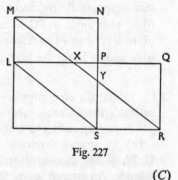

Fig. 227

**7** For a certain arrangement of pulleys the relation between the load W and the effort P is of the form $P = aW + b$, where $a$ and $b$ are constants. The following values are obtained in an experiment:

| P | 2·75 | 3·31 | 4·32 | 4·77 | 6·10 | 7·21 |
|---|------|------|------|------|------|------|
| W | 2    | 4    | 8    | 10   | 15   | 20   |

Find the values of $a$ and $b$, and also P when W = 12.   (*C*)

**8** A particle starts from rest at a point 6 m from O, and moves in a straight line away from O with a velocity $v$ m s$^{-1}$ at time

$t$ s, given by $v = t - \frac{1}{18}t^2$. Find (i) its acceleration and distance from O, each in terms of $t$; (ii) the time at which it begins to return, and the time at which it again reaches its starting-point. $(OC)^*$

**9** A circular cylinder, open at the top, is to be made out of 1 square metre of thin sheet metal. Show that the greatest volume will be obtained when the area of the base is $\frac{1}{3}$ m². $(N)^*$

**10** Differentiate $\sqrt[3]{x}$ and use your result to find an approximate value of $\sqrt[3]{126 \cdot 5}$. $(O)$

## XL

**1** (i) Given $V = \pi h^2 \left( r - \frac{h}{3} \right)$, find V correct to 3 sig. fig., if $\pi = 3 \cdot 142$, $r = 6 \cdot 87$, $h = 3 \cdot 94$.

Express $r$ in terms of V, $h$ and $\pi$.

(ii) Evaluate $\dfrac{\sqrt{8 \cdot 246} + \sqrt{0 \cdot 794}}{(5 \cdot 248)^2}$. $(W)$

**2** Two places P and Q are both in latitude 61° 30′ N. Calculate the distance in nautical miles of either P or Q from the North Pole.

Taking the circumference of the earth to be 40 000 km, calculate

(i) the distance in kilometres along the latitude line from P to Q, given that their longitudes are 44° W and 31° E respectively.

(ii) the latitude, correct to the nearest minute, of a place 960 km due south of Q. $(C)^*$

**3** Prove that the areas of similar triangles are proportional to the squares on corresponding sides.

ABC is a triangle inscribed in a circle, and the tangent at A meets $\overline{BC}$ produced at D. Prove that BD : CD = AB² : AC². $(L)$

*New General Mathematics*

**4** Draw on the same diagram the graphs of $\dfrac{x^3}{20} - 1$ and $\dfrac{6}{x}$ from

$x = 1$ to $x = 5$, taking 2 cm as unit on both axes.

Use the graphs to find a solution of the equation

$$x^4 - 20x - 120 = 0. \qquad (S)$$

**5** (i) If $x^3 - 3x + 2 = (x - 2)(x + 1)(x + a)$ when $x = 3$, find the value of $a$.

(ii) If

$x^3 - 3x + 2 = (x - 2)(x + 2)(x + b) + (x - 2)(x + c)$

when $x = 3$ and when $x = 4$, find the values of $b$ and $c$.

(iii) If $x^3 = Ax + Bx(x - 1) + Cx(x - 1)(x - 2)$ for all values of $x$, find the values of A, B and C. $\qquad (O)$

**6** The flow of water over a weir is given by the equation $Q = kH^n$, where Q is the volume in $m^3\ s^{-1}$ and H is the depth of the water in metres. The following values are recorded for Q and H:

| H | 0·5 | 0·9 | 1·5 |
|---|-----|-----|-----|
| Q | 0·283 | 1·229 | 4·409 |

Plot log Q against log H as follows:

log Q on the horizontal axis, scale 0·2 units = 2 cm,

log H on the vertical axis, scale 0·1 units = 2 cm.

(All logarithms are to base 10.)

Draw the graph showing the relation between log .H and log Q, and explain why this shows that the relation between H and Q is of the form $Q = kH^n$.

Deduce the values of $k$ and $n$, each correct to one decimal place. $\qquad (MEI)$

**7** A variable rectangle ABCD is such that its perimeter, 2(AB + AD), is always equal to 12 cm. Draw a graph to show its area, plotted along the $y$-axis, for values of AB, plotted along the $x$ axis. Take 2 cm along the $y$-axis to represent

1 cm² of area, and plot points for integral values of AB from 0 to 6 cm.

If P is any point on the curve and $\overline{PN}$ the perpendicular on to the x-axis, show that the corresponding length of AD in centimetres is represented by tan $\hat{PON}$, where O is the origin.

$(OC)^*$

8 The parabola $y = ax^2 + bx + c$ goes through the points $(0, 1), (2, 3), (4, 7)$. Find the values of $a$, $b$, $c$ and show that the area between the curve, the axes, and the line $x = 4$ is $13\frac{1}{3}$ square units. $(N)$

9 While a train is travelling from its start at A to its next stop at B, its distance $x$ km from A is given by $x = 90t^2 - 45t^3$, where $t$ hours is the time taken. Find, in terms of $t$, its velocity and its acceleration after time $t$.

Hence find (i) the time taken by the journey from A to B, (ii) AB, (iii) the greatest speed attained. $(OC)^*$

10 A conical vessel with its axis vertical and vertex downwards has a base radius of 6 cm and a depth of 10 cm. If the vessel is filled with water to a depth of $x$ cm, what is the volume of water in the vessel? ($\pi$ may be left in the answer.)

If water is being poured into the vessel at the rate of 2 cm³ s⁻¹, at what rate is the surface rising at the moment when the depth of the water is 2 cm? $(O)^*$

*Answers*

# Answers

*Exercise* 1 (*p.* 3)

| | | | |
|---|---|---|---|
| **1** £270·40 | **2** £578·8 | **3** £424·36 | **4** £657·95 |
| **5** £152·45 | **6** £95·60 | **7** £30·33 | **8** £129·79 |
| **9** £228·93 | **10** £56·08 | **11** £187·37 | **12** £357·60 |
| **13** £4·79 | **14** £16·56 | **15** £24·94 | **16** £4·33 |
| **17** £15·69 | **18** £26·93 | **19** £25·75 | **20** £29·06 |
| **21** £88·34 | **22** £23·16 | **23** £26·64 | **24** £18·31 |
| **25** £37·26 | **26** £171·40 | **27** £72·69 | **28** £162·37 |
| **29** £175·23 | **30** £312·96 | **31** £14·64 | **32** £2·61 |
| **33** £12·88 | **34** £60·27 | **35** £30·81 | **36** £112·55 |
| **37** £264·98 | **38** £11·93 | **39** £45·45 | **40** £307·56 |
| **41** £172·39 | **42** £1 369·50 | **43** £686 | **44** £271·66 |
| **45** 1% quarterly, 4·06% | | **46** £2·44 | **47** £468·20 |
| **48** £1 397·38 | **49** £700 | **50** £367 | **51** 482 447 |
| **52** £10·06 greater | **53** £338·12 | | |

*Exercise* 2a (*p.* 10)

**1** (i) £187   (ii) £56·25   (iii) £2 510   (iv) £129   (v) £70
**2** (i) 500   (ii) 960   (iii) 768   (iv) 75   (v) 128
**3** £123·50   **4** £130   **5** 65¼p   **6** 390p
**7** £125 gain   **8** No   **9** 32   **10** £6·30, £1 642·50
**11** £20, 6¼%   **12** £75, 12%   **13** £60, 2⁷⁄₉%   **14** £30, 7½%
**15** £2·10, 1⅔%   **16** £31·50, 5⁵⁄₉%   **17** £90, 4⅘%   **18** £69·30, 8⅓%
**19** (i)   **20** (i)   **21** (ii)   **22** Equal
**23** (i)   **24** 72%, 7½%   **25** 2 000, £760, 11·2%
**26** £32·31   **27** £10·19   **28** £1 684·45   **29** 100, £19
**30** B.L. £105, B.A. £250

*Exercise* 2b (*p.* 14)

**1** (i) £460   (ii) £290·50   (iii) £512·20   (iv) £411·80   (v) £165·38
**2** (i) £23·75   (ii) £12·25   (iii) £14·30   (iv) £17·40   (v) £10·12
**3** (i) £250   (ii) £333·33   (iii) £250   (iv) £745·34   (v) £454·55
**4** (i) £10   (ii) £16·67   (iii) £13·75   (iv) £26·09   (v) £22·73
**5** (i) 5·8%   (ii) 5·4%   (iii) 5·3%   (iv) 4·3%   (v) 4·5%
**6** £866·67   **7** 90   **8** 4%   **9** £2 520
**10** 48¾   **11** £999   **12** 4%   **13** 93½
**14** 6%   **15** £601·25
**16** (i) First   (ii) First   (iii) Second   (iv) First   (v) Second
**17** 80   **18** 75   **19** 65   **20** 140
**21** £41·07   **22** 87   **23** £2 285·71; £30   **24** 80

*New General Mathematics*

*Exercise* 3 (*p.* 20)
1 $(1, 1)$; $(1\frac{2}{3}, 2\frac{1}{3})$  2 $(5, -3)$; $(-3, 5)$  3 $(3, -1)$; $(-3, 1)$
4 $(1, \frac{2}{3})$ twice  5 $(3, -2)$; $(\frac{1}{3}, 6)$  6 $(6, -3)$
7 $(5, -2)$  8 $(2, -1)$  9 $(5, -3)$  10 $(3, 4)$
11 $(-3, 1)$; $(-4, \frac{1}{2})$  12 $(0, \frac{1}{2})$; $(1, 3)$
13 $(2, 1)$; $(-1\frac{1}{3}, -1\frac{1}{2})$  14 $(2, -8)$
15 $(4, 6)$; $(-2, -6)$  16 $(4, -1)$; $(8, -3)$
17 $(7, -2)$; $(-4, 3\frac{1}{2})$  18 $(2, -9)$; $(-1, -12)$
19 $(-1, 3)$; $(1\frac{1}{2}, -2)$  20 $(0, \frac{1}{3})$; $(5, 2)$
21 $(6, 1)$; $(-2\frac{1}{2}, -2\frac{2}{5})$  22 $(-1, 1)$; $(3, -5)$
23 $(-6, 1)$; $(-1\frac{1}{2}, 4)$  24 $(-\frac{4}{5}, 2)$ twice
25 $(3, -\frac{1}{2})$; $(-\frac{2}{3}, 2\frac{1}{4})$  26 $(4, 2)$; $(-2, -\frac{2}{5})$
27 $(-3, 5)$; $(2, -2\frac{1}{2})$  28 $(2, 3)$
29 $(2, -3)$; $(3, -5)$  30 $(4, 1)$; $(-5, -3\frac{1}{2})$
31 $(-3, \frac{1}{2})$; $(5, -\frac{1}{2})$  32 $(13, 9)$; $(-9\frac{1}{2}, 1\frac{1}{2})$
33 $(-3, -1)$; $(3\frac{2}{3}, \frac{1}{3})$  34 $(-3, 2)$; $(-4, 2\frac{1}{3})$
35 $(3, -2)$; $(-5, -7\frac{1}{3})$  36 $(15, 12)$; $(12, 10)$
37 $(\frac{1}{3}, \frac{2}{3})$; $(\frac{3}{8}, \frac{3}{8})$  38 $(5, 3)$; $(-1\frac{1}{2}, -10)$
39 $(2, 2)$; $(-1\frac{1}{2}, 3\frac{3}{4})$  40 $(1, -1)$; $(2\frac{1}{2}, -3)$


*Exercise* 4a (*p.* 24)
1 $x > 3$ or $x < 0$  2 $x > 0$ or $x < -3$  3 $\{x: 0 < x \leqslant 2\}$
4 $\{x: -4 < x < 0\}$  5 $0 < x \leqslant \frac{1}{6}$  6 $\{x: 0 < x < \frac{1}{3}\}$
7 $-10 \leqslant x < 0$  8 $\{x: x < -1\frac{1}{2}\} \cup \{x: x > 0\}$
9 $\{x: 0 < x < 8\}$  10 $x > 0$ or $x \leqslant -\frac{2}{3}$
11 $\{x: x < 0\} \cup \{x: x > \frac{4}{3}\}$  12 $x > 0$ or $x \leqslant -2\frac{1}{2}$

*Exercise* 4b (*p.* 26)
1 $x > 3$ or $x < 2$  2 $\{x: 3 > x > 2\}$  3 $-3 < x < -2$
4 $\{x: x < -3\} \cup \{x: x > -2\}$  5 $x > 6$ or $x < -6$
6 $\{x: -10 > x > 10\}$  7 $\{x: -2 < x < 3\}$  8 $x > 4$ or $x < -1$
9 $x \geqslant 4$ or $x \leqslant -4$  10 $x > 4$ or $x < -3$  11 $\{x: -6 \leqslant x \leqslant 2\}$
12 $\{x: x < -4\} \cup \{x: x > 2\frac{1}{2}\}$  13 $-1\frac{1}{2} < x < 2$
14 $x > 1\frac{1}{2}$ or $x \leqslant -2\frac{1}{2}$  15 $\{x: -1 \leqslant x \leqslant 0\}$
16 $0 < x < 4$ or $x < -2$  17 $x \geqslant 3$ or $-\frac{1}{3} \leqslant x < 0$
18 $\{x: x < -1\frac{1}{2}\} \cup \{x: x > \frac{2}{3}\}$

*Exercise* 4c (*p.* 28)
1 $(3, 9)$, $(4, 9)$  2 $(1, 4)$, $(2, 2)$  3 $(6, 2)$, $(7, 2)$, $(7, 3)$
4 $(4, 3)$, $(5, 3)$, $(5, 4)$, $(5, 5)$, $(6, 5)$  5 $(5, 4)$, $(6, 4)$, $(6, 5)$, $(7, 3)$
6 $(3, 4)$, $(4, 4)$, $(3, 5)$  7 $(5, 2)$, $(6, 2)$, $(7, 2)$, $(8, 2)$, $(10, 3)$
8 $(2, 4)$, $(2, 5)$, $(3, 5)$, $(3, 6)$  9 $(1, 7)$  10 $(2, 8)$, $(2, 9)$
11 $(2, 5)$, $(2, 6)$, $(2, 7)$, $(3, 7)$  12 $(3, 4)$, $(3, 5)$, $(4, 5)$
13 $(3, 2)$, $(4, 2)$  14 $(2, 7)$

*Exercise 5a (p. 32)*

| | | | | | | | | | |
|---|---|---|---|---|---|---|---|---|---|
| **1** | 0·939 7 | **2** | −0·342 0 | **3** | −2·747 5 | **4** | 0·454 0 | **5** | 0·990 3 |
| **6** | −0·275 6 | **7** | −0·788 0 | **8** | −0·230 9 | **9** | −19·08 | **10** | −0·615 7 |
| **11** | 0·398 7 | **12** | −0·109 5 | **13** | −0·947 4 | **14** | −1·117 1 | **15** | 0·998 3 |
| **16** | −0·715 1 | **17** | −0·227 0 | **18** | −1·812 8 | **19** | 0·024 7 | **20** | −23·06 |
| **21** | −0·005 2 | **22** | 0·262 5 | **23** | −0·473 6 | **24** | −0·522 7 | **25** | −11·06 |

*Exercise 5b (p. 34)*

| | | | | | | | |
|---|---|---|---|---|---|---|---|
| **1** 36° | **2** 144° | **3** 75° | **4** 105° | **5** 67°, 113° | **6** 117° |
| **7** 160° | **8** 25°, 155° | **9** 98° | **10** 148° | **11** 136° 42′ |
| **12** 37° 30′, 142° 30′ | **13** 74° 42′, 105° 18′ | **14** 115° 24′ |
| **15** 162° 26′ | **16** 115° 10′ | **17** 56° 24′, 123° 36′ |
| **18** 144° 8′ | **19** 73° 37′, 106° 23′ | **20** 141° 41′ |
| **21** 120° 47′ | **22** 15° 14′, 164° 46′ | **23** 48° 9′, 131° 51′ |
| **24** 94° 38′ | **25** 162° 15′ |

*Exercise 6 (p. 38)*

**1** $\frac{3}{5}, \frac{3}{4}$   **2** $\frac{5}{13}, 2\frac{2}{5}$   **3** $\frac{8}{17}, 1\frac{5}{7}$   **4** $\frac{24}{25}, \frac{7}{24}$   **5** $\frac{9}{41}, \frac{9}{40}$

**6** 0·581, 0·814   **7** 0·903, 0·430   **8** 0·904, 0·474   **9** 0·943, 2·83

**10** 0·917, 2·29   **11** $\dfrac{t}{\sqrt{1+t^2}}, \dfrac{1}{\sqrt{1+t^2}}$   **12** $\dfrac{\sqrt{x^2-1}}{x}, \dfrac{1}{\sqrt{x^2-1}}$

**13** 1·880 7   **14** 0·559 2   **15** 1·057 6

*Exercise 7 (p. 41)*

**1** (i) 176·8   (ii) 248·4   (iii) 48   (iv) 208·4   (v) 30 000
**2** (i) £9·62   (ii) £41·81   (iii) £17·49   (iv) £8·76   (v) £6·67

| | | | | |
|---|---|---|---|---|
| **3** +3p | **4** 50·6% | **5** 10p | **6** 23p |
| **7** 94p | **8** 62p | **9** £10·67 | **10** £4·03 |
| **11** £2·70 | **12** £24·09 | **13** 0·52p | **14** £14·39 |
| **15** 277% | **16** 22·41 F | **17** $52\frac{1}{4}$% | **18** 10·21 f |
| **19** 67p | **20** £8·54$\frac{1}{2}$ exactly | | |

*Revision Examples (p. 43)*

I

**1** £29·97   **2** 6   **3** 7·86   **4** 44° 25′, 135° 35′
**5** (3, −2), (4, −1$\frac{1}{2}$)   **6** 10 days   **7** $\frac{1}{3}$
**9** The second; 5%, $5\frac{5}{16}$%   **10** (i) $x < 0$ or $x > 3$   (ii) $x > 4$ or $x < 2$

II

**1** 2; −$\frac{4}{5}$   **2** 3·97 cm   **3** +84p   **4** (8, 3)
**5** {4, 8, 16}, {3, 6, 9, 15}   **6** 56° 26′, 74° 13′   **7** 50 km
**9** £9·57   **10** 1·18, 8·45

### III

**1** 4·8%, £1 150 **2** 885 km h⁻¹ **3** 122° 50′; 3
**4** (i) {x : 0 < x ⩽ 1½} (ii) {x : −5 < x < 5} **5** (4, −1), (−5, 2)
**6** £899·50 **8** 15 min **9** £7·40 **10** 3·52

### IV

**1** (−1½, 2) **2** £14·21 **3** (i) 2·385 × 10⁵, 4·7 × 10⁻⁶ (ii) −1⅕
**5** 1 800, £63 **6** 29 800 km h⁻¹ **7** 17° 28′, 24° 35′
**8** French, by 5p **10** (3, −6), (6, 6), (−6, −3)

### V

**1** (i) 5·267 (ii) 0·112 1 **2** (2, 5), (10, 1) **3** £191·20
**4** (i) 1 (ii) 1 **5** £32·30
**6** (i) 2 × 10⁻³, 3 × 10⁻⁶, 6 × 10⁻⁹
 (ii) 1·2 × 10⁵, 4 × 10⁻², 3 × 10⁶
 (iii) 5 × 10⁻³, 1·25 × 10⁻⁷ (iv) 8·1 × 10⁵, 3 × 10¹
**7** −17 **9** 35p, 42p **10** 116° 34′

### VI

**1** 113° 35′ **2** 9·8 cm **3** £1 = $2·88, $1 = 35p
**4** (4, −2), (−2, 4) **5** £9·09 **6** 9·55 cm **7** £5·90%
**8** 7·95 × 10⁻⁵ **10** 4·56, 0·44

### VII

**1** £1 602·83 **2** 25° 40′, 154° 20′ **3** (−2, 1), (1¾, −1½)
**4** 49° 6′, 75° 58′
**5** (i) {x : x > 0} ∪ {x : x < −4} (ii) {x : x > 4} ∪ {x : x ⩽ −2}
**6** 10 km h⁻¹ **8** 48° 11′, 52° 14′ **9** £136·50, £30 **10** 1·22, 3·28

### VIII

**1** (3, 2), (12, −4) **2** £2 878·56 **3** 8·72 cm, 8·00 cm

**4** $\begin{pmatrix} -11 & 13 \\ -16 & 18 \end{pmatrix}$, $\begin{pmatrix} 0 & -2 \\ 5 & 7 \end{pmatrix}$ **5** 10·4 km, 71° 52′ **6** $x = \dfrac{5y + 2}{3 - 2y}$; 7, 1

**7** −£1·59 **8** 14° 44′ **9** (i) −2·68, −0·52 (ii) 3, −4 **10** 18°

### IX

**1** 0·035 2, 0·003 80, 1·78 **2** (−4, 2), (−1½, −3) **3** 4 317
**5** 800, £48, 12·8% **6** 99 **7** £46·59
**8** 3·00 × 10⁵ km s⁻¹, 9·46 × 10¹² km, 5·18 × 10⁵
**9** 32 at 25p **10** −1, −1, 2

### X

**1** ⅔, −0·8 **2** (4, 9), (−1½, −2)
**4** (−7, 3), (2, −1), (−6, −3) **5** 0 < x < 3 *or* x < −2

**6** $y = \dfrac{x^2}{2(x + z)}$        **7** £1 623·47

**9** 90               **10** $35\frac{1}{4}°$, $144\frac{3}{4}°$

*Exercise 8a (p. 58)*

**3** 13·03 m    **4** 14·50 cm    **5** 21·52 cm    **6** 48° 48′    **7** 41° 37′

**8** 13·44 m, 7·643 cm, 20·72 cm, 143·5 m, 2·680 m

**9** B = 26° 30′, C = 38° 30′, $c$ = 44·64 m

**10** A = 30°, $a$ = 23·74 m, $b$ = 20·54 m

**11** A = 98° 52′, $b$ = 9·84 cm, $c$ = 15·48 cm

**12** B = 29° 9′, C = 112° 33′, $c$ = 375·6 m

**13** A = 67° 22′, B = 16° 25′, $a$ = 36·58 cm

**14** 8·15 km        **15** 294° 47′, 188 m      **16** 190 m

**17** 4·06 m         **18** $25\frac{1}{2}$ m            **19** 13·6 km h$^{-1}$

**20** 23·6 m, 21·7 m     **21** 165 m, 116 m     **22** 2·54 km

**23** $240\frac{1}{2}$ m

*Exercise 8b (p. 62)*

**1** B = 60° 45′, $a$ = 4·826 cm, $c$ = 3·275 cm

**2** $\begin{cases} C = 63°\ 44',\ A = 74°,\ a = 2\ 572\ \text{m} \\ C = 116°\ 16',\ A = 21°\ 28',\ a = 979·2\ \text{m} \end{cases}$

**3** $\begin{cases} A = 41°\ 54',\ B = 122°\ 44',\ b = 7·934\ \text{m} \\ A = 138°\ 6',\ B = 26°\ 32',\ b = 4·213\ \text{m} \end{cases}$

**4** B = 35° 59′, C = 20° 54′, $c$ = 7·709 cm

**5** $\begin{cases} C = 70°\ 9',\ B = 71°\ 1',\ b = 4·223\ \text{cm} \\ C = 109°\ 51',\ B = 31°\ 19',\ b = 2·321\ \text{cm} \end{cases}$

**6** B = 21° 36′, $a$ = 24·40 cm, $b$ = 11·45 cm

**7** $\begin{cases} A = 75°\ 45',\ C = 39°\ 7',\ c = 101·6\ \text{m} \\ A = 104°\ 15',\ C = 10°\ 37',\ c = 29·66\ \text{m} \end{cases}$

**8** $\begin{cases} B = 72°\ 36',\ C = 50°\ 4',\ c = 4·099\ \text{cm} \\ B = 107°\ 24',\ C = 15°\ 16',\ c = 1·407\ \text{cm} \end{cases}$

**9** 13·6 km h$^{-1}$      **10** 526 m, 2 850 m; 257° 32′, 352° 24′

**11** 1 630 m         **12** 1·74 km      **13** 550 m *or* 61 m

**14** 1 110 m *or* 648 m    **15** 201° 24′ *or* 158° 36′

*Exercise 9a (p. 65)*

**1** $a$ = 3·785 cm      **2** $b$ = 1·490 cm      **3** $c$ = 1·583 m

**4** $a$ = 2·313 m       **5** $a$ = 16·64 cm     **6** $b$ = 4·182 cm

**7** $c$ = 5·740 m       **8** $b$ = 12·08 cm     **9** $a$ = 6·682 cm

**10** $c$ = 18·19 m

*Exercise 9b (p. 67)*

**1** $a$ = 4·973 cm, B = 47° 19′, C = 66° 41′

**2** $c$ = 9·871 cm, B = 29° 9′, A = 76° 51′

## New General Mathematics

**3** $c = 12.23$ m, A $= 25°\ 25'$, B $= 15°\ 35'$
**4** $b = 374.8$ m, C $= 32°\ 6'$, A $= 52°\ 54'$
**5** $a = 9.084$ m, B $= 69°\ 14'$, C $= 52°\ 38'$
**6** $b = 9.458$ cm, C $= 28°\ 31'$, A $= 25°\ 15'$
**7** $c = 3.227$ cm, A $= 126°\ 10\frac{1}{2}'$, B $= 28°\ 5\frac{1}{2}'$
**8** $a = 65.26$ m, B $= 26°\ 14'$, C $= 13°\ 38'$
**9** $c = 5.809$ cm, A $= 13°\ 42'$, B $= 23°\ 1'$
**10** $b = 3.209$ cm, C $= 29°\ 37'$, A $= 115°\ 54'$

### Exercise 9c (p. 69)

**1** $29°\ 55'$, $63°\ 54'$, $86°\ 11'$      **2** $81°\ 47'$, $38°\ 13'$, $60°$
**3** $62°\ 43'$, $80°\ 57'$, $36°\ 20'$      **4** $108°\ 13'$, $22°\ 20'$, $49°\ 27'$
**5** $33°\ 34'$, $50°\ 42'$, $95°\ 44'$      **6** $110°\ 55'$, $43°\ 14'$, $25°\ 51'$
**7** $41°\ 24',$ $55°\ 46'$, $82°\ 50'$      **8** $46°\ 30'$, $39°\ 24'$, $94°\ 6'$
**9** $98°\ 9'$, $50°\ 21'$, $31°\ 30'$      **10** $45°\ 44'$, $78°\ 57'$, $55°\ 19'$
**11** $\frac{2}{3}$; 7 m      **13** $-\frac{23}{40}$; 4.24 cm      **14** 7.42 m
**15** 6.36 cm; $61°\ 23'$      **16** $82°\ 49'$; 8.89 cm      **17** 5 units
**18** 5.01 cm, 4.04 cm, 5.06 cm

### Exercise 9d (p. 70)

**1** C $= 59°$, $a = 42.16$ m, $c = 36.95$ m
**2** B $= 61°\ 37'$, C $= 40°\ 9'$, $a = 9.703$ cm
**3** $\begin{cases} \text{A} = 69°\ 39', \text{C} = 65°\ 14', c = 8.640 \text{ cm} \\ \text{A} = 110°\ 21', \text{C} = 24°\ 32', c = 3.951 \text{ cm} \end{cases}$
**4** A $= 27°\ 40'$, B $= 111°\ 48'$, C $= 40°\ 32'$
**5** C $= 31°\ 43'$, $a = 4.011$ m, $c = 5.627$ m
**6** $\begin{cases} \text{C} = 65°\ 7', \text{B} = 70°\ 31', b = 26.28 \text{ cm} \\ \text{C} = 114°\ 53', \text{B} = 20°\ 45', b = 9.881 \text{ cm} \end{cases}$
**7** B $= 29°\ 45'$, C $= 46°\ 25'$, $a = 36.58$ cm
**8** A $= 21°\ 12'$, $b = 36.78$ cm, $c = 25.95$ cm
**9** A $= 18°\ 50'$, B $= 150°\ 36'$, C $= 10°\ 34'$
**10** A $= 59°\ 40'$, C $= 11°\ 6'$, $c = 33.24$ m
**11** 5.99 km      **12** $23\frac{1}{4}$ m      **13** 3.53 m, $56°\ 24'$
**14** $11°$      **15** 6.94 km      **16** AXB, by 55 s
**17** 8.72 km, $054°\ 9'$      **18** $117°\ 2'$, 9.40 cm      **19** 171 m
**20** 82.0 m      **21** 36.1 km, $73°\ 9'$      **22** 7.63 cm, 3.12 cm
**23** 9.57 km, $302°\ 30'$      **24** 19.2 km      **25** 44.5 km, $134°\ 10'$
**26** 11.1 cm      **27** $154\frac{1}{2}$ m      **28** 5.65 km, N $9°\ 32'$ W
**29** 75 seconds      **30** 2 350 m

### Exercise 10a (p. 75)

**1** $\frac{2}{5}$    **2** $\frac{9}{25}$    **3** $\frac{8}{11}$    **4** $1:2$    **5** $125:8$
**6** $1:7$    **7** $1:2$    **8** $2:3$    **9** $4:21$    **10** $5:3$
**11** $2:7$    **12** $\pm5:4$    **13** $-2:3$    **14** $5:4$    **18** $5:7$

**19** $\pm 2:3$     **20** $1:2$ *or* $1:3$     **21** $2:1$ *or* $-1:2$
**22** $3:4$ *or* $-5:2$     **23** $11:4$     **24** $23:20$

**25** Decreased in the ratio $n:m$     **26** $\dfrac{bx}{a}$

**27** $n:m, n-m:m$     **28** $h-k:h$
**29** $23m:22n$     **30** $45°, 63°, 72°$     **31** £21, £35, £49, £63

**32** £$\dfrac{ax}{a+b+c}$, £$\dfrac{bx}{a+b+c}$, £$\dfrac{cx}{a+b+c}$

**33** $4:5, 3:2$    **34** $15:20:24$    **35** $20:24:15$    **36** $4:3, 2:3$
**37** $21:30:26$    **38** $3:2$    **39** $7:1$    **40** $45:53$
**41** $25:9$    **42** $15:8$    **43** Decreased, $27:28$
**44** $16:25$    **45** $27:8$    **46** $36:25$    **47** $64:45$
**48** $32:27$    **49** $b^2:a^2$    **50** $ad:bc$    **51** $\frac{85}{42}$
**52** $11:4$    **53** $16:39$    **54** $32:39$    **55** $5:8$

*Exercise* 10*b* (*p.* 79)
**1** 16 cm, 6 cm    **2** 2·7 cm, 3·6 cm    **3** $8\frac{3}{4}$ cm, $5\frac{1}{4}$ cm
**4** 32 cm, 12 cm    **5** 3·2 cm, 5·6 cm    **6** $24\frac{3}{4}$ cm, $13\frac{3}{4}$ cm
**7** 9 cm, 6 cm, 45 cm, 30 cm    **8** $7\frac{1}{2}$ cm, $17\frac{1}{2}$ cm, $18\frac{3}{4}$ cm, $43\frac{3}{4}$ cm
**9** 10·5 cm    **10** 7·2 cm    **11** 12 cm, 3 cm, 48 cm

**12** $\dfrac{mx}{m+n}$ cm, $\dfrac{nx}{m+n}$ cm, $\dfrac{mx}{m-n}$ cm, $\dfrac{nx}{m-n}$ cm

**13** $\dfrac{x(m-n)}{2(m+n)}$ cm, $\dfrac{x(m+n)}{2(m-n)}$ cm

*Exercise* 11*a* (*p.* 82)
**1** $3:2, 3:5, 2:5$    **2** $3:4, 5:7, 5:6$    **3** $x=6\frac{2}{3}, y=8$
**4** $a=6, b=8, c=20, d=5\frac{1}{3}, e=13\frac{1}{2}$
**6** $p=5, q=18, x:y=1:3$

*Exercise* 11*b* (*p.* 84)
**1** $a=15, b=5$    **2** $c=13\frac{1}{2}, d=12$    **3** $3:5$
**4** $4:5$    **5** $1:3$    **6** $3:5$
**7** $a=15, b=9$    **8** $c=8, d=4$    **9** $f=12$
**10** $g=21$    **11** $h=7\frac{7}{9}$    **12** $l=3, m=24$

*Exercise* 11*c* (*p.* 88)
**1** $a=16, b=13\frac{1}{3}$    **2** $c=10, d=9$    **3** $e=10, f=4·8$
**4** $g=6$    **5** $h=18$    **6** $k=9$

*New General Mathematics*

*Exercise* 11*d* (*p.* 94)

**1** $a = 2$  **2** $b = 1$  **3** $c = 5$
**4** $d = 18, e = 9$  **5** $g = 6, h = 8$  **6** $k = 6, l = 8$
**7** $m = 6, n = 4, p = 7.8$  **8** $q = 4, r = 9$
**9** 7·5 m  **10** $12\frac{1}{2}$ cm  **11** 80 cm; $76\frac{12}{13}$ cm  **12** 4 m

*Exercise* 11*e* (*p.* 98)

**1** (i) $2:5$, (ii) $4:25$, (iii) $4:21$  **2** (i) $2:3$, (ii) $2:5$
**3** $\frac{1}{9}, 1:8$  **4** $4:5$  **5** 4 cm, $1:4$
**6** $4:9:12$  **7** $4:32:45$  **8** $4:9:6$
**9** (i) $1:4$, (ii) $9:16$  **10** $3:2$  **11** $2:1:2$

**12** $9:40$  **26** $\begin{pmatrix} 0 \\ 0 \end{pmatrix}, \begin{pmatrix} 6 \\ -2 \end{pmatrix}, \begin{pmatrix} 10 \\ 14 \end{pmatrix}; 4:1$

**27** $\begin{pmatrix} 10 & 0 \\ 0 & 10 \end{pmatrix}; 100$  **28** $\begin{pmatrix} 1 \\ -1 \end{pmatrix}, \begin{pmatrix} 5 \\ 3 \end{pmatrix}, \begin{pmatrix} 7 \\ -3 \end{pmatrix}; 4:1$

**29** $\begin{pmatrix} 2 \\ 0 \end{pmatrix}, \begin{pmatrix} 0 \\ 0 \end{pmatrix}, \begin{pmatrix} 1 \\ 3 \end{pmatrix}$  **30** $\begin{pmatrix} 2 \\ 1 \end{pmatrix}, \begin{pmatrix} 4 \\ -5 \end{pmatrix}, \begin{pmatrix} 6 \\ -3 \end{pmatrix}$

*Exercise* 12*a* (*p.* 104)

**1** (i) one-to-one  (ii) many-to-one  (iii) one-to-many
   (iv) many-to-many  (v) many-to-one  (vi) one-to-many
   (vii) many-to-many  (viii) many-to-many  (ix) many-to-one
   (x) one-to-many

**2** $0, 1, 9, 4, 9, y^2, x^2 + 2x + 1, 4x^2, 4z^2, x^2 + 2xh + h^2$

**3** $-1, 3, 0, 15, \dfrac{4}{x^2} - 1$  **4** $2, 8, \frac{1}{2}, 1, \frac{1}{4}$  **5** $1\frac{1}{3}, 2, 4, 0, 0$

**6** $x, x^2 + 2x, x^2 + 5x, x^3 + 3x^2 + 3x + 1, \dfrac{2x + 2}{x^2 + 4x + 4}$

**7** $1, 2x + h, 3x^2 + 3xh + h^2, -\dfrac{1}{x(x + h)}, 4x + 2h - 1$

*Exercise* 12*b* (*p.* 107)

**1** 6, 2, 11  **2** 1, 4, 16  **3** 0, 12, 18  **4** $-1, 3, -19$
**5** 0, 0, 12  **6** $-\frac{1}{2}, 13\frac{1}{2}, -28\frac{1}{2}$  **7** $14\frac{1}{2}, \frac{4}{9}, 2\frac{2}{9}$

*Exercise* 12*c* (*p.* 108)

**1** $(x - 1)(x + 2)(x + 3)$  **2** $(a + 1)^2(a - 2)$
**3** $(d - 2)(d + 3)(d - 4)$  **4** $(m - 3)(m + 3)(m + 4)$
**5** $(c + 2)(c - 3)^2$  **6** $(u + 2)(u^2 + u + 1)$
**7** $(n - 3)(n^2 + 2n + 3)$  **8** $(y - 1)(y + 3)(2y - 1)$
**9** $(x + 2)(x - 3)(2x + 3)$  **10** $(m - 2)(m + 4)(m - 7)$
**11** $(n - 1)^2(n + 2)$  **12** $(a - 2)(a + 2)(a + 3)$

338

**13** $(b + 2)(b + 3)(b - 5)$      **14** $(z - 2)(2z - 3)(3z + 2)$
**15** $(x - 5)^2(x + 7)$      **16** $(a - 2)(a + 3)(a + 4)(a - 5)$
**17** $(c - 1)(c - 2)(c^2 - c + 3)$      **18** $(d + 1)(d + 2)(d^2 + 2d - 4)$
**19** $(e - 8)(2e - 1)(2e + 1)$      **20** $(n + 2)^2(n - 3)(n + 5)$
**21** $(m + 1)(m - 2)(m + 4)(3m - 2)$
**22** $(b + 5)(b - 7)(2b + 1)$      **23** $(y + 2)(y - 3)(y - 4)(y + 5)$
**24** $(u - 1)(u - 3)(u + 3)(3u + 2)$      **25** $(v + 3)^2(v + 5)(2v - 5)$
**26** $(w + 2)(w + 3)(w + 4)(w + 5)$      **27** $(a - 2)(a + 3)(a^2 - a + 1)$
**28** $(m - 2)^3(m + 4)$      **29** $(n + 2)^3(n - 3)^2$
**30** $(m + 1)(2m - 3)(3m^2 + 2m + 2)$

*Exercise 12d (p. 110)*
**1** $-5, 2x^2 + x - 2$      **2** $-2, 26$      **3** $(x - 1)(x - 2)$
**4** $-11, -9, (x - 1)(x + 3)$      **5** $6, 19, 3x + 2$
**6** $3, -4$      **7** $2x^2 - 5x - 3$      **8** $2, 1, -5$
**9** $x - 2$      **10** $(x + 1)(x - 5)$

*Exercise 13 (p. 122)*
**1** $19 \cdot 7$ km h$^{-1}$, $258°$ $(257° 34')$      **2** $3 \cdot 83$ km h$^{-1}$, $026°$ $(026° 24')$
**3** $22 \cdot 2$ km h$^{-1}$, $191°$ $(190° 47')$      **4** $53° 8'$, $3 \cdot 2$ km h$^{-1}$
**5** $1 \cdot 73$ m s$^{-1}$, $3 \cdot 46$ m s$^{-1}$, $35$ s      **6** $339°$ $(339° 5')$
**7** $13 \cdot 3$ km h$^{-1}$, $045°$ $(044° 55')$
**8** $70\frac{1}{2}°$ $(70° 32')$ to the bank; straight across
**9** $4 \cdot 29$ km h$^{-1}$, $258°$ $(257° 58')$
**10** $2 \cdot 55$ m s$^{-2}$, $11° 19'$ to original direction
**11** $16° 4'$ to direction of $6 \cdot 1$ N force
**12** $1 \cdot 86$ N      **13** $1 \cdot 73$ N
**14** $11 \cdot 8$ m s$^{-2}$ at $4° 52'$ to original direction
**15** $511(\frac{1}{2})$ km h$^{-1}$, $200(\frac{1}{2})°$      **16** $380$ km h$^{-1}$, $122(\frac{1}{2})°$
**17** $430$ km h$^{-1}$, $306°$      **18** $681$ km h$^{-1}$, $023°$
**19** $70 \cdot 0$ km h$^{-1}$ from $302°$      **20** $56 \cdot 6$ km h$^{-1}$ from $033°$
**21** $137$ km h$^{-1}$ from $332°$      **22** $61 \cdot 6$ km h$^{-1}$ from $142°$
**23** $444$ km h$^{-1}$, $329°$      **24** $416$ km h$^{-1}$, $074°$
**25** $445(\frac{1}{2})$ km h$^{-1}$, $204°$      **26** $356$ km h$^{-1}$, $118°$
**27** $017°$      **28** $229°$      **29** $002°$      **30** $267°$

*Exercise 14a (p. 127)*
**1** $\frac{1}{4}$      **2** $\frac{1}{13}$      **3** $\frac{2}{5}$      **4** $\frac{5}{26}$      **5** $\frac{125}{676}$
**6** $\frac{1}{3}, \frac{1}{9}$      **7** $\frac{3}{8}$      **8** $\frac{1}{10}$      **9** $\frac{19}{20}$      **10** $\frac{1}{18}, \frac{1}{12}, \frac{5}{36}$

*Exercise 14b (p. 131)*
**1** $\frac{11}{36}, \frac{1}{6}$      **2** $\frac{21}{25}$      **3** $\frac{1}{4}, \frac{3}{4}, \frac{25}{169}$      **4** $\frac{1}{8}, \frac{7}{8}$
**5** $\frac{2}{27}, \frac{19}{27}$      **6** $\frac{1}{64}, \frac{37}{64}$      **7** $\frac{1}{25}, \frac{9}{25}, \frac{1}{5}$      **8** $\frac{1}{3}, \frac{5}{6}$
**9** $\frac{19}{27}, \frac{4}{9}$      **10** $\frac{29}{30}, \frac{3}{10}$      **11** $\frac{1}{8}$      **12** $\frac{5}{12}$

**13** $\frac{27}{64}, \frac{27}{64}$     **14** $\frac{6}{25}$     **15** $\frac{1}{9}, \frac{52}{81}$     **16** $\frac{16}{25}, \frac{8}{25}$
**17** $\frac{48}{625}$     **18** $\frac{1}{25}$     **19** $\frac{2}{9}$     **20** $\frac{1}{4}$

*Exercise* 14c (*p.* 134)

**1** $\frac{3}{8}, \frac{7}{8}$     **2** $\frac{4}{17}, \frac{13}{17}$     **3** $\frac{8}{663}, \frac{1}{221}$     **4** $\frac{28}{57}, \frac{8}{19}$
**5** $\frac{1}{4}, \frac{3}{8}$     **6** $\frac{4}{25}, \frac{9}{100}$     **7** $\frac{31}{125}$     **8** $\frac{3}{11}, \frac{4}{11}$
**9** $\frac{3}{64}$     **10** $\frac{5}{16}$     **11** $\frac{1}{6}, \frac{1}{2}$     **12** $\frac{62}{95}$

*Revision Examples* (*p.* 136)

## XI

**1** (i) $\frac{1}{5}$ (ii) $1\cdot7$     **2** (i) $6:8:7$ (ii) $15:18:14$ (iii) $18:30:55$
**3** 3 cm     **4** $55°\,56'$     **5** $92°\,58', 53°\,2', 28$ m
**6** $1\frac{1}{2}$, 6, 11, 5         **7** 2 040 cm³, $23\cdot3$ kg
**8** (i) $(y + 1)(y - 3)(2y - 1)$ (ii) $(z + 2)(2z - 3)(3z + 2)$
**9** (i) $(3, 1); (0, 2\frac{1}{2})$ (ii) $x^2 + xy + y^2$
**10** $x < -1, x \geqslant 2 \text{ or } x \leqslant -3$

## XII

**1** (i) $(6m - 7)(4m - 7), (12m + 7)(2m - 7)$ (ii) $(3, -2); (-1, 6)$
**2** $1:2$     **4** $40°\,10', 58°\,50', 21\cdot49$ cm
**5** $-5, 2x^2 - x + 3$     **6** £8·40     **7** $\frac{20}{221}$
**8** $60°, 10\cdot4(4)$ cm     **9** $8°$, 1 h $19\frac{1}{2}$ min     **10** 16 cm

## XIII

**1** 480; $+£25$     **2** S $49°$ E, $32\cdot1$ km h⁻¹     **5** $4\cdot50$ cm
**6** $5\cdot62, 3\cdot38$     **8** 764 m
**9** (i) $(x - 2)(x + 3)(2x - 3)$     (ii) $(m - 1)(m + 2)(m - 4)(3m - 2)$
**10** 5 cm, 3 cm

## XIV

**1** $\frac{1}{15}, \frac{4}{15}, \frac{11}{15}$     **2** $2\cdot56, -1\cdot56$     **3** 11 cm     **4** 2; 7

**5** (i) $r = \sqrt{R^2 - \dfrac{V}{\pi h}}$ (ii) $6\cdot04$     **6** 6 h 8 min, $4\cdot27$ kg

**7** $1\cdot37$ N     **8** $3\frac{1}{3}$, 6, 5
**9** $65°\,6', 72°\,37', 16\cdot73$ cm; $30°\,20', 107°\,23', 9\cdot313$ cm     **10** $40:33$

## XV

**1** (i) $(m - 2)(m - 4)(m - 7)$ (ii) $(n - 1)^2(n - 2)$     **2** $52\frac{1}{2}$p more
**3** 14 cm     **5** $224°\,41'$     **6** $(1\frac{2}{3}, -1\frac{1}{3})$     **7** 10 kg
**8** $-2\cdot89, 0\cdot12, 2\cdot76$     **9** $\frac{44}{25}$     **10** $22°\,20', 27°\,7\frac{1}{2}', 130°\,32\frac{1}{2}'$

## XVI

**1** 38 200 cm³, 68·4 kg      **2** S 83° W, 27¼ km h⁻¹

**3** $3 < x < 4$, $x \leqslant -\frac{1}{2}$ or $x \geqslant \frac{1}{3}$    **4** 5, 7, 2½     **5** 41 : 9

**6** 21° 36′, 24·40 cm, 11·45 cm    **7** $(3, -5)$; $(-2\frac{1}{3}, 5\frac{2}{3})$

**8** 32·4 s      **9** $(x + 1)(x - 3)$    **10** 167° 8′, 10·93 cm

## XVII

**1** 34° 31′, 103° 12′, 16·50 m

**2** (i) $(a - 2)(a + 2)(a - 3)$ (ii) $(d + 1)(d + 2)(d^2 - 2d - 4)$

**3** 35 min      **4** (i) 0·48, 2 (ii) 2·6 km      **5** 245°

**6** £678·72      **7** 7      **8** 108 : 125

**10** $(-1, -4)$; $(\frac{1}{2}, -2\frac{1}{2})$

## XVIII

**1** 8·54 cm, 44·1 cm²    **2** $\frac{5}{108}$      **3** 24, 24, 32, 33

**4** 47·7 km, 38·3 km    **5** $63\frac{13}{19}\%$

**6** (i) 3 : 4 (ii) 3 : 1 *or* 5 : 1 (iii) 3 : 2 *or* 5 : 3    **7** 185°, 355°

**8** 1 cm      **9** 2·00 cm (1·995)     **10** $-4, -5, (x - 2)(x - 3)$

## XIX

**1** 52° 24′, 97° 55′, 29° 41′     **2** $(3\frac{1}{2}, -2\frac{1}{2})$; $(-7\frac{1}{2}, 1\frac{1}{6})$

**3** £61·75      **5** 9 cm

**6** (i) $(b - 5)(b + 7)(2b + 1)$ (ii) $(x - 2)(x + 5)^2(x - 7)$

**8** $\frac{17}{105}$      **9** 3·63 km     **10** 567, 504, 588

## XX

**1** 6, 5, $3x - 2$    **2** $\frac{5}{7}, \frac{1}{4}, \frac{7}{6}, -\frac{8}{17}, \frac{10}{33}$     **3** £8·00

**4** (i) 4·31 (ii) 3·47      **5** 19·1 km, 339° 45′

**6** (*a*) 12 km h⁻¹, 20 km h⁻¹ (*b*) 64 km h⁻¹, 72 km h⁻¹

**8** 6·504 m, 97° 42′, 52° 19′      **9** 140·8 cm²

**10** 140 km h⁻¹ from 209°

*Exercise 15a (p. 149)*

**1** 26·8 cm²      **2** 14·7 cm²      **3** 9·80 cm²

**4** 6·61 cm²      **5** 2·79 cm²      **6** 1·54 cm²

**7** 12·9 cm²      **8** 5·31 cm²      **9** 344 m²

**10** 59·4 cm²     **11** 2·24 m²     **12** 4·11 cm²

**13** 90·0 cm²     **14** 655 m²

*Exercise 15b (p. 153)*

**1** 9·85 cm²      **2** 2·23 cm²      **3** 14·1 cm²

**4** 34·3 cm²     **5** 6·50 cm²     **6** 15·1 cm²

**7** 35·0 cm²     **8** 15·6 cm²     **9** 64·9 cm²

**10** 51·8 cm²     **11** 15·5 cm²     **12** 25·8 cm²

*New General Mathematics*

| | | |
|---|---|---|
| **13** 13·8 cm² | **14** 5·12 cm² | **15** 49·7 cm² |
| **16** 41° 49′ *or* 138° 11′ | **17** (i) 8·19 cm² (ii) 537 m² (iii) 121 000 cm² | |
| **18** 75 cm² | **19** 283 cm² | **20** 111 cm² |
| **21** 315 cm²; 314 cm² | **22** 47·0 cm² | **23** 92·1% |
| **24** 90·8 cm²; 13·5% | **25** 6·79 ha | **26** 30·8 cm² |
| **27** 363 cm² | **28** 932 cm² | **29** 2·24 t |
| **30** 5·49 ha | **31** 1·78 ha | **32** 1 130 m, 8·44 ha |

*Exercise 16a (p. 157)*

**1** M = 5L; M = $\frac{15}{2}$L    **2** i, ii, iv, v, vii, viii    **3** D = 4S; S = 44
**4** $x = \frac{5}{2}y$; $x = 25$, $y = 5\frac{3}{5}$    **5** P = $\frac{3}{5}$Q; P = 6, Q = 6·4
**6** A = $\frac{2}{4}$B; A = 0·9, B = 3$\frac{1}{3}$    **7** E = 2·6T; E = 19·5; T = 7·7
**8** B = 5·6A; A = 8·5, B = 67·2    **9** £1 = \$2·40; £6·67, \$16·80
**10** H = 0·87V; V = 8·0, H = 3·3

*Exercise 16b (p. 159)*

**1** (*a*) M ∝ L,     (*b*) M ∝ D³,     (*c*) L ∝ $\frac{1}{B}$,

(*d*) N ∝ M,     (*e*) D ∝ $\sqrt{C}$,     (*f*) A ∝ $\frac{1}{N}$

*Exercise 16c (p. 161)*

**1** $x = 5y^2$; $x = 80$, $y = 5$     **2** A = $\frac{1}{2}$B³; A = 108, B = 3
**3** P = $\frac{5}{2}\sqrt{Q}$; P = 7$\frac{1}{2}$, Q = $\frac{9}{16}$     **4** Z² = 3Y; Z = 12, Y = 12

**5** V = $\frac{1}{2}$D³; V = 13$\frac{1}{2}$, D = 1·6     **6** D = $\sqrt{\dfrac{3H}{2}}$; D = 15, H = 73$\frac{1}{2}$

**7** (i) +21%, (ii) −19%     **8** +20%
**9** 72·8%     **10** 27$\frac{3}{4}$%     **11** $k = 1·5$     **12** 7 g

*Exercise 16d (p. 164)*

**11** (i) V = $k$HD², (ii) E = $k$MV², (iii) $s = k$M$l$³,

(iv) $d = a + kv^2$, (v) F = $k\dfrac{Mm}{d^2}$, (vi) D = $a$V + $b$V²

**2** A = 5, C = 8; −1%     **3** $x = 37\frac{1}{2}$, $y = \pm4$. Doubled
**4** $p = 37\frac{1}{2}$     **5** $x = 5y − 10$; $x = 5$     **6** $x = 2$

**7** A = 100     **8** $x \propto z^3$     **9** $x \propto z^4$     **10** A ∝ $\frac{1}{C}$

**1** 58·4%     **12** 63 cm     **13** £63 500     **14** £7·85
**15** $y = \dfrac{1}{2x}$, $z = \dfrac{x^3}{24}$; 33·1%     **16** 3·53 cm

**17** 80 km h⁻¹    **18** 104 min    **19** (ii) £321

**20** (i) $R = \dfrac{42Mv^2}{x}$ (ii) $v = \sqrt{\dfrac{Rx}{42M}}$ (iii) 80 km h⁻¹

*Exercise* 17 (*p.* 172)

  **1** 6 cm            **2** 8 cm           **3** $1\frac{12}{13}$ cm, $11\frac{1}{13}$ cm
  **4** 1·8 cm, 33° 42′, 3·51 cm²          **9** 4·90 cm
**12** $2\sqrt{3}$ cm, 4 cm, $\sqrt{3}$ cm, 3 cm, 1 cm
**13** 2·038 cm, 1·816 cm, 4·489 cm, 3·564 cm
**14** 5·09 cm          **15** 5·02 cm         **18** 6·32 cm
**23** 5·80 cm        **24** 2·76 m²        **25** 51·2 cm, 28·8 cm

*Exercise* 18 (*p.* 179)

  **1** $5\frac{1}{4}$ cm, $3\frac{3}{4}$ cm      **3** 20 cm        **4** 14 cm
  **5** 10 cm, 6 cm, 24 cm                **8** 11·5 cm
  **9** 17·68 cm       **11** 8 : 3        **14** $3\frac{1}{2}$ cm
**16** 1 020 cm²      **18** 20·2 cm      **19** 32·7 cm
**21** 5·05 cm, 7·58 cm, 3·62 cm, 5·45 cm      **24** 2·183 cm

*Exercise* 19a (*p.* 184)

**1** (i) 0·628 4ᶜ   (ii) 0·481 8ᶜ   (iii) 1·478ᶜ   (iv) 2·557ᶜ   (v) 3·816ᶜ
**2** (i) 143° 12′   (ii) 30° 25′   (iii) 80° 51′   (iv) 208° 54′   (v) 119° 24′
**3** (i) 90°     (ii) 36°     (iii) 18°     (iv) 120°     (v) $67\frac{1}{2}$°

**4** (i) $\dfrac{\pi^c}{4}$   (ii) $\dfrac{\pi^c}{6}$   (iii) $\dfrac{\pi^c}{9}$   (iv) $\dfrac{5\pi^c}{12}$   (v) $\dfrac{7\pi^c}{10}$

**5** (i) $\dfrac{3\pi^c}{4}$   (ii) $\dfrac{\pi^c}{3}$   (iii) $\dfrac{3\pi^c}{7}$   (iv) $\dfrac{13\pi^c}{18}$   (v) $\dfrac{14\pi^c}{17}$

**6** (i) $\dfrac{\pi^c}{4}$   (ii) $\dfrac{\pi^c}{6}$   (iii) $\dfrac{\pi^c}{3}$   (iv) $\dfrac{3\pi^c}{8}$   (v) $\dfrac{7\pi^c}{18}$

**7** (i) $\dfrac{\pi^c}{6}$   (ii) $\dfrac{7\pi^c}{12}$   (iii) $\dfrac{\pi^c}{3}$   (iv) $\dfrac{2\pi^c}{5}$   (v) $\dfrac{5\pi^c}{16}$

*Exercise* 19b (*p.* 186)

  **1** (i) α = 34° 23′, β = 91° 41′ (ii) x = 6·37 cm, y = 14·05 cm
    (iii) A = $7\frac{1}{2}$ cm², B = 20 cm²
  **2** 24 cm²          **3** 7·42 cm        **4** 35 cm²
  **5** 201° 36′, 82° 48′, 50° 24′, 25° 12′        **6** 8 : 1
  **7** 1·5 cm        **8** 10 cm s⁻¹       **9** 0·105 rad s⁻¹
**10** $\dfrac{10\pi}{3}$ rad s⁻¹, 189 cm s⁻¹        **11** 15 rad s⁻¹, 143
**12** $1\frac{1}{32}$ cm²       **13** 6·28 cm, 4·57 cm²

*New General Mathematics*

**14** (i) 11·3 cm (ii) 14·7 cm (iii) 32·4 cm²

**15** 9·27 cm, 11·2 cm²   **16** 11·2 cm, 18·2 cm²   **17** 72·6 cm

**18** 1·16 m          **19** 542 m        **20** 794 m        **21** 8·17 cm²

**22** 47·4 m          **23** 31·9 cm      **24** 26·1 cm      **25** 202 cm

**26** 231 cm          **27** 237 cm       **28** 7·61 m²

**29** (i) 2·39 : 1 (ii) 6·03 : 1       **30** $\dfrac{2v}{d}$          **31** $\dfrac{l}{r}$

**32** $\theta = \dfrac{l}{r} - 2$       **33** $\frac{1}{2}lr - r^2$       **34** $\dfrac{200l^c}{d}$          **40** 149°

*Exercise 20a (p.* 195)

**1** 10·07 cm          **2** 23·45 cm        **3** 2 333 km        **4** 5 667 km

**5** 7·217 cm          **6** 3 881 km        **7** 4 111 km        **8** 2° 23'

**9** 2 386 km          **10** 29 730 km      **11** 50·44 km       **12** 4 122 km

**13** 2 777 km         **14** 36 680 km      **15** 1 600 km       **16** 63° 15' N or S

**17** 996 km           **18** 393 km         **19** 68° N or S     **20** 16 820 km

**21** (i) 4 444 km (ii) 6 840 km       **22** 2 076 km        **23** 841 km

**24** (i) 15 800 km (ii) 11 600 km

*Exercise 20b (p.* 202)

**1** 2° 10'                    **2** 1 620 naut mile        **3** 5° 20'

**4** 44° 20' S                 **5** 4 h 21 min             **6** 9 h 15 min

**7** 7 min 20 s               **8** 8 min 48 s             **9** 7 h 33 min

**10** 10 h 1 min              **11** 1 740 naut mile       **12** 1 920 naut mile

**13** 6° 30' S                **14** 5° 5' S               **15** 19.24

**16** 28 min 52 s, 491 km             **17** 15 min 20 s, 259 km

**18** 18 min 32 s, 298 km

**19** (i) 5 h 14 min (ii) 8 710 km (iii) 4 710 naut mile

**20** (i) 6 240 km (ii) 3 370 naut mile

**21** (i) 7 180 km (ii) 3 880 naut mile

**22** (i) 9 200 km (ii) 4 970 naut mile

**23** (i) 15·7 cm (ii) 16·3 cm (iii) 24·7 cm

**24** 44 cm, 88½° E                    **25** 9 h 12 min, 15 100 km

**26** 3 530 km, 3 350 km               **27** 3 160 km, 1 710 naut mile

**28** (i) 2 060 km (ii) 1 974 km; 1 070 naut mile

**29** 4 h 40 min; (i) 3 890 km (ii) 3 700 km; 2 000 naut mile

**30** (i) 11 300 km (ii) 6 110 naut mile (iii) 12 700 km

*Exercise 21 (p.* 207)

**1** 149·5 m      **2** 64·6 m      **3** 2 160 m     **4** 478 m       **5** 155 m

**6** 293 m        **7** 885 m       **8** 2 970 m     **9** 2·28 km     **10** 314 m

**11** 2 060 m     **12** 255 m      **13** 410 m      **14** 9 960 m    **15** 74·3 m

**16** 20° 53'     **17** 20·4 m     **18** 510 m      **19** 2 620 m

**20** N 75° 28' E, 1 540 m

*Revision Examples* (*p.* 210)

## XXI

**1** $(x + 3)(3x + 7)$; $103 \times 307$

**2** (i) $(3, 5), (3, 6), (4, 5)$ (ii) $+ - +$; imaginary

**4** $40°\ 16'$, $13\cdot7$ cm     **5** $102$, $R = \dfrac{V + \pi a t^2}{2\pi a t}$

**7** (i) $158$ m (ii) $27\frac{1}{35}$ cm²    **8** $4$ h $20$ min     **9** $10$ yr

**10** $360$ cm², $13\cdot9$ cm, $67°\ 23'$

## XXII

**1** $16\frac{2}{3}\%$, £$5\cdot10$, £$29\cdot15$    **3** $\dfrac{12x - 11y}{15}$, $\dfrac{3(b - a)}{2(a^2 + ab + b^2)}$

**4** $0\cdot660\ 7$; $41°\ 21'$, $138°\ 39'$

**6** (i) $\frac{3}{5}$ (ii) $\frac{3}{10}$ (iii) $\frac{9}{25}$ (iv) $\frac{1}{10}$, $\frac{9}{10}$     **7** $5$ km h⁻¹

**9** $98$ cm     **10** $-0\cdot8$ to $1\cdot46$; $0\cdot67$

## XXIII

**2** $\dfrac{c^2 - 1}{c}$, $\dfrac{1}{c + 1}$

**3** (i) $\begin{pmatrix} 6 & 10 \\ 5 & 11 \end{pmatrix}$, $\frac{1}{4}\begin{pmatrix} 3 & -2 \\ -1 & 2 \end{pmatrix}$

  (ii) $\begin{pmatrix} 0 & 2 \\ 2 & 0 \end{pmatrix}$, yes. $y = x$, $2$; $\begin{pmatrix} -k & 0 \\ 0 & -k \end{pmatrix}$

**4** $58\cdot9$ m, $64\cdot3$ m, $42°\ 29'$     **6** £$50$, $1\cdot85$ t

**7** $3\cdot37$, $0\cdot30$; $(2, 3)$, $\left(-\dfrac{20}{7}, -\dfrac{9}{14}\right)$

**8** $34\cdot8$ cm, $34\frac{1}{2}°$ E     **10** $16-$; $28\%$

## XXIV

**1** £$1\cdot44$, $8\frac{4}{17}\%$    **3** $24°\ 54'$     **4** $2\frac{1}{2}$p     **5** $30\frac{1}{2}$p, $12$ cm

**7** $3\cdot71$ cm, $5\cdot71$ cm, $106$ cm²    **8** $-0\cdot4$, $3\cdot9$; $-0\cdot45$, $3\cdot45$

**10** £$300\cdot60$, $24$p

## XXV

**1** $\frac{15}{8}$, $-\frac{8}{17}$; $600$ m

**3** $(3x - 2)(2x + 3)$, $(x + 2y)(x^2 - 2xy + 4y^2)$; $\dfrac{2(x + 2)}{2x^2 - 3x - 2}$

**4** £$4\ 500$     **5** $5\cdot63$ cm²     **7** $3\cdot14$, $-0\cdot64$; $(\frac{1}{2}, 1)$, $(\frac{1}{6}, 1\frac{2}{3})$

**8** $513$ t     **9** £$3\cdot30$     **10** $11$ men, $7$ women

## XXVI

**1** 4; −2, −6    **3** 30 t, 64 m²    **4** 5 cm, 3 cm    **5** 27 people
**7** (6, 4); H    **8** (i) 3·61 cm (ii) 3·46 cm    **9** 3·89 cm
**10** −1½; 0·79, −3·79

## XXVII

**1** 28·8 cm²      **2** 4, $(2x + 1)(2x − 3)$; 1·57, −0·32

**3** 3·5 mm      **4** 102 cm      **5** $\dfrac{5a}{x − a}$, 1

**7** £90, £82·50, 4·31%      **8** 26·56 km, 60·75 km      **10** 53

## XXVIII

**1** (1, −1), $(−\tfrac{3}{5}, 1\tfrac{2}{5})$; $\dfrac{b^2}{3a + 2b}$      **2** 5·59 cm, 4·51 cm

**3** 28 cm, 21 cm, 3 080 cm²
**5** 8      **7** 5·13%      **4** $−\tfrac{20}{29}$, $−\tfrac{20}{21}$; 79° 28′
**8** 16·0 m
**9** (i) 4 220 km (ii) 6 510 km; 5 h 17 min      **10** 1·7, −1·2

## XXIX

**2** 8 890 km, 11 360 km      **3** 2·14 m²

**5** $\sqrt{13}$ cm ≃ 3·61 cm, 64° 20′, 46° 9′      **6** $\dfrac{x^2 + 3x + 9}{x^2 + 3x}$, $\dfrac{2}{x − a}$
**7** £2 250, £2 400; 35% increase      **10** 21° 20′

## XXX

**1** $a − b − 1$; $a − b, a + b, b − 1$      **2** 1 386 l, 97 mm min⁻¹
**4** 6·71 km, 5·23 km, 15 km h⁻¹      **5** (i) 0·621 7 (ii) 5·11, 0·39
**6** 1½ m      **7** £1 410      **8** 9·37 cm
**9** (i) 46·3 m (ii) 66° 42′      **10** 1·33

*Exercise 22a (p. 230)*

**1** $\tfrac{2}{7}$    **2** $\tfrac{3}{2}$    **3** $\tfrac{3}{5}$    **4** $−\tfrac{4}{5}$    **5** $−\tfrac{4}{3}$    **6** $\tfrac{2}{7}$
**7** −2    **8** $−\tfrac{3}{4}$    **9** 3    **10** $−\tfrac{1}{2}$    **11** 3    **12** 3
**13** −2    **14** 2    **15** $−\tfrac{2}{3}$    **16** $−\tfrac{2}{3}$    **17** $\tfrac{4}{3}$    **18** $\tfrac{2}{5}$
**19** $\tfrac{5}{2}$    **20** $−\tfrac{7}{4}$

*Exercise 22b (p. 232)*

**1** 2    **2** 2    **3** $\tfrac{1}{3}$    **4** $\tfrac{1}{3}$    **5** $\tfrac{5}{4}$    **6** $\tfrac{3}{5}$
**7** $−\tfrac{3}{7}$    **8** $−\tfrac{4}{3}$    **9** $\tfrac{4}{7}$    **10** $−\tfrac{8}{5}$

*Exercise 22c* (*p.* 233)
 **1** 1·2, 0·6, −0·8   **2** 4, 0, −4   **3** 2, 0, −3, −4
 **4** 4, 2, 0, −3   **5** 2, 0, −1, −3   **6** −5, −1, 7
 **7** 6, −6, −3   **8** ±¼, ±½, ∞   **9** 1, ½, 0, −½
**10** 7, 1, −5, −11

*Exercise 23* (*p.* 238)
 **1** 1 500 m   **2** (i) 4, 2, −2 (ii) 36, 0
 **3** (i) 4, 2, −4 (ii) 9, 1½   **4** 0·9 m s⁻², 0·15 m s⁻²; 1 600 m
 **5** 1 100 m², 1·2 × 10⁶ l s⁻¹   **6** 0·18 cm s⁻¹, 0·10 cm s⁻¹
 **7** 3, −1; vel. in m s⁻¹, stationary   **8** 1·2 cm s⁻², 3·68 cm s⁻²; 6·4 cm
 **9** 0·067 m s⁻², 0·047 m s⁻²; 5 600 m
**10** 600 m, 0·60 m s⁻², 0·15 m s⁻²; 45·3 km h⁻¹ after 43 s
**11** 1, 1·56   **12** 3, −2; (4·29, −0·95)
**13** 29·8 m s⁻¹ when *t* = 27; 0·38 m s⁻²; 1 360 m
**14** 0·5; 1·44, 5·56   **15** 1·67°C min⁻¹, 6·2°C min⁻¹, 4¾ min

*Exercise 24a* (*p.* 249)
 **1** 5·1 m s⁻¹, 5·01 m s⁻¹, 4·9 m s⁻¹, 4·99 m s⁻¹, (5 + *h*) m s⁻¹, 5 m s⁻¹
 **2** 6·1 m s⁻¹, 6·01 m s⁻¹, 5·9 m s⁻¹, 5·99 m s⁻¹, (6 + *h*) m s⁻¹, 6 m s⁻¹
 **3** 11·1 m s⁻¹, 11·01 m s⁻¹, 10·9 m s⁻¹, 10·99 m s⁻¹, (11 + *h*) m s⁻¹,
    11 m s⁻¹

*Exercise 24b* (*p.* 254)
 **1** $14x$   **2** $15x^2$   **3** $a$   **4** $2bx$   **5** $3cx^2$
 **6** $2x + 4$   **7** $6x - 5$   **8** $3x^2 + 2x$   **9** $4x^3$   **10** $24x^3$
**11** $6x^2 - 6x$   **12** $5x^4$   **13** $6x - 7$   **14** $6 - 14x$
**15** $3x^2 - 10x + 3$   **16** $4$   **17** $2t - 3$   **18** $-2t$
**19** $2 - 6t$   **20** $10t - 4$

*Exercise 24c* (*p.* 258)
 **1** $5x^4$   **2** $6x^5$   **3** $8x$   **4** $21x^2$   **5** $15x^4$

 **6** $-\dfrac{4}{x^5}$   **7** $-\dfrac{5}{x^2}$   **8** $\dfrac{6}{x^3}$   **9** $2x + 3$   **10** $3x^2$

**11** $8x^3 - 10x$   **12** $4$   **13** $6$   **14** $1 - \dfrac{1}{x^2}$

**15** $-\dfrac{3}{x^2} + \dfrac{4}{x^3}$   **16** $10x - 3$   **17** $2x - 7$   **18** $6x + 5$

**19** $5 - \dfrac{2}{x^2}$   **20** $40x^4$   **21** $14x - 3$   **22** $6x + \dfrac{6}{x^4}$

**23** $3x^2 - 4x + 1$   **24** $12x^2 - 3$   **25** $3x^2 + 14x - 4$

**26** $3x^2 - 2x - 1$    **27** $6x^2 - 8x + 3$    **28** $9x^2 - 14x - 9$

**29** $-\dfrac{1}{x^4} - \dfrac{1}{x^3} - \dfrac{1}{x^2}$    **30** $-\dfrac{15}{x^4} + \dfrac{6}{x^3} - \dfrac{2}{x^2}$

*Exercise* 24d (*p.* 259)

**1** $7, 5, 1, -3, -7$    **2** $22, -2, -5, 7, 22$

**3** $13, 5, -3, -11, -15$

**4** $-\frac{1}{4}, -1, -\frac{9}{4}, -64, -4, -\frac{4}{9}, -16$

**5** $-9, -5, -1, 3, 7$    **6** $(3, 5)$    **7** $(3, 0)$

**8** $(2, 3)$    **9** $(-1, -4)$    **10** $(-1, 5)$

**11** $(2, 4), (-2, -4)$    **12** $-9, -3, 3, 6$    **13** $0, -\frac{5}{4}, -3, \frac{3}{4}$

**14** $8, -4, -1, 23$    **15** $3, -1, 19, 38$    **16** $\frac{1}{8}, 8, -2\frac{7}{8}, -1$

**17** $12, 0, 6, -12$    **18** $1, -9, -7, 7$    **19** $-3, 4, 12$

**20** $(1, 1), (2, 0)$    **21** $(2, -64), (-3, 61)$    **22** $(-1, 26), (3, -26)$

**23** $(-1, -4), (-3, 14)$    **24** $(-3, 20), (\frac{1}{3}, 1\frac{13}{27})$

**25** $(2, -1), (-\frac{2}{3}, -4\frac{23}{27})$

*Exercise* 24e (*p.* 266)

**1** $3\,\text{m s}^{-1}, 7\,\text{m s}^{-1}$    **2** $3\,\text{m s}^{-2}, 5\,\text{m s}^{-2}, 0\,\text{m s}^{-2}$

**3** $2\,\text{m s}^{-2}$    **4** $3\,\text{m s}^{-1}$

**5** $6\,\text{m s}^{-1}, 0\,\text{m s}^{-1}, -2\,\text{m s}^{-1}$    **6** $-2\,\text{m s}^{-2}, -6\,\text{m s}^{-2}$

**7** $12\,\text{m s}^{-1}, 20\,\text{m s}^{-1}$, after $\frac{1}{2}$ s    **8** $8\,\text{m s}^{-2}, 18\,\text{m s}^{-2}$

**9** $29\,\text{m s}^{-1}, 8\,\text{m s}^{-2}$    **10** $2\,\text{m s}^{-2}; 0\,\text{m s}^{-1}, 4\,\text{m s}^{-1}, 6\,\text{m s}^{-1}$

**11** $3$ s, $44\cdot1$ m, $29\cdot4\,\text{m s}^{-1}$

**12** $24\,\text{cm s}^{-1}, 4$ s, $-24\,\text{cm s}^{-1}, 0, -6\,\text{cm s}^{-2}$

**13** After $1$ s and $3$ s; after $2$ s; $9\,\text{m s}^{-1}, -12\,\text{m s}^{-2}; 9\,\text{m s}^{-1}, 12\,\text{m s}^{-}$

**14** $68\,\text{m s}^{-1}, 12\,\text{m s}^{-2}; 77\,\text{m s}^{-1}, -6\,\text{m s}^{-2}$; after $5$ s

**15** After $2$ s; $38\,\text{m s}^{-1}, 12\,\text{m s}^{-2}; 20\,\text{m s}^{-1}, -24\,\text{m s}^{-2}$

*Exercise* 25a (*p.* 273)

**1** $3$, min., $-6$    **2** $-2$, max., $11$    **3** $3$, max., $9$

**4** $-1\frac{1}{2}$, min., $-2\frac{1}{4}$    **5** $0$, min., $0$; $1\frac{1}{3}$, max., $1\frac{5}{27}$

**6** $1$, min., $-3$; $-1$, max., $1$

**7** $-\frac{1}{3}$, min., $-5\frac{1}{3}$    **8** $-2$, max., $16$    **9** $1\frac{1}{4}$, max., $3\frac{1}{8}$

**10** $2$, min., $-14$; $-2$, max., $18$    **11** $1$, max., $1$; $2$, min., $0$

**12** $3$, max., $28$; $-1$, min., $-4$    **13** $-1$, pt. of infl., $2$

**14** $2$, pt. of infl, $-3$    **15** $1$, min., $4$; $-1$, max., $0$

**16** $3$, min., $-75$; $-2$, max., $50$    **17** $1$, max., $13$; $-2$, min., $-14$

**18** $0$, pt. of infl., $3$    **19** $2$, min., $-50$; $-3$, max., $75$

**20** $0$, pt. of infl., $2$    **21** $1$, min., $3$

**22** $2$, min., $11$; $-2$, max., $-5$    **23** $1$, max., $0$; $2\frac{1}{3}$, min., $-1\frac{5}{27}$

**24** $3$, pt. of infl., $2$    **25** $-2$, min., $12$

*Exercise 25b* (*p.* 275)

| | | |
|---|---|---|
| **1** $7\frac{11}{27}$ cm³ | **2** 18 cm³ | **3** 27 |
| **4** 24 | **5** 64 m² | **6** 3-cm cube |
| **7** 48 m² | **8** 490 m | **9** $3\frac{1}{3}$ |
| **10** 20 cm | **11** 1 024 cm³ | **12** 20 |
| **13** 891 m² | **14** 48 cm³ | **15** $\frac{2}{27}$ m³ |

**16** $0\cdot094\ 3$ m³$\left(\dfrac{8}{27\pi}\ \text{m}^3\right)$

**17** $x = y = 24$

**18** 12 cm by 12 cm by 13 cm

**19** 6-cm cube

**20** $\dfrac{800}{3\pi + 8}$ m

**21** $2\pi$ cm³

**22** $24\pi$ cm²

**23** $\dfrac{360°}{\pi}$

*Exercise 26a* (*p.* 280)

| | | | |
|---|---|---|---|
| **1** $\dfrac{x^3}{3} + c$ | **2** $x^3 + c$ | **3** $\dfrac{5x^3}{3} + c$ | **4** $\dfrac{x^5}{5} + c$ |
| **5** $x^5 + c$ | **6** $\dfrac{3x^5}{5} + c$ | **7** $\dfrac{x^2}{2} + c$ | **8** $x^2 + c$ |
| **9** $\dfrac{3x^2}{2} + c$ | **10** $5x + c$ | **11** $\dfrac{x^2}{4} + c$ | **12** $\dfrac{x^3}{6} + c$ |
| **13** $-\dfrac{x^4}{16} + c$ | **14** $-\dfrac{1}{x} + c$ | **15** $\dfrac{1}{x^2} + c$ | |

*Exercise 26b* (*p.* 282)

| | | | |
|---|---|---|---|
| **1** $\dfrac{3x^4}{4} + c$ | **2** $\dfrac{x^4}{12} + c$ | **3** $-\dfrac{3}{2x^2} + c$ | **4** $\dfrac{1}{x^3} + c$ |
| **5** $\dfrac{1}{2x^4} + c$ | **6** $c$ | **7** $2x^2 - 3x + c$ | **8** $\dfrac{x^2}{2} + x + c$ |

**9** $2x^3 - x^2 + x + c$  **10** $2x - 3x^2 + c$  **11** $\dfrac{3x^2}{2} - \dfrac{x^2}{3} + c$

**12** $3x^3 + 8x + c$  **13** $\dfrac{x^3}{3} + \dfrac{1}{x} + c$  **14** $\dfrac{x^4}{4} - \dfrac{1}{2x^2} + c$

**15** $\dfrac{x^4}{4} + \dfrac{x^3}{3} + \dfrac{x^2}{2} + x + c$  **16** $\dfrac{x^4}{8} + \dfrac{x^3}{9} + \dfrac{x^2}{8} + \dfrac{x}{5} + c$

**17** $x^6 - x^4 - x^2 + 3x + c$  **18** $\frac{1}{8}x^4 - \frac{1}{9}x^3 + c$

**19** $-\dfrac{2}{x} + \dfrac{5}{2x^2} + c$  **20** $-\dfrac{5}{x} + \dfrac{3}{x^2} - \dfrac{2}{x^3} + c$

*New General Mathematics*

**Exercise 26c (p. 285)**

**1** $u = 2v^2 - 3v + 3$      **2** $y = x^2 + 3x - 7$

**3** $y = 3x + 7$      **4** $s = 6 + 36t - 2t^2$

**5** $w = 3u^3 + 3u^2 - 3u + 29$      **6** $y = -3x + 13$

**7** $y = -\dfrac{x^2}{2} + 2x - 3$      **8** $s = 48t - \dfrac{3t^2}{2}$, 32 seconds

**9** $v = t^2 + t + 5$      **10** $(-2, -16)$

**11** $y = \dfrac{x^3}{3} - 2x + \dfrac{4}{3}$      **12** $y = x^2 + \dfrac{1}{x} + 1$

**13** 13·5 m      **14** $h = 147t - 4.9t^2$, 1 102·5 m

**15** $y = 5x - 3x^2$      **16** $-2, 4$

**17** $y = x^3 - 3x^2 - 2x$      **18** $(-3, 14)$

**19** $v = 9t - 2t^2 + 3$      **20** $y = 1 + 3x + 4x^2 - 2x^3$

**21** $x = 2 \; or \; -5$      **22** $s = 12t - \frac{1}{9}t^3$, 6 s, 48 m

**23** $y = x^3 - 2x^2 - \dfrac{2}{x} - 3$      **24** 3 m, 3 m, 39 m

**25** $v = 58.8 - 9.8t$, $h = 58.8t - 4.9t^2$, 171·5 m, 171·5 m

**Exercise 26d (p. 291)**

| | | | | | |
|---|---|---|---|---|---|
| **1** $2\frac{1}{3}$ | **2** 60 | **3** 16 | **4** $-37$ | **5** $-50$ | **6** 15 |
| **7** 375 | **8** 162 | **9** $2\frac{1}{2}$ | **10** $-1$ | **11** 115 | **12** 39 |
| **13** $13\frac{3}{4}$ | **14** $-6$ | **15** $26\frac{1}{6}$ | **16** $8\frac{2}{3}$ | **17** $24 \cdot$ | **18** 22 |
| **19** $9\frac{1}{3}$ | **20** $21\frac{1}{3}$ | **21** $4\frac{1}{2}$ | **22** $57\frac{1}{6}$ | **23** $11\frac{1}{6}$ | **24** 55 |
| **25** $21\frac{3}{10}$ | **26** 36 | **27** 150 | **28** $57\frac{1}{6}$ | **29** $10\frac{2}{3}$ | **30** 36 |

**Exercise 26e (p. 294)**

| | | | | | |
|---|---|---|---|---|---|
| **1** $34\pi$ | **2** $\dfrac{27\pi}{5}$ | **3** $\dfrac{500\pi}{3}$ | **4** $14\pi$ | **5** $36\pi$ | **6** $7\pi$ |
| **7** $\dfrac{\pi}{30}$ | **8** $\dfrac{25\pi}{3}$ | **9** $\dfrac{70\pi}{3}$ | **10** $\dfrac{81\pi}{10}$ | | |

**Quick Revision Tests (p. 296)**

### I

**1** 14   **2** (i) $\frac{9}{10}$, $\frac{11}{12}$ (ii) 16, 22 (iii) $5a^4$, $-6a^5$ (iv) $3\frac{5}{9}$, $2\frac{10}{27}$ (v) 26, 37

**3** 45°, 60°, 75°      **4** 0·6, 0·3, 60, 27

**5** (i) 0·3, $\frac{13}{40}$, $\frac{1}{3}$ (ii) $2a^2$, $(1\frac{1}{2}a)^2$, $(2a)^2$      **6** (i) 2 000 (ii) 140

### II

**1** (i) $\frac{1}{5}$, $\frac{3}{20}$, $\frac{9}{25}$, $\frac{1}{8}$, $\frac{3}{16}$ (ii) 30%, $37\frac{1}{2}$%, $41\frac{2}{3}$%, $6\frac{2}{3}$%, 16%

**2** (i) 5, $-1$ (ii) 2, 2 (iii) 0, 4 (iv) $\pm 2$      **3** 68°, 64°, 44°, 84°

**4** (i) 25 m (ii) £3·60 (iii) £16·20     **5** 19; 1p

**6** $\dfrac{2c - 3a}{abc}$, $\dfrac{9a - 7b}{12}$, $\dfrac{a^2 + 5ab + b^2}{ab}$, $\dfrac{m - 7n}{m^2 - n^2}$

## III

**1** 068°, N 68° E; 158°, S 22° E; 270°, due W
**2** (i) $(x - a)(x + b)$ (ii) $(x - a)(x + a - b)$
(iii) $(x - a + b)(x - a - b)$

**3** $\frac{3}{4}$, $\frac{5}{4}$     **4** $4a^2$, $\dfrac{2}{a^2}$, $\dfrac{1}{4a^2}$, $\pm 1\frac{1}{4}$     **5** (i) $-1$ (ii) 7     **6** 4, 4

## IV

**1** (i) $x^2 - 5x + 6 = 0$ (ii) $8x^2 + 2x - 3 = 0$ (iii) $x^3 - x^2 - 2x = 0$
**2** (i) $\frac{1}{11}$ (ii) $\frac{3}{11}$ (iii) $\frac{8}{11}$     **3** $\bar{2}\cdot3$, $0\cdot5$, $\bar{7}\cdot36$, $\bar{1}\cdot41$     **4** 370 cm³
**5** £50·83     **6** $22\frac{1}{2}°$

## V

**1** 3, 2, $-1$, 4
**2** (i) $300a^3b^3$ (ii) $42x^2y^3z$ (iii) $12a(a + b)(a - b)$
(iv) $6(2a + b)(2a - b)$ (v) $6(2a + b)^2(2a - b)$

**3** £409·20     **4** $a - b$, $\dfrac{b}{a}$, $\dfrac{a}{b}$, $\dfrac{b - a}{c}$     **5** (i) $\frac{1}{3}$ (ii) $\frac{16}{81}$     **6** $3\frac{1}{3}$, 6, 5

## VI

**1** $\dfrac{a + b}{a}$, $\dfrac{a - b}{a}$, $\dfrac{a^2 + b^2}{a(a + b)}$, $\dfrac{a + b}{a}$, $\dfrac{a - b}{a}$

**2** $4\frac{2}{3}$ cm, $3\frac{1}{3}$ cm, 14 cm, 10 cm     **3** $2\frac{1}{2}$

**4** Volumes 15 cm³, $\dfrac{9\pi}{2}$ cm³, $16\pi$ cm³, $12\pi$ cm³, 64 cm³

Areas $39\frac{1}{2}$ cm², $9\pi$ cm², $\dfrac{248\pi}{9}$ cm², $24\pi$ cm², 144 cm²

**5** $2\cdot7 \times 10^4$, $3\cdot6 \times 10^{-4}$, $4\cdot5 \times 10^{-6}$, $6\cdot7 \times 10^{13}$
**6** (i) 24° 2′ (ii) 65° 58′ *or* 114° 2′

## VII

**1** 50·8, 0·063 1, 76 800, 0·301, 6·67     **2** $1\frac{1}{3}$ cm

**3** (i) 0, $1\frac{2}{3}$ (ii) 3, $-1\frac{1}{3}$ (iii) $\dfrac{5 \pm \sqrt{37}}{6}$     **4** 65°, 66°, 105°, 125°

**5** 3, 0·948 7, 9·487, 30, 0·3, $\frac{1}{3}$
**6** $(4a + 1)(a + 9)$, $(2b + 1)(2b + 9)$, $(c + 3)(4c + 3)$, $(d + 1)(4d + 9)$

## VIII

**1** $5x^4, \dfrac{1}{2\sqrt{x}}, -\dfrac{2}{x^3}, 6x + \dfrac{2}{\sqrt{x^3}};$

$\dfrac{x^6}{6} + c, \dfrac{2}{3}\sqrt{x^3} + c, x - \dfrac{1}{x} + c, x^3 - 8\sqrt{x} + c$

**2** $3^{-2}, 3^{1\frac{1}{2}}, 3^{2x}, 3^{-4}, 3^0$ **3** 2 cm, 3 cm, 6 cm **5** 6 m, 600 m

**6** $\dfrac{1 \pm \sqrt{7}}{3}, \dfrac{-3 \pm \sqrt{5}}{2}, \dfrac{-4 \pm \sqrt{31}}{5}$

## IX

**1** $-4\%$ **2** 6, 15; 9 : 16 **3** $1\frac{1}{4}$

**4** (i) $\dfrac{\dot{n}(b - m)}{m - a}$ (ii) $y - z^2$ (iii) $\pm\sqrt{y^2 + z^2}$ **5** 792 cm³

**6** 3, $-2, 2\frac{1}{2}, 1\frac{1}{2}, 0$

## X

**1** 54, 120 **2** $\dfrac{2bc}{a}, \dfrac{2c^2 - a^2}{a}$ **3** 5 kg **4** 7, 18

**5** (i) $2 \cdot 3 \times 10^9$ (ii) $1 \cdot 2 \times 10^5$ **6** $6\frac{3}{4}$ kg

## XI

**1** $1 \cdot 9 \times 10^{-7}$ **2** $9 \cdot 2 \times 10^{-6}$ **3** $2 \cdot 4 \times 10^{-5}$ **4** $1 \cdot 4 \times 10^{12}$
**5** $1 \cdot 8 \times 10^{-10}$ **6** $1 \cdot 7 \times 10^{26}$ **7** $2 \cdot 5 \times 10^9$ **8** $1 \cdot 1 \times 10^{18}$
**9** $1 \cdot 8 \times 10^{-8}$ **10** $9 \cdot 1 \times 10^8$ **11** $6 \cdot 6 \times 10^{16}$ **12** $4 \cdot 2 \times 10^{10}$

## XII

**1** $(a + 1)(3a + 2)$ **2** $(b + 2)(3b - 1)$ **3** $(c - 1)(3c - 2)$
**4** $(d - 2)(3d + 1)$ **5** $(t - 6)(t - 9)$ **6** $(s + 3)(s - 18)$
**7** $(h - 9)(2h + 3)$ **8** $(k - 3)(2k - 9)$ **9** $(l - 5)(10l + 9)$
**10** $(2m - 5)(5m - 9)$ **11** $(d + e)(m - n)$ **12** $(ax - by)(x - y)$
**13** $(a + 1)(a^2 + 1)$ **14** $(a + 1)^2(a - 1)$ **15** $(l - n)(l + m + n)$
**16** $(p - s)(q - r)$ **17** $(x - 2)(x^2 + 2x + 4)$
**18** $(2a + 3b)(4a^2 - 6ab + 9b^2)$ **19** $(a + b - c)(a - b + c)$
**20** $(x + 1)(x - 1)(x^2 + 21)$

*Revision Examples (p. 305)*

## XXXI

**1** $\frac{1}{3}(2a + b), \frac{1}{3}(a - 3b)$ (i) $\frac{3}{7}, \frac{6}{7}$ (ii) $\frac{1}{7}(2a + b)$ **2** (i) 7·7 (ii) 7·3

**3** (i) $(1, 1), (\frac{1}{3}, 1\frac{2}{3})$ (ii) R $= 42 + \dfrac{3V^2}{200}$, 79·5 N t$^{-1}$

**4** BMC = 35·3 cm², △ CAP = △̇ MAP = 13·8 cm²
**5** (i) $\frac{61}{432}$ (ii) $\frac{7}{72}$     **7** $\frac{1}{3}$       **8** 4 units²
**9** min $x = 4$, max $x = -\frac{2}{3}$
**10** $(24n - 5)$ m; $(7 + 24n)$ m s⁻¹; 24 m s⁻²

## XXXII

**1** (i) 1·11 (ii) 36, 125    **2** £4 050; £960, £2 060    **3** (ii) 3¾ cm
**5** (i) $\frac{1}{32}$ (ii) $\frac{37}{128}$ (iii) $\frac{3}{16}$ (iv) $\frac{1}{128}$    **6** (a) 454 m (b) 16·5 m
**7** −0·85, 1·65

**8** (i) $6(2x + 3)^2$ (ii) $5x^4 + 12x^5$; $y = 2x - \dfrac{1}{x} + 2$

**9** 14 m s⁻²; 44 m     **10** (i) 2¼ (ii) 4½ units²

## XXXIII

**1** (i) 107 m² (ii) 105 m³    **2** (i) 39 (ii) 31; (a) 100 (b) 30 (c) 10
**3** 3·753 cm, 17·97 cm²    **4** $a = 2, b = -5$; $-3, \frac{1}{2}, 5$
**5** 32 m    **6** (i) 1·387 (ii) 1·468 (iii) 2, 8    **7** $\frac{27}{125}, \frac{44}{125}$

**8** (i) (a) $4x(x^2 - 1)$ (b) $1 + \dfrac{1}{x^2} + \dfrac{4}{x^3}$ (ii) (a) 6¾ (b) 1⅓

**9** (i) −1 (ii) 8¼ units²
**10** (i) $-7\frac{1}{2}$ m s⁻¹, −9 m s⁻² (ii) 16 m (iii) 6 m s⁻¹, 6 m s⁻²

## XXXIV

**1** 7p, 15p    **2** $\frac{29}{50}$    **3** 4·83 cm, 49° 50′    **4** 6·30 cm *or* 2·70 cm
**5** $250 < x + y < 350$; $x < 2y$; 183 to 208    **6** 8 200 km    **7** 62° 54′

**8** $y = \dfrac{3}{4}x^4 + 2x^2 - \dfrac{2}{x} + \dfrac{1}{4}$

**9** $\left(x^2 + \dfrac{432}{x}\right)$ m²; 6m × 6m × 3m; £162

**10** 42⅔ units²; $128\pi$ units³

## XXXV

**1** 9, 5    **2** $D = p^2 - (Z + Z^{-1})p + 1$; $D = (1 + p)^2 - 4pC^2$
**3** 0·29       **5** 6·25 cm       **6** 139 m; 14° 58′

**7** (i) (a) T (b) F (c) T (ii) $\binom{30}{19}$ (iii) $\binom{6}{6}, \binom{30}{42}$ (iv) 3, 4

**8** (i) 7 (ii) $-\dfrac{1\,000}{v^2}$ (iii) 10⅔ units²

**9** 10 cm × 10 cm × 5 cm, 500 cm³
**10** (i) 68 cm s⁻¹ (ii) 95 cm s⁻¹ (iii) 825 cm

## XXXVI

**1** (i) (a) 25; (2½, 5) (b) $10\frac{5}{6}$; (4⅙, 3⅓) (ii) (a) 26; (2, 6) (b) 11; (5, 3)

**2** (i) 22 kg (ii) $1\cdot2$ g cm⁻³       **3** $1 : 8, 2 : 1$

**4** (i) $-\frac{3}{5}$ (ii) $\frac{4}{5}$ (iii) $\frac{8}{17}$; 36 cm²       **5** $2\cdot46$ cm

**6** (i) $\frac{2}{3}\mathbf{a}$ (ii) $\frac{1}{2}(\mathbf{a} + \mathbf{b})$ (iii) 2**b** (iv) $\frac{1}{6}(3\mathbf{b} - \mathbf{a})$ (v) $\frac{1}{2}(3\mathbf{b} - \mathbf{a})$; 1 : 3

**7** $1\cdot44$       **8** (i) 12 (ii) (2, 4), (−2, 16)       **9** 10 knots, £1 200

**10** $a = b = 2$; 53 m s⁻¹; 53 m s⁻²; 42 m

## XXXVII

**1** $\frac{3}{4}$       **2** 873 m

**3** (i) (a) H (b) M$_y$ (c) H (ii) (2, 0); $\tan^{-1}(\frac{4}{3})$       **4** $4\cdot08$ cm

**5** (i) $-1$; $(x - 1)(x + 1)(x + 2)$ (ii) $2\frac{1}{2}$ (iii) $0\cdot869$       **6** 30 km h⁻¹

**7** (b) $\frac{1}{2}$ unit² (c) $\begin{pmatrix} 1 & -\frac{1}{2} \\ 4 & 1 \end{pmatrix}$       **8** $6\frac{2}{3}$ cm × 10 cm × 4 cm

**9** 19 cm       **10** (i) 36 (ii) (a) $\frac{1}{4}$ unit² (b) $-\frac{1}{4}$ unit² (iii) $8\pi$ unit³

## XXXVIII

**1** 16 mm, 227 g       **2** 4° 47′, 3° 49′, 143° 8′

**3** 1 170 naut mile       **4** (i) $0\cdot176\ 09$, $0\cdot079\ 18$ (ii) $1\cdot93$

**5** 5, 8, $3\cdot2$; $6\cdot1$       **7** (i) £3·20 approx (ii) 18

**8** (−1, 0), (2·2, 1·6)       **9** (i) 30 m s⁻¹; 42 m s⁻² (ii) $-6\frac{3}{4}$ m

**10** −2 min, $\frac{1}{2}$ max, 3 min

## XXXIX

**1** £810, £420, £75       **2** (i) 23° 35′ (ii) $3\cdot5$ m

**3** (i) $30\cdot6$ km (ii) (a) $17\cdot33$ (b) 74° N, 4° 26½′ E       **4** F, N, T, N

**6** (i) $4\frac{1}{2}$ cm (ii) 10 cm (iii) $3\cdot6$ cm       **7** $a = \frac{1}{4}$, $b = 2\cdot3$; $5\cdot3$

**8** (i) $\left(1 - \dfrac{t}{9}\right)$ m s⁻²; $(\frac{1}{2}t^2 - \frac{1}{54}t^3 + 6)$ m (ii) 18 s, 27 s       **10** $5\cdot02$

## XL

**1** (i) 271; $r = \dfrac{V}{\pi h^2} + \dfrac{h}{3}$ (ii) $0\cdot136\ 6$

**2** 1 710 naut mile (i) 3 977 km (ii) 53° 26′ N       **4** $3\cdot74$

**5** (i) $a = 2$ (ii) $b = -3$, $c = 17$ (iii) A = 1, B = 3, C = 1

**6** $1\cdot6$, $2\cdot5$       **8** $\frac{1}{4}$, $\frac{1}{2}$, 1

**9** $(180t - 135t^2)$ km h⁻¹; $(180 - 270t)$ km h⁻²

    (i) $1\frac{1}{3}$ h (ii) $53\frac{1}{3}$ km (iii) 60 km h⁻¹

**10** $\dfrac{3\pi x^3}{25}$ cm³; $\dfrac{25}{18\pi}$ cm s⁻¹